The
Trypanosome
Surface

Bibliothèque Scientifique Francqui
Francqui Scientific Library
Wissenschaftliche Bibliothek Francqui
Wetenschappelijke Bibliotheek Francqui

3 Bibliothèque Scientifique Francqui
Francqui Scientific Library
Wissenschaftliche Bibliothek Francqui
Wetenschappelijke Bibliotheek Francqui

The Trypanosome Surface

Proceedings of
the Third Francqui Colloquium,
26-27 May 1997, Brussels

Etienne Pays (Ed.)

 De Boeck
Université

La Bibliothèque Scientifique Francqui est publiée avec le concours de la Fondation Francqui.

Les textes du colloque ont fait l'objet d'une première publication dans *Molecular and Biochemical Parasitology*, Elsevier, Vol. 91, Number 1, 1 March 1998.

Imprimé en Belgique
D 1999/0074/2

ISBN 2-8041-3010-X

1

Contents

Keywords : Trypanosoma brucei; Surface glycoproteins; Expression site-associated gene

Expression and function of surface proteins in *Trypanosoma brucei* [1]

Etienne Pays,
Derek P. Nolan

*Department of Molecular Biology,
University of Brussels 67, rue des
Chevaux, B-1640 Rhode St Genèse,
Belgium*

1 • Introduction

Trypanosoma brucei is the paradigmatic species of African trypanosomes, protozoan flagellate parasites transmitted by *Glossina* flies (generally termed tsetse flies), which cause sleeping sickness in humans and the nagana disease in cattle. While sleeping sickness is devastating (probably more than 50 000 death cases per year in recent years), the economic impact of nagana is even more important. As a consequence of this disease, at least 10 million square kilometers of potential grazing land, in 37 countries of sub-Saharan Africa, are rendered unsuitable for livestock breeding [1]. Thus, there is no need to stress the impact of trypanosomes on public health, both through direct human infection and because of the considerable cons-

1. *Abbreviations :* ES, expression site; *esag,* expression site-associated gene ; GPI, glycosylphosphatidylinositol ; Isg (*isg*), invariant surface glycoprotein (gene) variant surface glycoprotein (gene)

traint on meat and milk production [2]. Current methods of control include treatment with trypanocides, use of livestock which are less productive economically but more resistant to disease, and control of tsetse populations. However, all these methods have proven unsatisfactory, and clearly the development of a vaccine, if ever possible, would represent the ideal solution.

The plasma membrane of African trypanosomes, as is the case for all unicellular parasitic protozoans, represents an important biological interface between the extracellular environment of the mammalian host or arthropod vector and the intracellular milieu of the parasite. The nature, function and expression of surface proteins in these cells is shaped to a large extent by two, potentially conflicting, requirements. On one hand, these parasites must be able to take up essential growth factors, solutes and ions from the extracellular environment and also respond rapidly to the dramatic changes that occur upon the ingestion of a bloodmeal by the tsetse fly vector. At the same time, the externally disposed proteins on the parasite surface that mediate these processes must either avoid detection or be otherwise protected from the immune/lytic responses of the host or vector. The aim here is to review our knowledge concerning the function and expression of surface proteins in African trypanosomes, especially those of the *T. brucei* subgroup, and to examine the strategies by which these unicellular eukaryotes alter the composition and organization of their plasma membrane in order to survive and grow in a variety of mammalian hosts and the *Glossina* fly vector. In this context, the perspectives for vaccination against trypanosomiasis are discussed.

2 • The major surface glycoproteins

Studies of the proteins on the surface of trypanosomes have been dominated by two glycoproteins, namely the Vsg (variant surface glycoprotein) of the bloodstream stage and procyclin (also termed Parp for procyclic acidic repetitive protein) of the procyclic stage (Fig. 1). These two proteins cover the entire surface of the trypanosome, are absolutely stage-specific, and are by far the most abundant surface proteins during these stages of the life cycle. The Vsg coat is acquired when trypanosomes undergo their final maturation in the fly salivary glands, i.e. during the metacyclic stage. This coat persists throughout the development in the bloodstream of the mammalian host and is replaced by procyclin when the trypanosomes are ingested by the fly and differentiate into procyclic forms.

2.1   The Vsg coat of the bloodstream form

The Vsg consists of an N-terminal domain of 350 to 400 residues and a C-terminal domain of 50 to 100 residues, and is attached to the plasma membrane by a C-terminal glycosyl-phosphatidylinositol (GPI) anchor which contains two myristic acid residues. The Vsg molecules associate as dimers, which adopt an extended configuration perpendicular to the cell surface, due to the folding of the N-terminal domain into two long antiparallel α-helices separated by a turn [3]. A comparison of several Vsgs from different clones and isolates has shown that the entire N-terminal domain is extremely variable, whereas the C-terminal domain is more conserved, especially around cysteine residues which form disulphide bridges. Despite this sequence variability, the tertiary structure of the N-terminal domain of different Vsgs appears to be quite similar. All Vsgs described so far are *N*-glycosylated, at least near or within the C-terminal domain.

The main function of the Vsg is to form a protective coat that covers the entire surface of the parasite. Each cell is surrounded by 10^7 molecules of the same Vsg. These molecules are so tightly packed that only a very limited stretch of their amino acid sequence is accessible to the extracellular environment and the C-terminal domain is completely buried. This organization not only prevents the immune recognition of conserved epitopes present in the C-terminal region of the Vsg, but it also shields invariant proteins present on the surface of the cell that are potentially vulnerable to attack by the immune system [4]. In addition, the Vsg also protects the cell against lytic elements present in the serum, even from a non-immune host. Interestingly, bloodstream forms of *T. brucei* contain high levels of a GPI specific phospholipase C (PLC) termed Vsg lipase, the only characterized PLC in *T. brucei*, that efficiently cleaves the GPI anchor of the Vsg and releases the protein from the cellular surface under a variety of stress conditions [5, 6]. Although it has been postulated that this lipase may play a role in Vsg processing, to date, the evidence remains equivocal. Significantly, a null Vsg lipase mutant is able to complete its life-cycle [7], indicating that this enzyme is not essential for Vsg synthesis, processing and variation nor for cellular differentiation. However, it may influence the efficiency of growth of the parasite since the bloodstream form of the null Vsg lipase mutant has a longer doubling time and exhibits a significantly lower level of parasitaemia.

2.2   Antigenic variation of the Vsg

Rather than avoiding the recognition by the immune system, trypanosomes manage to survive for long periods in their mammalian

FIGURE 1

The life-cycle of *Trypanosoma brucei*. The major developmental stages are named with indication of the major surface antigen. The insert (top, right) represents the parasitaemia waves developing in the bloodstream, which consist of successive trypanosome populations expressing different Vsgs (1, 2, 3 etc.).

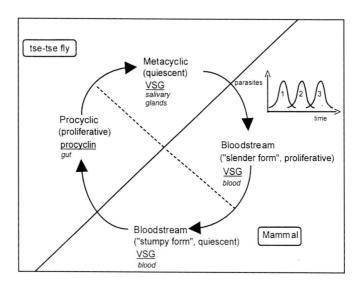

host by exploiting the high immunogenicity, coupled to the extraordinary variability, of their Vsg coat. Epitopes exposed on the surface of the Vsg are readily detected by the host, and the resultant humoral response leads to an efficient and rapid clearing of the parasites from the bloodstream. However, at any given time the trypanosome is able to change its Vsg coat, which always allows some parasites to escape the antibody response directed against the previous Vsg. The continuous interplay between the immune reaction of the host and antigenic variation of the parasite shapes the pattern of parasitaemia in a succession of trypanosome populations that differ only in their Vsg (see insert in Fig. 1).

Thus, in one sense, the parasite makes use of the immune system to control its own growth, by exhibiting and then changing this immunodominant surface antigen. The benefit of this strategy is that it leads to a persistent infection due to the presence of a relatively constant and tolerable number of parasites in the blood, rather than a rapid killing of the host as would occur in the case of uncontrolled growth.

The ability of *T. brucei* to vary the Vsg seems to be essentially unlimited and each parasite can express sequentially more than one hundred different Vsgs. This variation is independent of external stimuli, such as antibodies, but occurs spontaneously, at a frequency which is strikingly different for laboratory-adapted and wild type strains, respectively about $10^{-7}/10^{-6}$ and 10^{-2} switches per cell and per generation [8, 9]. Interestingly, the Vsgs are not produced totally at random, but occur with a loose hierarchy which prevents a rapid exhaustion of the total antigen repertoire. In a given trypanosome strain, some Vsgs are frequently found early after the inoculation of parasites, whereas others appear somewhat later and the last, probably the majority, are only observed late during the development of a chronic infection. This semi-programming is relatively conserved : in a naive animal the early Vsgs of a given trypanosome strain are generally the same and independent of which Vsg is expressed in the parasite inoculum.

2.3   The Vsg genes and expression sites

Several dozen Vsg cDNAs have been characterized. While most of the sequences are extremely variable, the 3'-terminal regions of the mRNAs are more conserved. This conservation is particularly important in the 3'-untranslated region (3'-UTR) and, to a lesser extent, in the sequence encoding the C-terminal domain of the protein. This characteristic has been exploited to evaluate the number of these genes in the trypanosome genome. Based on the level of hybridization of probes from this region, it has been estimated that the genomic DNA of *T. brucei* contains more than 1000 *vsgs* [10]. Thus, a large fraction of the trypanosome genome (more than 2%) is devoted to coding for Vsgs. While the majority of these genes are clustered in discrete locations in different chromosomes, many appear to be located near telomeres. This is particularly true for *vsgs* located at the ends of mini-chromosomes of 50–150 kilobase pairs, which appear to act as reservoirs for Vsg sequences [11]. The telomeric *vsgs* are usually flanked by two extensive stretches of repeats, upstream imperfect 70 bp repeats and downstream telomeric repeats [12, 13]. These sequences are known as « barren » regions as they are devoid of sites for most restriction endonucleases. Interestingly, remnants of 70 bp-repeats can be found upstream of some non-telomeric *vsgs*, suggesting that this subset of genes was originally translocated from a telomeric position. The variability in the number of these repeats between non-telomeric and telomeric *vsgs* (typically zero to a dozen and several dozen to hundreds, respectively) may influence the programming of Vsg expression (Section 2.5).

The non-telomeric *vsgs* and the telomeric *vsgs* present in the mini-chromosomes are never transcribed in situ, presumably because they are not preceded by a transcription promoter. In contrast, most, if not all, telomeric *vsgs* of the large chromosomes appear to have the potential to be transcribed in situ. These telomeric loci are usually termed the *vsg* expression sites (*vsg* ESs). Currently it is estimated that about 20 *vsg* ESs can be active in bloodstream trypomastigotes [14]. In addition, probably a similar number of telomeric

FIGURE 2

Structure and function of an expression site for bloodstream Vsg genes (essentially based on the AnTat 1.3A ES) [19–21]. On top, the boxes represent the different genes contained in this polycistronic transcription unit, with the *esags* numbered from 1 to 10. The flags indicate the transcription promoters. The open and dark dots, respectively, represent the arrays of 70 bp repeats and telomeric repeats, and the terminal vertical bar represents the chromosome end. A schematic subcellular localization and function is proposed for the proteins encoded by these genes.

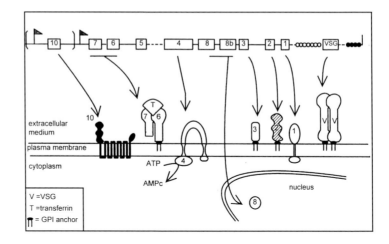

vsgs, particularly from the largest chromosomes, are selectively transcribed in metacyclic forms [15, 16]. At present it is unclear to what extent, if any, the sets of bloodstream and metacyclic *vsg* ESs overlap [15]. Therefore, it is possible that up to 40 telomeres from the large chromosome fraction, maybe all telomeres of this fraction, contain *vsg* ESs.

The bloodstream and metacyclic *vsg* ESs differ in their length and general organization. While the former are polycistronic units of 45–60 kilobase pairs which contain about ten different genes [17–21], the latter are much shorter and appear to contain only the Vsg gene [15, 16]. The genes contained in the polycistronic units of the bloodstream *vsg* ESs have been termed *esags,* for expression site-associated genes [22]. Curiously, some of the metacyclic *vsg* ESs are preceded by *esags,* but these genes are transcribed independently [23, 24]. Similarly, in the bloodstream form, genes related to some of the *esags* are transcribed independently of the *vsg* ESs [25]. The nucleotide sequences of several *esags* suggest that they code for amphipathic proteins with typical membrane signal sequences and consensus sites for *N*-glycosylation but the functions of only some of them are known (Fig. 2). *Esag 10* is contained in a DNA fragment located between two identical copies of the transcription promoter, but this fragment is only present in half the ESs [26]. The protein encoded by this gene resembles a transmembrane transporter [27]. The protein encoded by *esag 8* is located in the nucleus and probably plays a regulatory role in gene expression [28–30]. *Esag 7* and *6* encode the two subunits of a heterodimeric receptor for transferrin [31–33]. *Esag 4* encodes a transmembrane adenylate cyclase with a receptor-like structure [20, 34, 35], while *esag 3, 2* and *1* appear to encode minor surface proteins of unknown function [19, 22, 36]. Attempts to establish the function of *esag 1* by disruption of the gene in two ESs were unsuccessful due to expression of *esag 1* family members from chromosomal internal sites, albeit at lower levels than the transcripts from the active ES in wild type trypanosomes [37]. This result may have implications for the use of gene disruption techniques to establish the function of other *esags*.

As a rule, only a single telomere is transcribed at a time, leading to the synthesis of a single type of Vsg and, consequently, to a uniform surface coat. The significance of this observation is unclear, since it has been found experimentally that trypanosomes expressing two Vsgs simultaneously are perfectly viable [38]. It is probable that the mechanisms ensuring the selective activity of a single ES from the collection of 20–40 potentially transcribable telomeres are related to those allowing the alternative activation of different ESs during chronic infection.

2.4   Genetic mechanisms of antigenic variation

The last 15 years have seen the characterization of the genetic mechanisms involved in the switching of Vsgs in *T. brucei*. Several recent reviews should be consulted for detailed discussions on different aspects of this topic [25, 39–42].

Essentially, two different processes can lead to antigenic variation of the surface coat. The Vsg switches arise either by the alternative use of different *vsg* ESs or by DNA recombination events which change the *vsg* present in the active ES. These mechanisms are summarized in Fig. 3.

2.4.1   *In situ activation*

The first process, often termed in situ activation, is manifested by the inactivation of the former ES and the simultaneous activation of a new one from the repertoire. Although these events are usually coupled, trypanosomes acquire a propensity to uncouple them in vitro, in support of other observations indicating that under unusual circumstances more than one Vsg can be expressed at a given time [43]. However, rigorous demonstration that more than a single ES can be fully transcribed within a given cell has not been provided so far, and it is possible that a strict cross-talk only allows for the full expression of a single ES at a time. The only salient feature concerning the switching of ESs is that it does not necessarily require DNA rearrangements in and around the promoter region. Occasionally large deletions in this area may occur together with Vsg switching, but these events are not always observed [26]. Present speculation suggests a relationship between the in situ inactivation of ESs and the presence of a modified base, β-D-glucosyl-hydroxymethyluracil,

FIGURE 3

The genetic mechanisms for antigenic variation in the bloodstream form. In each diagram, the symbols are the same as those in Fig. 2, except that the boxes represent the Vsg genes involved in antigenic switching, with a black terminal block depicting the conserved sequence usually present at the 3'-extremity. Notice that in each case the transcribed *vsg* (preceded by a flag) switches, from a white to a (partially) grey box in this scheme. See text for details.

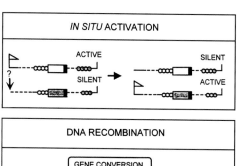

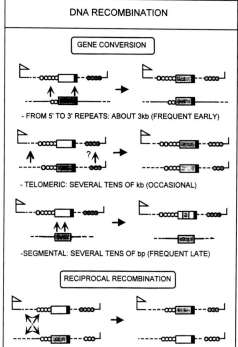

which is found only in the non-transcribed telomeres of the bloodstream form [44, 45]. Whether this modification is the cause or a consequence of transcriptional silencing is unclear. In this respect, it is worth noting that differential DNA accessibility in chromatin can be experimentally uncoupled from DNA modification, since the release from chromatin of proteins soluble in 0.35 M NaCl completely abolished the hypersensitivity of the active ES to DNAase, under conditions where it is impossible that DNA modification takes place (1 h incubation at 0–4 °C) (Fig. 4). Therefore, DNA modification does not seem to be necessary to induce a repressed chromatin structure (heterochromatin). It has been proposed that the telomeres with modified DNA would be unable to interact with elements of the nuclear matrix, which would exclude them from the transcription machinery. For example, the association of a telomeric ES with the nucleolus may be necessary to trigger its transcription, since the RNA polymerase active on the *vsg* ES resembles the ribosomal pol I which is present in the nucleolus [47]. Although recent results tend to exclude this interpretation (see the paper by P. Borst in this issue), it is still possible that a discrete nuclear site yet to be discovered contains the pol I-like enzyme recruited by the *vsg* promoter. More generally, the reversible (in)activation of the telomeric ESs can be compared with the instable control of transcription operating in the direct vicinity of heterochromatin in yeast, the so-called position effect [39, 46]. This control reflects the variable spreading into protein encoding sequences of a locked chromatin structure associated with repetitive DNA such as telomeric repeats, and is mediated by the interaction of several proteins, called Sir for silent information regulator, with the N-terminal domain of histones [48]. In the *vsg* ESs this type of control could spread from both 5'- and 3'-flanking sequences, since large regions of repeated DNA are present at both ends of these transcription units (upstream arrays of 50 bp-repeats and downstream arrays of telomeric repeats). However, this model does not easily account for the high selectivity of the ES control. Thus, exactly why a

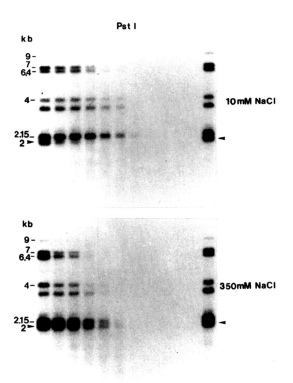

FIGURE 4

Chromatin components released from nuclei by salt extraction between 10 and 350 mM NaCl are responsible for the selective hypersensitivity of the active *vsg* ES to DNAaseI. Among all members of the AnTat 1.1 *vsg* gene family, the active gene (in a 2 kb *Pst* I fragment, arrowhead) is preferentially digested by DNAaseI (top panel), unless the nuclei are previously washed in 350 mM NaCl (bottom panel). The different lanes show *Pst* I digests of nuclei from the AnTat 1.1A clone, incubated for different periods with DNAaseI under the conditions defined in [46], except the last lane, which shows DNA from nuclei incubated in vitro as long as for the previous lane, but without DNAaseI. This result allows us to exclude that DNA modification is necessary for the induction of a repressed chromatin structure in the *vsg* ESs.

single ES always escapes silencing and how this site is changed from time to time remains a mystery.

The case of the metacyclic *vsgs* deserves special comment. This subset of *vsgs,* which is selectively transcribed during the final maturation of trypanosomes in the fly salivary glands, seems to be exclusively activated in situ. In metacyclic, as in bloodstream forms, usually a single *vsg* ES is active in any given cell. However, contrary to what occurs in bloodstream forms, at this stage all ESs seem to be triggered simultaneously in the different cells, so that the metacyclic population expresses the whole repertoire of metacyclic Vsgs at the same time [49]. It is not known if the mechanisms ensuring the selective activation of the metacyclic *vsg* ESs are of the same type as those operating in the bloodstream. The simultaneous activation of the different metacyclic ESs in the fly salivary glands, as well as their rapid inactivation in the bloodstream, strongly suggests the involvement of specific factors from the fly. Interestingly, a metacyclic ES has been reported to be active in a bloodstream variant [15]. Whether this activation was accidental or forced by the selection is unclear.

2.4.2 *DNA recombination*

The DNA recombination events involved in Vsg switching fall into two classes: gene conversion and reciprocal recombination (Fig. 3). Both processes are dependent on the recognition of sequence homology between two partners, the *vsg* ES on one hand and another *vsg*-containing DNA fragment on the other hand. They reflect the high potential of trypanosomatids for homologous recombination, which is the underlying basis of methods for transformation of the trypanosome genome with exogenous DNA [50–53]. Although both processes in effect tend to the same result, these two recombinations differ fundamentally in their relative symmetry.

Gene conversion consists of the replacement of a DNA sequence by the copy of another. Thus, this process is asymmetric, with a target, the *vsg* ES, and a donor, one of the *vsgs* contained in the silent repertoire. It is probable that the chromatin structure of the partner sequences dictates the orientation of the recombination, defining the respective roles of target and donor. The chromatin of the active *vsg* ES is the only one open for transcription, which renders the DNA of this locus more susceptible to cleavage by nucleases [54] (Fig. 4), hence its designation as the target. If this DNA is cut upstream from the *vsg* and downstream from the transcription promoter, the free double-stranded DNA end generated by the cleavage will tend to invade other sequences sharing homology, namely the upstream environment of silent *vsgs.* Base pairing between the invading and recipient strands triggers the synthesis of a copy of the invaded *vsg.*

Therefore, a copy of another *vsg* is inserted downstream from the transcription promoter of the *vsg* ES, while the former *vsg* present in this site is degraded and lost. The resolution of the conversion in the 3'-region of the *vsgs* involves recombination in a downstream region of homology (for details about this model, see [42, 55]). As this process depends on the recognition of sequence homologies between the invading DNA and another DNA fragment, the location of sequences shared between the two partners will determine the end-limits of gene conversion, or, in other words, the length of the copy and replacement (often termed duplication-transposition). The location of these blocks of homology may vary considerably between different *vsgs*, so that the extent of gene conversion is extremely variable. As shown in Fig. 3, the converted region is frequently about 3 kilobases long, because this distance separates the two blocks of homology which are the most frequently found between *vsgs* : the upstream 70 bp-repeats and the downstream 3'-end region of the gene which includes the 3'-UTR of the mRNA. However, gene conversion can occur independently of 70 bp-repeats [56]. Depending on the presence of homologies in other regions, much longer and much shorter conversion events, from several tens of kilobase pairs to several tens of base pairs, can be observed. It is worth noting that when the process of copy/replacement is short and occurs entirely within the gene coding region, hybrid *vsgs* are constructed by the assembly of the residual fragments of the target and the copied sequences from the donor (see segmental conversion in Fig. 3). Such type of chimeric genes are selected provided they encode Vsgs with a new antigenic specificity. Therefore, gene conversion allows for the generation of new *vsgs* by sequence reassortment, which considerably extends the potential of the parasite for antigenic variability [57, 58].

Reciprocal recombination is a second type of homologous recombination, which differs from gene conversion by its symmetry. As shown in Fig. 3, this process allows telomeric *vsgs* to be exchanged with the gene present in the active *vsg* ES. Thus, this process does not involve either gene copy or gene replacement. It was believed to be a rare event because only a few cases were reported for a long time [59]. Recently however, a detailed analysis of several Vsg switches led to the conclusion that this mechanism may contribute significantly to antigenic variation, at least early in experimental infections by a given strain of *T. brucei* [60]. The lower frequency of this process compared to gene conversion could be explained both by the need for telomeric *vsgs* as partners for the recombination, and by the necessity of DNA cleavage not only in the open chromatin of the active ES, but also in the repressed chromatin of silent telomeres.

2.5 Programming of Vsg expression

As noted previously, the pattern of Vsg appearance during a chronic infection is semi-predictable, at least in well-defined trypanosome strains. Certain Vsgs are expressed early, others can be observed later and many only appear very late in the infection. Moreover, the early Vsgs are again observed first when a clone expressing a late variant is injected in a naive animal, a result which clearly indicates that the different Vsgs are not expressed randomly but according to a loose programming. Experimental evidence supports the view that this phenomenon does not primarily depend on the *vsg* sequence, but rather on its genomic environment. A *vsg* that was expressed late in the infection can become expressed early if its genomic environment is experimentally forced to be changed, which normally only occurs rarely [61, 62]. As detailed below, the characteristics of the genetic processes underlying Vsg switching can explain these observations (Fig. 3).

At the beginning of the infection, the different *vsg* ESs are alternatively activated in situ, until a given site is preferred. The switching of ESs is obviously a simple way to trigger variation of the Vsg, because the ESs carry different *vsgs* and are potentially functional as such, so that their alternative activation leads to the synthesis of different Vsgs without the need for DNA rearrangements. Thus, it would appear that at least several ESs have similar probabilities of being activated and are stochastically selected. This process may actually be driven by a selective pressure, since it may reflect a scanning for the most suitable group of *esags* for a given host, for example those encoding the transferrin receptor (Section 3.5). Therefore, the *vsgs* present in potential ESs frequently encode Vsgs that are expressed the earliest.

Also synthesized early are the Vsgs encoded by telomeric genes which are not contained in ESs. These genes need to recombine with the active ES to be transcribed, but the probability of this recombination is high because there is extensive sequence homology between their genomic environment and the ES. Both are telomeric and share large arrays of upstream 70 bp repeats and downstream telomeric repeats. Presumably due to the presence of G-rich motifs which form G-quartets, the latter may force chromosome ends to pair [63]. Indirect evidence suggests that these interactions favour the recombinations between telomeric *vsgs* and the ES [62].

Non-telomeric *vsgs* are not flanked by extensive regions of homology with the ES, so that their recombination with the ES is less likely and these genes are consequently expressed later. Many of the non-telomeric *vsgs* are preceded by one or a few 70 bp repeats which allow them to recombine easily with the ES. However, the number of these repeats is variable among the non-telomeric *vsgs*, which directly influences the probability of gene activation. *Vsgs* preceded by only a few 70 bp repeats are expressed late in infection [57, 61]. When the repeats are absent, the recombination of the *vsgs* with the ES cannot occur with the usual recognition sequences, and must rely on the fortuitous presence of unusual homologies in this site. These improbable events can only be selected late, when the expression of easily activated genes is prevented by the presence of antibodies against the early variants. A typical event of this kind is the recognition of sequence similarities existing within the coding region of the two partner *vsgs*. This leads to intragenic recombination (segmental gene conversion) which creates new Vsgs by sequence reassortment (Fig. 3). Therefore, *vsgs* expressed late during chronic infection are frequently mosaic sequences constructed from several donors, in particular Vsg pseudogenes [64, 65]. The generation of new Vsg sequences is a powerful way in which to expand the *vsg* repertoire, enabling the parasite population as a whole to survive for long periods in the bloodstream [57, 58].

2.6   Mechanisms for Vsg diversification

The Vsg repertoires are subject to an extraordinarily rapid evolution. It is exceptional to find common Vsgs (termed isotypes) among different trypanosome strains, even if these strains originate from the same region. Accordingly, the patterns of Vsg-specific DNA sequences are highly variable between parasite isolates, with the notable exception of *T. brucei gambiense* [66–68]. The existence of two, basically different, mechanisms for switching *vsgs* may at least partly explain this observation. Indeed, we will see that the alternative use of these mechanisms allows the parasite to modify rapidly its Vsg repertoire by a continuous creation, storage and deletion of different *vsgs*.

2.6.1   *Creation of new genes*

In the active ES, the *vsg* is prone to segmental gene conversion which may involve several *vsg* sequences as donors (see above). Consequently, the ES may be considered as a workshop for the construction of novel *vsg* sequences by DNA rearrangement. Moreover, point mutations can also be generated during the process of gene conversion [69]. Although this observation is still controversial [42, 70], it may be tentatively ascribed to the presence of the modified base β-D-glucosyl-hydroxymethyluracil in the DNA of silent telomeres [44]. It is tempting to speculate that when silent telomeric *vsgs,* hence modified *vsgs,* are used as templates for gene conversion, mistakes are generated during the duplication of the donor. This view is supported by the fact that, so far, point mutations have only been found in conversion events involving telomeric *vsgs* as donors. Whatever the reason, the generation of point mutations also contributes to the hyper-evolution of *vsg* sequences, especially since these mutations can alter the antigenic specificity of the Vsgs [71].

2.6.2 *Storage of new genes*

There is a way for newly created *vsgs* to be stored in the genomic repertoire. When gene conversion and in situ activation are successively used as mechanisms for antigenic variation during chronic infection, the change of ES allows the conservation, as a silent gene, of the *vsg* previously transcribed. Since this gene was the result of an earlier conversion event, its sequence may be original due to either segmental conversion or point mutation, or both. In

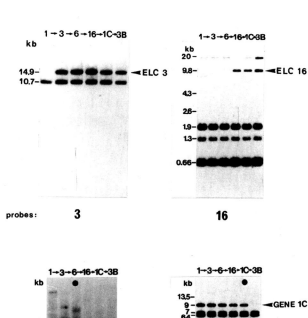

FIGURE 5

The use of alternate ESs for *vsg* expression allows for hyper-evolution of *vsg* repertoires. The four panels illustrate the evolution of different *vsg* families (AnTat 1.3, 1.16, 1.6 and 1.1, respectively, from left to right and top to bottom), during the five successive antigen switches indicated on the top of each panel. The repertoires evolve by gain and loss of different *vsgs*. In the two top panels the arrowheaded bands (ELCs, for expression-linked copies) contain new *vsg* family members generated by gene conversion in variants AnTat 1.3A and 1.16 respectively, whereas the arrowheaded bands in the bottom panels contain *vsgs* which are lost upon gene conversion in variants AnTat 1.16 and 1.3B, respectively. The dots in the bottom panels point to the DNAs of variants expressed following in situ activation.

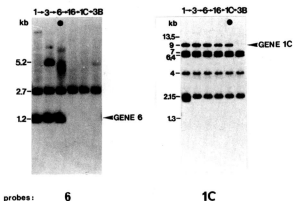

such a case the gene would encode a new Vsg, expanding the antigen repertoire of the parasite. Transcriptional silencing prevents this original gene from being rapidly lost by gene conversion since the structure of repressed chromatin probably inhibits endonucleolytic cleavages necessary to trigger the recombination process [54, 55]. Therefore, the succession of gene conversion followed by in situ activation allows for the acquisition of new *vsg* sequences.

2.6.3 *Loss of genes*

The reverse order of antigenic switching events can lead to the loss of *vsgs*. If a unique *vsg* present in a potential ES is activated in situ, any gene conversion targeted to this site will inevitably lead to its replacement and thus, to the disappearance of this antigen from the repertoire.

Therefore, the successive use of the different mechanisms for *vsg* activation continuously alters the antigen repertoire of the parasite by gain and loss of different genes (see Fig. 5 for an example of this evolution over five successive antigen switches).

This potential for continuous Vsg diversification, which obviously depends on the existence of two basically different *vsg* switching mechanisms, may constitute one of the evolutionary driving forces for the selection of a system with multiple ESs. Another reason is suggested in Section 3.5.

It should be added that genetic exchange could further contribute to the variability of the Vsg repertoires. Indeed, trypanosomes can sometimes exchange genetic information during their development in the fly [72–74]. This possibility allows for occasional transfer of *vsgs* between trypanosome strains and, thus, for massive rearrangements of Vsg repertoires.

2.7 Procyclin, the major surface protein of the procyclic form

When bloodstream forms are ingested by the fly, the Vsg coat is rapidly lost and replaced by another major glycoprotein termed procyclin which is present at approximately 6×10^6 copies per cell [75–77]. Actually the procyclin coat is heterogeneous, since it consists of four classes of related proteins, three of which contain an extensive array of Glu-Pro repeats differing by their length and level of *N*-glycosylation, and the fourth contains repeats of the pentapeptide GPEET and is not *N*-glycosylated. The repeats form a rod-like structure, presumably allowing procyclin to transiently protrude through the layer of Vsg during the process of differentiation. As is the case with the Vsg, procyclin is also attached to the plasma membrane by a GPI anchor, but the size and structure of this glycolipid is different [78, 79]. The GPI anchor of procyclin is much larger than that of the Vsg, and consists of a complex highly sialated structure. Furthermore, acylation of the inositol ring prevents cleavage of the anchor by the GPI-specific PLC. Interestingly, the Vsg acquires a procyclin-type of GPI anchor when experimentally forced to be expressed in procyclic forms [80], indicating that the nature of the GPI is independent of the protein but is dictated by the type of developmental form of the parasite.

The procyclin genes of *T. brucei* are organized as a family of eight to nine copies per diploid genome and are present at different, non-telomeric loci in tandem arrays of two or three copies, with at least two loci being transcribed in a given cloned line [81–83]. The genes are located immediately downstream from the promoter and, like *vsgs*, are also transcribed by an α-amanitin resistant RNA polymerase. They are contained in relatively short polycistronic transcription units with a few procyclin-associated genes (*pags*) [84]. The function of these genes is unknown, although two of them appear to be related to certain *esags* [36, 85].

Although the function of procyclin is unclear, it probably plays a role in the protection of the parasite against components from the fly, such as proteases present in the tsetse midgut. It seems reasonable to assume that the Glu-Pro repeat structure would be relatively resistant to proteases of the insect midgut and that covalently linked carbohydrate, especially that present in the extensive sialated anchor, may form a glycocalyx that offers additional shielding for other surface proteins. This view is supported by the observation that trypanosomes depleted of procyclin develop poorly in the fly (see the paper by I. Roditi and colleagues in this issue).

An alternative major surface glycoprotein has been identified in procyclic forms of *T. congolense* [86, 87]. Although this protein, termed Garp for glutamate and alanine rich protein, shows no significant sequence homology to procyclin from *T. brucei*, both proteins are extremely acidic, immunodominant, stage-specific surface proteins which demonstrate a subgenus-specific distribution. In addition, Garp is expressed with the same kinetics as procyclin during the differentiation of bloodstream to procyclic forms of *T. congolense*, and both Garp and procyclin mRNAs share common translational control elements in their 3'-terminal region (Section 6.2). Like procyclin, Garp is uniformly distributed over the cellular surface where it probably forms an extended polyanionic structure, and may also be attached to the membrane by a GPI anchor. However, there are clear differences between these proteins. Garp has a predicted molecular mass of about 26 kDa, which is almost double that of procyclin, and lacks any potential *N*-glycosylation sites but is probably heavily *O*-glycosylated. These considerations suggest that Garp and procyclin are structural analogues rather than homologues. Interestingly however, a gene related to *garp* has recently been characterized in *T. brucei*, and in this species it is only expressed in the bloodstream form of the parasite (D. Nolan and E. Pays, unpublished data).

2.8   Vsg and procyclin : different horses for different courses

Although Vsg and procyclin represent two classes of surface proteins that are as different as could be possibly imagined, it seems likely that both represent a topological solution to the same problem : the creation of a palisade that protects the parasite from extracellular elements detrimental to survival of the organism. Why have trypanosomes chosen such very different proteins to serve the same function ? Presumably, the answer lies in the nature of the challenge faced by the cells in the mammalian bloodstream and the insect gut. In the well buffered, glucose-rich milieu of the mammalian bloodstream the primary threat comes from the immune response of the host. Consequently, bloodstream trypomastigotes are obliged to present an immunodominant Vsg surface coat that changes constantly, even at a low frequency, in order to ensure that at least some cells survive the inevitable immune challenge against the dominant surface antigen. In contrast for procyclic cells an immune response is not the major problem. Instead, the primary, and a clearly immediate, challenge is from the abundant proteases of the insect midgut. Under these circumstances antigenic variation is unlikely to be rapid enough to afford much protection and procyclic cells probably rely on a relatively invariant surface coat which possesses a unique protease-resistant primary structure. By corollary, such an invariant surface coat would be useless for bloodstream trypomastigotes to avoid the more sophisticated challenge of the mammalian immune system. Thus, in a sense, the choice of these two different proteins as surface coats is a reflection of the different dietary requirements of the mammalian host and vector and, in a way, parallels the adaptive switch of trypanosomes from a metabolism based on a glucose-rich to an amino acid-rich external environment in these two life cycle stages.

There are several other relevant points to be made concerning these different adaptive strategies. First, the differential glycosylation of the two major surface proteins may be related to different types of sugar-lectin interactions with the host. That different glycans of the Vsg can be involved as both receptors and inducers for components of the immune system is discussed elsewhere (Section 3.4, Section 7.1). Similarly, it is possible that carbohydrates exposed on procyclin interact with lectin-like proteins from the fly to organise the development of the parasite in the different insect compartments ([75]; see the paper by I. Roditi and colleagues in this issue). Second, trypanosomes have utilized GPI-anchoring for the surface coat during both life-cycle stages and it is tempting to speculate that this form of anchoring is a solution to the topological requirements necessary to achieve a sufficiently dense packing of the protective coat during both life-cycle stages, but it may also relate to effective and rapid turnover of these proteins in the surface membrane [88]. Finally, the speed and efficiency with which the trypanosome can effectively remodel its entire surface from a Vsg to procyclin based coat during differentiation from bloodstream to procyclic forms are very impressive. Significantly, at no time are the differentiating trypanosomes devoid of a surface coat and at times both proteins are present on the surface [89]. The fact that both are GPI-anchored may assist in this intercalation.

3 • Surface receptors and transporters

Over the past few years there has been increasing interest in surface proteins located either beneath the surface coats of Vsg/procyclin or within the flagellar pocket [90–92]. There are several reasons why interest in these proteins is increasing. First, it is clear that some of these proteins must be involved in a range of cellular housekeeping processes such as the uptake of high-molecular-weight ligands and the transport of solutes and ions. Second, given their functional role, such proteins are unlikely to undergo antigenic variation in the same manner as the Vsg and, consequently, may represent suitable targets for the development of vaccines or chemotherapy. Third, even if the development of effective vaccines against these invariant surface antigens proves to be either impossible or impractical, the fact remains that plasma membrane proteins are likely to occupy a pivotal position in multiple signalling pathways, such as those involved in (i) interactions between the mammalian host and arthropod vector, (ii) switching between different life cycle stages, and possibly (iii) intercellular communication between trypanosomes. These topics are among the most exigent areas of research in molecular parasitology at present, and an important step towards improving our understanding of these processes must be the identification and characterization of the plasma membrane proteins that mediate them. To date, apart from the Vsg and procyclin, only three other surface proteins have been characterized at a molecular and functional level in *T. brucei* : the heterodimeric transferrin receptor, a family of adenylate cyclases and a family of hexose transporters.

One recurrent feature of receptors in *T. brucei* is their localization within the flagellar pocket. This region consists of an invagination of the plasma membrane where the flagellum emerges from the cytoplasm, is devoid of the underlying array of microtubules found in the pellicle and appears to be a specialized site for endo- and exocytosis [90]. Thus, the flagellar pocket represents a discrete functional and structural domain in the continuous phase of the plasma membrane. There are probably two reasons for the clustering of receptors in this region. First, this location essentially makes them invulnerable to the cellular arm of the immune system, although not necessarily from host antibodies. Second, the underlying subpellicular array of microtubules in the remainder of the cell body is probably prohibitive for the membrane fusion and fission events typical of endo- and exocytosis. Restriction of these pathways to a small area of the cellular surface does not appear to represent an impediment since the rate of membrane turnover within the pocket is equivalent to the entire surface area of the pocket every 1–2 min and a volume equivalent of almost an order of magnitude per hour [90]. Finally, although the pocket forms a partially shielded microenvironment the lumen of the pocket appears to be permeable to relatively large macromolecules; for example, ferritin, transferrin and antibodies can freely penetrate even at low temperature [31, 93].

3.1   The transferrin receptor

Transferrin is an essential host-derived growth factor for trypanosomes and the efficiency and nature of transferrin uptake suggested the presence of a specific receptor for this ligand. Over the past few years many of the issues concerning this receptor have been resolved and once again trypanosomes have proven to be a source of surprises. The starting point for these studies began with the finding that the product of one of the *vsg* ES associated genes, *esag 6*, was a component of the purified transferrin binding complex [94]. Subsequent work by several groups demonstrated that the functional complex was in fact a 1 : 1 heterodimer of the products of *esag 6* and *7* and no additional factors were required for transferrin binding [31–33]. Although Esag 6 and 7 share a high degree of sequence homology, Esag 6 possesses a C-terminal hydrophobic extension which leads to the addition of a GPI anchor that in turn is responsible for attachment of the complex to the membrane (Fig. 2). Thus, the transferrin receptor of *T. brucei* differs significantly from the larger homodimeric, transmembrane receptor of higher eukaryotes. Recent work in our laboratory has revealed that this receptor is evolutionary related to the Vsg, since Esag 7 and 6 not only share the structure of the N-terminal domain of Vsgs, but they also show high sequence homology with some Vsg variants [95]. Interestingly, the transferrin binding site of the receptor was found to correspond to the most surface-exposed loops of the Vsg.

Although the transferrin receptor of *T. brucei* is restricted to the flagellar pocket, curiously, both transferrin and the receptor were found to be mainly located inside the lumen of the pocket rather than on the surface of the pocket membrane proper [31, 32]. In the bloodstream form, the flagellar pocket appears to be filled with an electron opaque, glycoproteinic material which is also found in coated pits and vesicles derived from the pocket [31, 90]. Significantly, an experimentally engineered soluble form of the receptor, which lacks the GPI anchor, has been shown to bind the ligand in vitro [31]. Thus, it is possible that receptors are released from the cell surface and associate with luminal glycoproteins, bind transferrin and are then internalized. This hypothesis would allow the cell to achieve a higher density of functional receptor in the pocket than if it were restricted solely to the membrane surface and may also account for the discrepancy in the estimated number of receptors reported by different groups. Alternatively, the luminal material may represent receptors that have been internalized, unloaded of transferrin and recycled to the flagellar pocket for further rounds of uptake [92]. This process may require cleavage of the GPI anchor of Esag 6 by the GPI-specific PLC, which has been shown to release the receptor expressed in *Xenopus* oocytes [31]. Interestingly, as noted in a previous section null mutant trypanosomes for the GPI-specific PLC demonstrated significantly attenuated levels of growth.

3.2 Receptors for lipoproteins

Low-density lipoprotein (LDL) is required for growth of *T. brucei* and these cells specifically take up LDL from the mammalian host through the flagellar pocket. Scatchard plot analysis of the binding of iodinated LDL indicated the presence of high affinity receptors for LDL in bloodstream trypomastigotes [96]. An LDL binding protein (~145 kDa) has been isolated by affinity chromatography and appears to be located in the pocket membrane as well as the membrane covering the flagellum [97]. Although the gene for this protein has not been identified, the gene for a cysteine-rich, acidic membrane protein (~200 kDa), termed Cram, that shows homologies with the cysteine-rich repetitive motif characteristic of the human LDL receptor has been characterized [98]. Although both the LDL-binding protein and Cram shared a similar cellular location, it seems unlikely that they are the same protein. First, they differ significantly in apparent molecular weight. Second, two remarkable features of the LDL-binding protein are its conservation throughout the Kinetoplastida order [99] and its high antigenic similarity to the host receptor [100], both of which seem difficult to reconcile with the amino acid sequence of Cram. Finally, the Cram gene is preferentially expressed in procyclic forms, whereas immunoblotting demonstrated the presence of the LDL-binding protein in both bloodstream and procyclic forms of the parasite.

Host serum high density lipoprotein (HDL) is also specifically taken up by receptor-mediated endocytosis and a component of HDL, termed the trypanosome lytic factor or TFL, is responsible for the host range restriction of the *T. b. brucei* subspecies [101]. The lysis of susceptible strains of trypanosomes requires the binding of TLF to receptors in the flagellar pocket, specific uptake and delivery of the factor to the lysosome. Lysosomal disruption and subsequent autodigestion of the cell follow. Recently, a comparison of sensitive and resistant clones of *T. b. rhodesiense* revealed that the mechanism of resistance was related to a failure to efficiently process receptor bound TLF rather than the absence of a receptor [102]. This failure may relate to the presence of what appears to be a truncated form of Vsg in resistant clones only [103].

3.3   Trypanosome adenylate cyclases : a family of receptors ?

In addition to *esag 7* and *6,* another gene contained in the polycistronic transcription unit of the Vsg gene, termed *esag 4,* has been found to encode a cell surface protein [35]. This gene codes for an adenylate cyclase and belongs to a large family of genes, at least some members of which also encode adenylate cyclases [35, 104, 105]. Similar gene families have been identified in *T. equiperdum* [34] and *Leishmania donovani* [106]. All these cyclase isoforms share the same basic receptor-like structure, with a large and relatively variable region predicted to be extracellular and a C-terminal, conserved catalytic domain predicted to be located immediately underneath the plasma membrane (Fig. 2). Interestingly, at least some of these cyclases appear to be located on the flagellum [35]. It is tempting to postulate that the different cyclases are activated by the interaction of their extracellular domain with different specific ligands from the parasite environment. As observed in *Dictyostelium* [107], the activation of each of the cyclases could play a distinct role during the development of the parasite. Such a role is also consistent with the developmentally regulated expression of *esag 4,* which is specific to the bloodstream form.

A bloodstream-stage specific calcium-activated adenylate cyclase activity has been described in *T. brucei.* This cyclase, probably together with other isoforms, is strongly activated upon cellular stress such as acidic or osmotic shock [6], or high cell density (S. Rolin and E. Pays, unpublished data). No involvement of G-protein seems to be required for this activation. The stress-induced activation probably plays a role during the differentiation of bloodstream into procyclic forms [108, 109]. Although a variety of experimental membrane-perturbating conditions usually trigger Vsg release by the GPI specific PLC and activation of adenylate cyclase simultaneously [6, 110, 111], it has been shown directly that PLC mediated release of Vsg and adenylate cyclase activation are not obligatorily coupled [6]. It seems that the two processes are independent, but both may depend on inhibition of protein kinase C [6].

3.4   Surface receptors for other growth factors

Although less well defined than for the receptors described previously, data in the literature also suggest the presence of surface receptors for growth factors such as epidermal growth factor [112] and cytokines such as TNF-α [113] or IFN-γ [114]. The latter two molecules may be considered as growth regulators, as they appear to play opposite roles in the control of parasitaemia. The equilibrium between proliferation stimulated by IFN-γ [114] and lysis induced by TNF-α [113, 115, 116] may ensure a fine tuning of the number of parasites in the blood, to prevent rapid killing of the host and to maintain a chronic infection. Trypanosomes appear to direct this host-mediated regulation, as they secrete factors that trigger the production of both IFN-γ by CD8+ cells [114] and TNF-α by macrophages ([117]; S. Magez, B. Stijlemans, E. Pays, M. Ferguson and P. De Baetselier, unpublished data). The control of growth seems to depend on a differential sensitivity of the trypanosomes to the cytokines as a function of the stage of proliferation : TNF-α becomes lytic only late during parasitaemia, presumably when trypanosomes undergo cellular stress linked to either high parasite density or increasing immune response [116]. Interestingly, recent results indicate that some Vsg molecules that are released into the lumen of the flagellar pocket can act as specific binding sites for cytokines of the host (S. Magez, M. Radwanska, P. De Baetselier and E. Pays, unpublished results). These findings introduce the novel notion that the Vsg may have a receptor-like function on the cell surface.

3.5 Variation of receptors

The growth properties of trypanosomes differ considerably between variant clones of the same strain [118]. It is probable that this difference in growth reflects more the expression of different receptors encoded by the *esags*, for example the transferrin receptor (*esag 7* and *6*) and a receptor-like adenylate cyclase (*esag 4*), that are associated with the alternative activation of different *vsg* ESs, rather than the nature of the Vsg itself. In the case of the transferrin receptor the evidence for this proposal is rather convincing. Although the genes for these proteins are very similar, they are not absolutely identical between different ESs. Maybe *esags*, like *vsgs*, accumulate point mutations because of the modified base present in telomeric DNA (see Section 2.6). As a consequence of these amino acid variations, the receptors encoded by different ESs show large differences in affinity for transferrin from a given host [119, 120]. Indeed, it has been shown directly that only a single amino acid difference in the most exposed surface loop of Esag 6 can account for a more than 10-fold difference in the affinity of the receptor for the ligand [95]. In addition, the affinity of the same receptor differs greatly for transferrins from different mammalian species and depending on the species-specificity of transferrin, trypanosomes appear to switch *vsg* ESs until expression of the best adapted transferrin receptor is achieved [120]. As usual with the benefit of hindsight this is not so surprising given the diversity of mammalian transferrins. Since a large host range is a clear advantage to the parasite, the requirement for several host-specific Esags may actually be one of the underlying reasons for the existence of multiple ESs (another reason is provided in Section 2.6). Thus, in addition to being a mechanism involved in antigenic variation, in situ activation may also be a way for the parasite to select a set of receptors which is the most appropriate for the mammalian host.

These considerations suggest that the proteins encoded by other *esags* may represent surface components that are specific for different mammalian hosts. Such a hypothesis obviously implies that the host-specificity of the different Esags would be coordinated between ESs. Similarly, the relative resistance or susceptibility of trypanosomes to lytic factors present in human serum, at least in the *T. brucei rhodesiense* subspecies, may also be related to switching between ESs. In fact, resistance to human serum is acquired only after switching to certain Vsgs [121], an observation which would find an easy explanation if the gene for resistance was an *esag* present only in some *vsg* ESs. This hypothesis is actually supported by preliminary evidence (E. Chimfwembe, H.V. Xong and E. Pays, unpublished results).

3.6 A family of glucose transporters

Glucose is the primary carbon source for bloodstream trypo-mastigotes, and these cells possess a transporter that differs significantly from mammalian glucose transporters [122]. Molecular analysis of glucose transport, so far the only plasma membrane solute transport system thus characterized in any trypanosome, became possible with the isolation of a developmentally regulated gene, termed *tht* (for trypanosome hexose transporter), that is homologous to the glucose transporter in a range of organisms and is also widely distributed among Kinetoplastidae [123]. The deduced amino acid sequence suggested that the putative protein (~53 kDa) contained 12 membrane spanning regions and a single *N*-glycosylation site. One unusual feature of the protein is the presence of a cysteine-rich segment in the largest of the two hydrophilic loops. Subsequent work revealed the presence of two families of glucose transporter genes, *tht1* and *tht2*, that are developmentally regulated [124]. The *tht* locus contains six direct repeats of *tht1* followed by five direct repeats of *tht2*. Tht1 genes appear to be expressed only in bloodstream forms, whereas Tht2 genes are preferentially expressed in procyclic forms. The homology between the two sets of genes is about 80% and both proteins appear to have a similar topographic organization in the membrane. Interestingly the first hydrophilic loop, which probably corresponds to the extracellular domain of the proteins, is the region displaying the greatest divergence between the two amino acid sequences. These differences in a region of the polypeptide that may represent the external substrate binding site may be the molecular basis of the large difference in affinities observed in heterologous expression experiments [125]. The differential expression of two transporters is probably related to the fact that in the glucose-rich environment of the mammalian bloodstream a lower affinity transporter (Tht1) is sufficient for the needs of the cell, whereas during the insect stage of the life-cycle amino acids are the primary source of energy and glucose is of secondary importance. However, procyclic cells have the ability to respond rapidly should low concentrations of glucose become available in the insect gut by expressing a transporter with a higher substrate affinity (Tht2).

4 • Invariant surface glycoproteins

The use of classical biochemical approaches for the isolation of invariant surface proteins (Isgs) from trypanosomes is beset by the formidable technical problem of their relatively low abundance (100 to 10 000-fold less) compared to either of the two major surface glycoproteins, Vsg or procyclin. Furthermore, there is always the possibility of contamination by components derived from the host or culture medium. Nevertheless, surface labeling with membrane-impermeant protein modifying reagents, such as radioiodination [126–128] and biotinylation with NHS-LC-biotin [129, 130], has been employed for the identification, purification and characterization of a range of Isgs in bloodstream forms of *T. brucei* (see Table 1 for a summary).

Interestingly, both surface radioiodination and biotinylation identified the same glycoprotein, termed either Isg65 [129, 130] or Isg70 ([127]; D. Nolan and E. Pays, unpublished). This protein, along with another, termed Isg75, identified by biotinylation only, are both bloodstream stage-specific and are probably the most abundant surface proteins after the Vsg, with approximately $5–7 \times 10^4$ copies of each per cell. The genes for these Isgs show no significant homology to other known genes and code for proteins (46 and 55 kDa for Isgs 65 and 75 respectively) with N-terminal leader sequences, large hydrophilic extracellular domains, single transmembrane spans followed by short cytoplasmic domains. Multiple copies of both genes appear to be present, probably in tandem repeats, and in the case of *isg75* at two different loci [131]. Immunofluorescence microscopy demonstrated that both are uniformly distributed over the entire surface of fixed cells but are not detectable in live cells [4, 127, 129]. This finding suggests that under physiological conditions the proteins are not accessible to antibodies due to shielding by the Vsg. It has been proposed that both proteins form compact globular structures that can be hidden within niches formed by the extended rod-like Vsg molecules. Although the function of these proteins remains unknown, it is tempting to speculate that they may have some form of structural role, perhaps associated with the organization of the Vsg on the cell surface given their relative abundance and proposed surface topology. In this respect it is interesting to note that both proteins are lost from the cellular surface during the differentiation of bloodstream into procyclic forms with approximately the same kinetics as the Vsg [132].

Surface radioiodination has also revealed the presence of a distinctly different Isg, termed Isg100 on the basis of its electrophoretic mobility [128]. This protein, which contains two large N-linked carbohydrate chains, is expressed only in bloodstream forms. The nucleotide sequence of the gene,which has no homology with other known genes, predicts a large, highly reiterative polypeptide (~143 kDa) that contains three distinct domains : a unique N-terminal domain containing *N*-glycosylation sites which is followed by a large internal domain consisting of 72 consecutive copies of a serine-rich, 17 amino acid motif and a unique C-terminal region containing a transmembrane spanning domain and a unique tyrosine which must

TABLE 1

Summary of the molecular features of plasma membrane proteins in *Trypanosoma brucei*. The size of the proteins is given either as the M_r determined by SDS-PAGE (kDa) or alternatively the predicted number of amino acid residues (aa) from the putative open reading frame of the gene

Protein	Identification	Stage	Size	Copy number/cell	Cellular location	Gene	Comments	Ref.
Vsg	Purification and cloning	BF	55–65 kDa	10^7	Cell surface	Multiple	GPI-anchored major surface antigen	[3]
Esag1	Cloning	BF	360 aa	?	?	Multiple	Transmembrane protein ?	[20,23]
Esag2	Cloning	BF	453 aa	?	Cell surface*	Multiple	GPI-anchored protein ?	[20]**
Esag3	Cloning	BF	367 aa	?	?	Multiple	GPI-anchored protein ?	[20]
Esag4	Cloning	BF	140 kDa	low	Flagellum and cell surface***	Multiple	Adenylate cyclase, transmembrane protein	[21,36,107]
Esag6/7	Purification and cloning	BF	50–60 and 42 KDa	$\sim 3 \times 10^{3a}$	FP	Multiple	Heterodimetric transferrin receptor	[21,32–34,96]
Esag10	Cloning	BF	686 aa	?	?	Multiple	Transmembrane protein	[28]
Tht1	Cloning	BF	527 aa	?	Cell surface ?	Multiple	Glucose transporter	[126]
Tht2	Cloning	BF/PF	530 aa	?	Cell surface ?	Multiple	Glucose transporter	[127,128]
LDL-binding protein	Purification	BF/PF	145 kDa	5.4×10^3 total sites (BF)[b]	FP/flagellar membrane	?	Not yet cloned	[98,99,101]
Isg100	Iodination	BF	100 kDa	low	FP/endosomal and lysosomal	Single	Reiterative membrane protein heavily *N*-glycosylated	[131]
Isg75	Biotinylation	BF	75 kDa	5×10^4	Cell surface	Multiple	Transmembrane protein	[132–134]
Isg65/70	Biotinylation and iodination	BF	65/70 kDa	$5–7 \times 10^4$	Cell surface	Multiple	Transmembrane protein with N-linked sugars	[130,132,133]
Isg64	Iodination	BF	64 kDa	?	?	?	Not yet cloned	[130]
Cb1-gp	Immunodetection	BF	180 kDa	?	FP/lysosomal	?	Not yet cloned	[135,136]
Procyclin	Purification and cloning	PF	40–50 kDa[c]	$3–6 \times 10^6$	Cell surface	Multiple	Major surface antigen, GPI-anchored protein	[76–78]
Cram	Cloning	PF	130 kDa	?	FP	?	Cysteine rich protein	[100]
Pssa2	Cloning	PF	412 aa	3×10^5	?	Multiple	Transmembrane protein	[137]
Kmp11	Purification	PF	11 kDa	$0.2–1 \times 10^6$	Flagellum	?	Not yet cloned	[138]
Pag1	Cloning	PF	406 aa	?	?	Single	GPI-anchored protein ?	[86]
Pag3	Cloning	PF	202 aa	?	?	Single	Transmembrane protein ?	[85]
Gresag2.1	Cloning	PF	451 aa	?	Cell surface*	Single	GPI-anchored protein ?	[37]

BF, bloodstream forms; PF, procyclic forms; FP, flagellar pocket.

[a] Variable numbers of transferrin receptors have been reported.

[b] Includes 52 000 low affinity ($K_d = 250$ nM) and 1800 high affinity ($K_d = 5.7$ nM) sites in bloodstream forms.

[c] The M_r of procyclin varies depending on the SDS-PAGE conditions.

*M. Berberof, personal communication.

**Sequence corrected in data base.

***H.P. Voorheis, personal communication.

be at least transiently accessible to the extracellular medium. Unlike the genes for other Isgs, the Isg100 gene is present as a single copy. Although present in the flagellar pocket, Isg100 is predominantly associated with a large digestive vacuole as well as smaller vesicles and collecting tubules located in the proximity of the pocket. While the function of the protein remains unknown, its cellular location and distribution are consistent with it being a constituent of the endocytotic machinery of the cell. The cellular location of Isg100 is similar to that of another glycoprotein, Cb1-gp, which is transiently present on the cell surface as it cycles from the Golgi to the endocytic/lysosomal compartments via the flagellar pocket [133, 134]. At present it is not clear whether the two proteins are related since no sequence data is available for Cb1-gp but this glycoprotein migrates as a heterogenous band of about 180 kDa compared to the homogenous 100 kDa band of Isg100. Interestingly, two other highly reiterative proteins have been found in *T. brucei* that share a similar cellular location to both Isg100 and Cb1-gp. One of these proteins, Cram, is located in the flagellar pocket [98], whereas the other is present in the membranes of the vesicular network that underlies the pocket [135]. Both proteins contain shorter repeat motifs than Isg100 that are rich in acidic amino acids and only one, Cram, demonstrates stage-specific expression, being more abundant in procyclic than bloodstream forms.

Catalysed surface radioiodination has also been used to identify surface antigens in procyclic forms of *T. brucei* [126, 136]. Although a minimum of 25 proteins were labeled using this procedure and the overall pattern of labeling was distinctly different from that observed for bloodstream forms, none of these proteins has been characterized to date. However, a low molecular weight membrane protein (11 kDa), termed Kmp-11, that is significantly more abundant in procyclic than bloodstream forms has been purified from *T. brucei* [137]. Unexpectedly, the protein cross-reacts with monoclonal antibodies against the lipophosphoglycan-associated protein of *Leishmania donovani* and is present in a variety of kinetoplastids. The gene for the protein was not cloned but analysis of the purified protein demonstrated that it is non-glycosylated, relatively abundant ($0.2–1 \times 10^6$ copies per procyclic cell), rich in Asx and Glx residues and present along the length of the flagellum and concentrated at the flagellar base. The protein was not labeled by biotinylation reagents nor was it detected by antibodies in live cells, suggesting that it may not be exposed at the cellular surface.

A completely different approach to the search for surface proteins in *T. brucei* has been developed by Jackson et al. [138]. This strategy has involved the transient expression of procyclic cDNAs in COS-7 cells followed by immunopanning for trypanosomal surface proteins using polyclonal antisera against procyclic cells. In addition to an isoform of procyclin, the cDNA for another surface protein, termed Pssa-2 for procyclic stage surface antigen, was identified. The Pssa-2 cDNA exhibited no homology with any known sequences and coded for a procyclic stage-specific protein with a hydrophilic extracellular domain, a single transmembrane spanning region and a short cytoplasmic tail. An unusual feature of the latter region was the presence of a proline rich tandem repeat. Potential *N*- and *O*-glycosylation sites were also present in the sequence. It was estimated that the protein was approximately 20 times less abundant than procyclin. The function of this protein is not known but given its abundance relative to procyclin, predicted size and membrane topography and allowing for a degree of symmetry between the cell surface in the two life-cycle forms, it is tempting to suggest that Pssa2 has a role analogous to the surface Isgs of bloodstream forms.

5 • Surface proteins identified by functional assays

A variety of studies have suggested the presence of enzymes, solute transporters and ion pumps in the plasma membrane and flagellar pocket. For example, in addition to the glucose transporter, several transporters for a variety of solutes, including amino acids, nucleosides, ethanolamine and fatty acids, are known to be located in the plasma membrane [139–142]. However, the proteins which mediate these transport processes have yet to be identified and characterized. Subcellular fractionation experiments and enzyme cytochemical localization experiments have suggested the presence of hydrolases and other enzymes [143–146], as well as glycoproteins and other antigens in the flagellar pocket [147, 148]. However, assignment of these components to this localization should be considered with caution because of possible contamination from other cellular fractions, most notably lysosomal and microsomal fractions. In contrast to the flagellar pocket, relatively pure preparations of whole sheets of the plasma membrane from the pellicle have been reported [149, 150]. In both these studies there was a significant enrichment for a Na^+/K^+ ATPase as judged by enzyme activity measurements. Presumably this pump may be involved in maintaining cellular ionic homeostasis as is the case for higher eukaryotes. The presence of this ATPase is consistent with the finding that *T. brucei* has high and low intracellular concentration of K^+ and Na^+, respectively [151, 152], and there is physiological evidence for a passive electrogenic K^+ channel in bloodstream forms of *T. brucei* [152–154]. In addition to an ion motive ATPase for these monovalent cations there is also strong evidence for a plasma membrane Ca^{2+} ATPase [155] with properties different from the Ca^{2+} ATPase of the endoplasmic reticulum [156]. Interestingly, in highly purified plasma membranes prepared by free-flow electrophoresis there is an apparent enrichment of a total of 15 proteins, ranging from 24 to 210 kDa as judged by SDS PAGE, only two of which could be identified as the Vsg or a fragment derived from the Vsg [150]. Phase separation experiments with Triton X-114 suggested that most of these proteins behave as integral membrane proteins.

6 • Mechanisms of antigen switching during cellular differentiation

A profound rearrangement of the entire cellular surface occurs during the differentiation of bloodstream into insect-specific, procyclic forms of the parasite. Among other changes, procyclin quickly replaces the Vsg as the predominant antigen. Since these two proteins and their mRNAs are by far the most abundant during their respective developmental stages, they constitute excellent markers for the study of the genetic mechanisms involved in the switching of surface proteins during cellular differentiation.

6.1 Transcriptional regulation

A remarkable feature of the genome organization of kinetoplastids is that genes are devoid of introns and are generally arranged into long polygenic transcription units [157]. Protein-encoding genes can be divided in two categories, depending on the nature of the RNA polymerase used to transcribe them. While most of the genes are transcribed by an α-amanitin-sensitive pol II, the units containing the genes

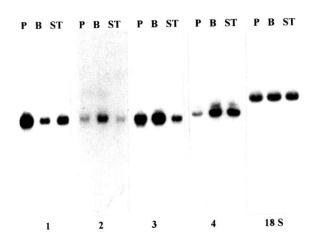

P B ST   P B ST   P B ST   P B ST   P B ST

1   2   3   4   18 S

FIGURE 6

Developmental regulation of mRNA abundance in *T. brucei*. The same Northern blot was successively hybridized with different probes for genes transcribed by pol II (panels 1 to 4). The last panel is a control of the RNA loading (hybridization with 18S rRNA probe). P, B and ST designate RNA from procyclic, bloodstream slender and bloodstream stumpy forms, respectively.

for the two major surface antigens, Vsg and procyclin, are transcribed by an α-amanitin-resistant pol I [47]. Presumably, this form of polymerase is employed because very high levels of transcripts are required for the most abundant antigens, and transcription by pol I is 5 to 10-fold more efficient than by pol II. To date, transcription promoters have been characterized only in the Vsg and procyclin gene units. The available evidence points to the ribosomal nature of these promoters [158–163]. Promoters able to recruit pol II have yet to be described, although weakly active candidates have been proposed [164, 165].

The levels of the different mRNAs are generally highly regulated during the parasite life-cycle (see different examples in Fig. 6).

The stage-specific regulation of mRNA abundance may differ even among genes belonging to the same transcription unit, so that bloodstream-specific and procyclic-specific proteins can be encoded by genes co-transcribed by the same molecule of RNA polymerase. Therefore, primary transcription by pol II seems to be constitutive. As yet no evidence has been found for any developmental control of this process, as determined by measuring the rate of transcription in nuclei isolated from both forms of the parasite [41]. This is true for all genes examined so far. In contrast, the pol I-mediated transcription of the Vsg and procyclin units is clearly regulated [41, 166, 167]. Indeed, strikingly opposite controls ensure the stage-specific transcription of the Vsg gene in the bloodstream form and of the procyclin genes in the procyclic form. In the case of the *vsg*, an additional regulation is also involved which limits transcription to a single ES in the bloodstream form.

Interestingly, it seems that the only transcriptional controls known in *T. brucei*, those acting on the *vsg* and *procyclin* units, do not primarily operate at the level of transcription initiation. First, a number of studies on the RNA synthesis occurring immediately downstream from the promoters in the *vsg* and *procyclin* units have concluded that this region is transcribed even during the developmental stage where these units are not functionally expressed [168–170]. Second, in both transient and permanent assays of a reporter function the *vsg* and *procyclin* promoters can exhibit a comparable activity at both stages of the parasite life-cycle [159, 170–173]. Taken together these findings indicate that all the necessary components required for recruitment of the RNA polymerase and initiation of transcription on these promoters are present during both bloodstream and procyclic stages, and that the activity of these promoters is essentially constitutive, in keeping with their probable ribosomal nature. However, it should be pointed out that in situ, full promoter activity is clearly dependent on the chromosomal context. Both the *vsg* and *procyclin* promoters, but also the ribosomal promoter, are less active when inserted in the *procyclin* units at the bloodstream stage, or in the *vsg* unit at the procyclic stage [170, 173]. In addition, when inserted within the *tubulin* transcription unit the *vsg* promoter is always inactivated, whereas in the same location the *procyclin* promoter can recruit its polymerase, but only in procyclic forms [174, 175]. The latter property appears to depend on the presence of upstream sequence elements (M. Berberof and E. Pays, unpublished data) which are presumably also those able to stimulate the activity of the *vsg* promoter when placed in its vicinity, even in opposite orientation [176, 177]. Therefore, in the chromosomal context a modulation of the pol I (like) promoter activity is possible due to cis-acting and non-specific elements, presumably through a regulation of the relative accessibility of DNA in chromatin.

If regulation of promoter activity is not primarily responsible for the stage-specific transcription control of the *vsg* and *procyclin* units, where is this control effected ? Analysis of transcription in isolated nuclei has shown that elongation of the RNA chains is subject to a stage-specific control operating in a clearly inverse fashion in the *vsg* and *procyclin* units [178]. Thus, abortive transcription occurs both in the *vsg* unit in the procyclic form and in the *procyclin* units in the bloodstream form. The stimuli for cellular differentiation from the bloodstream to the procyclic form (in particular a cold shock and the presence of cis-aconitate in the medium) appear to change these RNA elongation controls very rapidly. Again, these observation point to cis-acting controls of transcription, probably mediated by chromatin components. The opposite symmetry of these controls suggests a cross-talk between the two transcription units, but its nature remains obscure at present. It may be relevant to note that a common single-stranded DNA-binding protein appears to be shared by the two transcription promoters [162], evoking the possibility of a mutually exclusive use of the same factor(s) in only one of the two units at a time, depending on the developmental conditions (see the paper by L. Vanhamme and E. Pays in this issue). The hypothesis of the developmentally-controlled use of a common transcriptional element present in only limited amounts could possibly account both for the exclusive expression of a single *vsg* ES in bloodstream forms (alternative *vsg* ESs and *procyclin* units would be all restrained to abortive transcription) and for the exclusive expression of the *procyclin* units in procyclic forms (all *vsg* ESs are restrained to abortive transcription, and it is even possible that one of the different *procyclin* units is favoured over the others : see the paper by I. Roditi et al., in this issue).

6.2   Post-transcriptional regulation

The maturation of the polygenic transcripts into individual mRNAs is achieved by cleavage in the intergenic region of the primary transcripts followed by processing of the RNA extremities : trans-splicing at the 5'-end and polyadenylation at the 3'-end. These processing events are coupled. Both seem to depend on the recognition of polypyrimidine tracts present in the intergenic regions [166, 179]. Evidence is accumulating which indicates that the nature of the intergenic RNA sequences (UTRs), in particular the 3'-UTR, is the key element which determines the final amount of each individual mature mRNA in a stage-specific manner. This feature seems to be general for all genes irrespective of the polymerase used for transcription. The controls of RNA processing and stability appear to represent the principal levels where the differential expression of genes occurs as a function of development and, therefore, they underly the cellular differentiation of the parasite [41, 167]. Not surprisingly, in the case of the *vsg* and *procyclin* mRNAs the 3'-UTRs give rise to a high level of transcripts from reporter genes in the bloodstream and in the procyclic form, respectively [173, 180, 181]. The 3'-UTR of the *vsg* mRNA was found to cause two effects : it up-regulates the mRNA level in the bloodstream form by increasing the RNA stability and it down-regulates the mRNA level in the procyclic form by slowing down the rate of mRNA maturation [175]. The mechanisms by which the 3'-UTRs differentially influence the RNA amounts are presently unknown. In both *vsg* and *procyclin* mRNAs the available evidence points to the importance of polypyrimidine stretches present in the 3'-terminal region, and suggest that the control is mediated by short-lived proteins [175, 182–184]. Since polypyrimidine tracts are also trans-splicing signals [166, 179], it would appear that these sequences can recruit factors able to cleave the primary transcripts. Cleavage in the 3'-UTR may lead to inefficient processing of the free RNA ends and subsequent RNA degradation, and, therefore, it is possible that the sequences surrounding the polypyrimidine tracts can shield them against endonucleolytic cleavage, either by their folding or by the binding of proteins, or both. The differential mRNA stability as a function of the parasite development strongly suggests that the factors controlling the accessibility of the polypyrimidine tracts are stage-specific. However, to date not a single specific RNA-binding protein has been described in *T. brucei.*

In addition to determining the level of mRNA, sequences in the 3'-UTR, as well as in the coding region, also appear to influence the translation of the mRNA. This is particularly clear for the *procyclin* and *garp* mRNAs, which contain a stem-loop structure involved in translation [185]. So far there is no evidence that this last control is developmentally regulated.

Under steady-state conditions, gene expression in the *vsg* and *procyclin* units is already regulated at the primary transcription level.

Therefore, in these cases the different post-transcriptional controls discussed above concerning the *vsg* and *procyclin* mRNAs probably play a role only during the transition between successive developmental stages, and experimental evidence supports this view [175]. These controls presumably ensure a rapid change of the major surface antigens when cellular differentiation is triggered. Indeed, when bloodstream forms are induced to transform into procyclics, the amount of *vsg* mRNA switches from 10% of the polyadenylated transcripts to almost nothing within 4 h, whereas at the same time exactly the opposite occurs for the *procyclin* mRNA [186]. Presumably post-transcriptional controls acting on the stability and processing of the transcripts as well as on mRNA translation allow for accelerated disappearance of both the *vsg* mRNA and the protein it encodes, at a moment when the *procyclin* mRNA must rapidly accumulate and be expressed at very high levels.

6.3 Relevance for the adaptation of the parasite

The trypanosome genes are generally contained in long polycistronic units which appear to be continuously transcribed and cellular differentiation is dependent on stage-regulated post-transcriptional controls which determine the selective accumulation of some mRNAs, while the others are degraded. A priori, this system may seem less flexible and more wasteful than what generally occurs in other eukaryotes, namely controls of transcription initiation in monocistronic units. However, a remarkable feature of this system is the speed and precision at which the concerted changes linked to cellular differentiation occur, as revealed in particular during the experimentally-induced switching from the bloodstream to the procyclic form in vitro (see [187], for a timing of these events). Consequently, it appears that modulating gene expression at the level of RNA processing is at least as efficient and accurate as controlling transcription promoters. Presumably the constitutive transcription of most genes is a system that allows for a continuous supply of all primary RNA sequences, whatever the developmental stage of the parasite. Such a strategy would provide an immediate source of different sets of transcripts in case of a sudden change of the environmental conditions, such as the abrupt transfer from the blood into the fly or vice-versa, which is the situation in the wild. Of course this system is not the most economical, but for parasites the supply of energy is probably not a major matter of concern. Moreover, this type of gene expression control has probably spared trypanosomes from developing a complex network of specific regulatory transcription factors and target DNA sequences.

At least for the genes encoding the major surface antigens, Vsg and procyclin, transcription elongation appears to be specifically controlled. Again, it is tempting to propose that the abortive engagement of transcription of each unit at the developmental stage where its expression is down-regulated allows the parasite to instantaneously trigger full transcription as soon as the environmental conditions require it. This could also be valid for the different *vsg* ESs in the bloodstream form : the abortive engagement of transcription in the *vsg* ESs that are not used for Vsg expression would allow immediate ES switching when the need for antigenic variation imposes it.

Full activation of either a *vsg* or a *procyclin* unit always appears to be linked to the relative inactivation of the other. Given the striking symmetry of this process, irrespective of the environmental conditions — cellular differentiation or experimental modifications of the incubation medium — it would seem that it depends on some factors shared between the two units, as if, for instance, the (de)phosphorylation of a component of the transcription machinery at work on these units would condition (in)activation of only one of these units, or, as if the presence of a stage-dependent factor would be required both to activate one unit and repress the other. Interestingly, the Vsg and procyclin genes are located at opposite ends of their respective transcription units, the *vsg* being the last and *procyclin* the first. This implies that inhibition of RNA elongation in the *vsg* unit immediately and completely stops transcription of the Vsg gene which is very far from the promoter, whereas at the same time full transcription of the procyclin genes is triggered. Presumably this synchrony relates to the necessity for abrupt switching of coats as soon as the parasite is ingested by the fly.

7 • The elusive vaccine

So far, trypanosomes have eluded not just the host antibodies, but also defeated all the best efforts of researchers to counteract their infection strategies. Almost certainly an effective anti-trypanosomal vaccine, should such a panacea be actually possible, will have to take into consideration not just antigenic variation but also another weapon in the arsenal of the parasite, namely immunosuppression.

7.1 Parasite surface components and immunosuppression

African trypanosomes, like many parasites, not only escape the defenses of their hosts, but also actively perturb these defenses. Infection by the parasite leads to a loss of both specificity and memory of the immune response, in a process generally termed immunosuppression. In the case of trypanosomiasis, this is manifested by the inhibition of the proliferative response by T-cells, as well as by a polyclonal activation of B-cells and the development of autoimmune antibodies. In mice, perturbation of the immune system appears to involve two phases : a primary rapid but transient suppression due to the production of nitric oxide in the spleen, followed by the progressive establishment of a long-lasting immunosuppression typical of chronic infection. The available evidence points to the crucial role of cells derived from the lymph nodes in this latter process. The parasite appears to induce the synthesis of IFN-γ by CD8+ cells from this cellular compartment, which in turn triggers the overall pattern of immunosuppression. IFN-γ stimulates macrophages to produce high levels of TNF-α and to adopt an immunosuppressive phenotype, ultimately leading to the inhibition of the production of both IL-2 and its receptor [188]. Whether the induction of IFN-γ synthesis by CD8+ cells is directly due to parasite components or results indirectly from interaction of macrophages with the parasite is a matter of controversy [114, 188]. So far, the nature of the parasite factors responsible for triggering immunosuppression is unknown. Nevertheless, it is interesting to note that the inositolglycan moiety which remains at the base of the Vsg after cleavage by the GPI-PLC is a potent stimulator of TNF-α synthesis by IFN-γ-primed macrophages, whereas the full anchor renders macrophages hyperresponsive to LPS ([117, 189]; S. Magez et al., unpublished data). Both processes lead to the accumulation of TNF-α in the host, contributing not only to the establishment of immunosuppression, but also to the development of the pathology of the disease [115]. Therefore, GPI-anchored surface proteins such as the Vsg could be involved in the immunosuppression and pathology associated with the disease, both in their membrane-bound and released forms.

7.2 Protective antigens

The strong immunosuppression established during a chronic parasitaemia does not allow the development of an appropriate reaction of the host. Therefore, protective antigens, either present on the parasite surface or released after lysis of the cells, may exist but are not subjected to an effective immune response.

It is clear that the main trypanosome antigen, the Vsg, has been evolutionary selected to be presented to the immune system for the benefit of the parasite. The extraordinary variability of this protein obviously prevents its exploitation for vaccination. Even immunization with a large collection of Vsg variants from a given serodeme could provide only partial protection since it would not inhibit infection by variants from other serodemes.

As discussed above, the non-Vsg surface components of African trypanosomes are either completely buried underneath the tight Vsg coat or secluded in the flagellar pocket. Interestingly, the latter contains most, if not all surface receptors. These proteins are theoretically the most promising vaccine candidates, since their function imposes at least three criteria which are very useful in this respect : accessibility from the extracellular environment, relative invariance and importance for the cell viability [190]. To date, only the transferrin and LDL receptors have been characterized in any detail. Experimental evidence confirmed that these receptors can be reached by antibodies in vivo, and that this interaction can interfere with cellular growth [31, 96, 119]. However, in the case of the transferrin receptor, the presence of variant genes in the different *vsg* ESs, as well as the evidence for alternative expression of these variants, precludes the immediate use of this protein as a vaccine. In particular, it would seem that antibodies can bind to the receptor, and interfere with its function, only in cases where the affinity of the receptor for its ligand is low [120]. This binding could force the selection for the activation of *vsg* ESs encoding receptors of higher affinity, which would then be resistant to antibody binding.

In addition to the transferrin receptor, which resembles a Vsg, it is possible that some of the other receptors present in the flagellar pocket are actually Vsg molecules released from the plasma membrane (Section 3.4). Therefore, it would appear that, at least for some receptors, trypanosomes have managed to reconcile the necessary invariant nature of the ligand binding sites with the need for antigenic variation of the exposed epitopes.

7.3   Experimental vaccination

Despite the difficulties discussed above, some encouraging results have been obtained in experimental attempts of vaccination with flagellar pocket preparations, both in mice and in cattle ([148, 191] ; M. Radwanska, D. Nolan and E. Pays, unpublished data). Significantly, in mice this vaccination not only completely blocked the development of immunosuppression but it also led to a drastic qualitative change in the nature of the antibody isotypes, with a strong increase in the production of IgGγ2a (M. Radwanska et al., unpublished). Therefore, it seems that the flagellar pocket contains useful targets for prophylaxy but also components able to block the development of immunosuppression. The nature of these molecules remains to be determined. As could be expected from the discussion above, it would seem that successful vaccination requires a level of Vsg contamination as low as possible (M. Radwanska et al., unpublished).

8 • Conclusions and perspectives

By any criteria the cellular surface of African trypanosomes represents an extremely dynamic biological interface, one that is subjected both to continuous modifications and dramatic changes throughout the life-cycle of the cell. In bloodstream trypomastigotes the plasma membrane is completely covered by a dense surface coat consisting of Vsg. This protein has two major functions. First, it elicits an efficient antibody response which down-regulates the number of parasites and, consequently, ensures prolonged survival of the host. Second, concomitant with the immune challenge mounted against the predominant Vsg antigenic variation of the Vsg in different generations always allows a certain number of parasites to escape destruction and give rise to new waves of infection. This variation of Vsg is driven by two basically different processes : the alternative activation of different *vsg* ESs and frequent DNA rearrangements due to spontaneous homologous recombination in the active telomeric *vsg* ES. The former mechanism probably also allows the parasite to express surface proteins and receptors that are best adapted for different mammalian hosts, whereas the latter provides the means by which trypanosomes can generate new Vsgs by sequence rearrangements. The sequential use of these different methods of varying the Vsg during a chronic infection provides an explanation of certain puzzling features of antigenic variation in *T. brucei,* such as the relative programming of Vsg expression and the hyper-evolution of Vsg repertoires.

It goes without saying that the most dramatic, but by no means the only, change in the composition of the plasma membrane occurs when the entire Vsg coat is replaced by procyclin, a completely different glycoprotein, during the differentiation of bloodstream to procyclic forms of the parasite. Significantly, the mechanisms responsible for this major reprogramming of gene expression do not operate primarily at the level of the transcription promoters but rather during the elongation and processing of the relevant transcripts. Presumably, the choice of this form of control is related both to the organization of the genome of the trypanosome into long polycistronic transcription units and to the need for immediate and simultaneous switching of the two relevant units as soon as the environmental conditions require it.

Although during the past few years several receptors and other minor proteins have been identified, apart from Vsg and procyclin, overall our knowledge of trypanosomal surface proteins at a molecular and functional level remains significantly less than that available for higher eukaryotes. Nevertheless, even from the limited data available certain interesting features are beginning to emerge. First, as exemplified by the case of transferrin, it is likely that trypanosomes have evolved receptors for macromolecules that are functionally analogous but are radically different to those of their host/vector. While at a biological level such novelty is very exciting, at a practical level it may have portentous implications for the hopes of establishing the potential function of trypanosomal surface proteins by homology with proteins in the data base. Second, in the case of bloodstream trypomastigotes several surface proteins appear to adopt a Vsg-like structure or to be related to Vsgs [192]. It is possible that this observation is related to an evolutionary selection for surface proteins with conformations compatible with the Vsg coat. Finally, it is striking to note that, where the appropriate information is available, all externally disposed surface proteins so far described in African trypanosomes, including Vsg, Esags, Isgs, Cb1-gp, receptors and transporters in bloodstream trypomastigotes and procyclin, Garp, Pssa2, Cram, Kmp11 and Tht2 in procyclic forms, are expressed in a life cycle stage-specific manner. By contrast as far as we know no externally disposed surface protein has been found to be expressed equally in both life cycle forms, with the possible exception, however, of adenylate cyclase isoforms encoded by the *gresag 4* family. Although it is too early to be certain, it is possible that stage-specific expression of external surface proteins in *T. brucei* may prove to be the rule rather than the exception. Thus, in a sense the entire externally disposed surface of the trypanosome may be stage specific! What would be the possible teleological basis for such a drastic life cycle asymmetry? One obvious possibility relates to the previous point of selecting for surface proteins with structures compatible with the dominant surface antigen in order to create a uniform and homogeneous surface coat. However, it seems unlikely that these structural considerations alone would be responsible since both Vsg and procyclin are compatible within the same surface as observed during differentiation in vitro, and both Vsg and Esags can be functionally and efficiently expressed in procyclic forms in transfection experiments. It is more likely that the basis for such an asymmetry in surface protein expression relates to functional and environmental considerations. For example, proteins which have been designed to operate and function in the mammalian bloodstream are unlikely to be as effective in the altogether different environment of the insect gut and, of course, visa versa. Moreover, if trypanosomes appear to have developed a battery of Esags to cope with the subtle differences between different mammalian hosts it seems entirely reasonable that they have also developed different families of surface proteins to cope with the far greater differences between the extracellular environments of the mammalian host and arthropod vector. Whatever the reason, it may well be that changes in the cellular surface that occur during the transition between these two life cycle stages are even more profound than originally suspected.

Although the past few years have seen significant progress in our understanding of the function and expression of trypanosomal surface proteins, as usual the answers have led to even more questions. What is the basis of the selective activation of a single ES in bloodstream trypomastigotes and how is switching between ESs accomplished ? What are the enzymes involved in the processes of homologous recombination and are these enzymes regulated during the development of the parasite ? At present our functional and molecular understanding of non-Vsg surface proteins in bloodstream trypomastigotes remains inadequate, while the situation in life cycle forms that occur in the arthropod vector is even worse. What is the nature of trafficking of proteins to and from the surface ? For example, are proteins recycled ? Are any of the surface proteins potential targets for vaccination ? Finally, how is the massive reorganization of the cell surface between life cycle stages accomplished so efficiently and rapidly ? Amid all of this uncertainty, the only thing certain for the future, is that, as in the past, trypanosomes will continue to surprise us.

Acknowledgements

The work in our laboratory was financed by the Belgian FRSM and FRC-IM, a research contract with the Communaute Française de Belgique (ARC), the Interuniversity Poles of Attraction Programme, Belgian State, Prime Minister's Office, Federal Office for Scientific, Technical and Cultural Affairs, and by the Agreement for Collaborative Research between ILRAD (Nairobi) and Belgian Research Centres. E.P. thanks the Francqui Foundation (Brussels) for helpful support.

R E F E R E N C E S

[1] Kuzoe F.A. Current situation of African trypanosomiasis. Acta Tropica; 54; 1993; 153-162.

[2] Hursey B.S., Slingenbergh J. The tsetse fly and its effects on agriculture in sub-Saharan Africa. World Animal Rev; 3 (4); 1995; 67-73.

[3] Blum M.L., Down J.A., Gurnett A.M., Carrington M., Turner M.J., Wiley D. A structural motif in the variant surface glycoproteins of *Trypanosoma brucei*. Nature; 362; 1993; 603-609.

[4] Ziegelbauer K., Overath P. Organization of two invariant surface glycoproteins in the surface coat of *Trypanosoma brucei*. Infect Immun; 61; 1993; 4540-4545.

[5] Carrington M., Walters D., Webb H. The biology of the glycosylphosphatidylinositol-specific phospholipase C of *Trypanosoma brucei*. Cell Biol Intern Rep; 15; 1991; 1101-1114.

[6] Rolin S., Hanocq-Quertier J., Paturiaux-Hanocq F., Nolan D., Salmon D., Webb H., Carrington M., Voorheis P., Pays E. Simultaneous but independent activation of adenylate cyclase and glycosylphosphatidylinositol-phospholipase C under stress conditions in *Trypanosoma brucei*. J Biol Chem; 271; 1996; 10844-10852.

[7] Webb H, Carnall N, Vanhamme L, Rolin S, Van Den Abbeele J, Welburn S, Pays E, Carrington M. The GPI-specific phospholipase C of *Trypanosoma brucei* is non-essential but influences parasitaemia in mice. J Cell Biol ; 139 ; 1997 ; 103-114.

[8] Turner C.M.R., Barry J.D. High frequency of antigenic variation in *Trypanosoma brucei* rhodesiense infections. Parasitology; 99; 1989; 67-75.

[9] Cross G.A.M. Cellular and genetic aspects of antigenic variation in trypanosomes. Annu Rev Immunol; 8; 1990; 83-110.

[10] Van der Ploeg L.H.T., Valerio D., De Lange T., Bernards A., Borst P., Grosveld F.G. An analysis of cosmid clones of nuclear DNA from *Trypanosoma brucei* shows that the genes for variant surface glycoproteins are clustered in the genome. Nucleic Acids Res; 10; 1982; 5905-5923.

[11] Weiden M., Osheim Y.N., Beyer A.L., Van der Ploeg L.H.T. Chromosome structure: DNA nucleotide sequence elements of a subset of the mini-chromosomes of the protozoan *Trypanosoma brucei*. Mol Cell Biol; 11; 1991; 3823-3834.

[12] Liu A.Y.C., Van der Ploeg L.H.T., Rijsewijk F.A.M., Borst P. The transcription unit of variant surface glycoprotein gene 118 of *Trypanosoma brucei*. Presence of repeated elements at its border and absence of promoter associated sequences. J Mol Biol; 167; 1983; 57-75.

[13] Aline R.F.J., Stuart K.D. *Trypanosoma brucei*: conserved sequence organization 3' to telomeric variant surface glycoprotein genes. Exp Parasitol; 68; 1989; 57-66.

[14] Navarro M., Cross G.A.M. DNA rearrangements associated with multiple consecutive directed antigenic switches in *Trypanosoma brucei*. Mol Cell Biol; 16; 1996; 3615-3625.

[15] Alarcon C.M., Son H.J., Hall T., Donelson J.E. A monocistronic transcript for a trypanosome variant surface glycoprotein. Mol Cell Biol; 14; 1994; 5579-5591.

[16] Graham S.V., Barry J.D. Transcriptional regulation of metacyclic variant surface glycoprotein gene expression during the life cycle of *Trypanosoma brucei*. Mol Cell Biol; 15; 1995; 5945-5956.

[17] Kooter J.M., Van der Spek H.J., Wagter R., d'Oliveira C.E., Van der Hoeven F., Johnson P., Borst P. The anatomy and transcription of a telomeric expression site for variant-specific surface antigens in *Trypanosoma brucei*. Cell; 51; 1987; 261-272.

[18] Johnson P.J., Kooter J.M., Borst P. Inactivation of transcription by UV irradiation of *T. brucei* provides evidence for a multicistronic transcription unit including a VSG gene. Cell; 51; 1987; 273-281.

[19] Alexandre S., Guyaux M., Murphy N.B., Coquelet H., Steinert M., Pays E. Putative genes of a variant-specific antigen gene transcription unit in *Trypanosoma brucei*. Mol Cell Biol; 8; 1988; 2367-2378.

[20] Pays E., Tebabi P., Pays A., Coquelet H., Revelard P., Salmon D., Steinert M. The genes and transcripts of an antigen gene expression site from *T. brucei*. Cell; 57; 1989; 835-845.

[21] Lips S., Revelard P., Pays E. Identification of a new expression site-associated gene in the complete 30.5 kb sequence from the AnTat 1.3A variant surface protein gene expression site of *Trypanosoma brucei*. Mol Biochem Parasitol; 62; 1993; 135-138.

[22] Cully D.F., Ip H.S., Cross G.A.M. Coordinate transcription of variant surface glycoprotein genes and an expression site associated gene family in *Trypanosoma brucei*. Cell; 42; 1985; 173-182.

[23] Graham S.V., Matthews K.R., Barry J.D. *Trypanosoma brucei*: unusual expression-site-associated gene homologies in a metacyclic VSG gene expression site. Exp Parasitol; 76; 1993; 96-99.

[24] Sterverding D., Overath P. *Trypanosoma brucei* with an active metacyclic variant surface gene expression site expresses a transferrin receptor derived from ESAG6 and ESAG7. Mol Biochem Parasitol; 78; 1996; 285-288.

[25] Pays E., Vanhamme L., Berberof M. Genetic controls for the expression of surface proteins in African trypanosomes. Annu Rev Microbiol; 48; 1994; 25-52.

[26] Gottesdiener K.M., Goriparthi L., Masucci J.P., Van der Ploeg L.H.T. A proposed mechanism for promoter-associated DNA rearrangement events at a variant surface glycoprotein gene expression site. Mol Cell Biol; 12; 1992; 4784-4795.

[27] Gottesdiener K.M. A new VSG expression site-associated gene (ESAG) in the promoter region of *Trypanosoma brucei* encodes a protein with 10 potential transmembrane domains. Mol Biochem Parasitol; 63; 1994; 143-151.

[28] Smiley B.L., Stadnyk A.W., Myler P.J., Stuart K. The trypanosome leucine repeat gene in the variant surface glycoprotein expression site encodes a putative metal-binding domain and a region resembling protein-binding domains of yeast *Drosophila*, and mammalian proteins. Mol Cell Biol; 10; 1990; 6436-6444.

[29] Revelard P., Lips S., Pays E. A gene from the VSG gene expression site of *Trypanosoma brucei* encodes a protein with both leucine-rich repeats and a putative zinc finger. Nucleic Acids Res; 18; 1990; 7299-7303.

[30] Lips S., Geuskens M., Paturiaux-Hanocq F., Hanocq-Quertier J., Pays E. The ESAG 8 gene of *Trypanosoma brucei* encodes a nuclear protein. Mol Biochem Parasitol; 79; 1996; 113-117.

[31] Salmon D., Geuskens M., Hanocq F., Hanocq-Quertier J., Nolan D., Ruben L., Pays E. A novel heterodimeric transfer-

rin receptor encoded by a pair of VSG expression site-associated genes in *Trypanosoma brucei.* Cell; 78; 1994; 75-86.

[32] Steverding D., Stierhof Y.D., Chaudhri M., Ligtenberg M., Schell D., Beck-Sickinger A.G., Overath P. ESAG 6 and 7 products of *Trypanosoma brucei* form a transferrin binding complex. Eur J Cell Biol; 64; 1994; 78-87.

[33] Ligtenberg M.J., Bitter W., Kieft R., Steverding D., Janssen H., Calafat J., Borst P. Reconstitution of a surface transferrin binding complex in insect form *Trypanosoma brucei.* EMBO J; 13; 1994; 2565-2573.

[34] Ross D.T., Raibaud A., Florent I.C., Sather S., Gross M.K., Storm D.R., Eisen H. The trypanosome VSG expression site encodes adenylate cyclase and a leucine-rich putative regulatory gene. EMBO J; 10; 1991; 2047-2053.

[35] Paindavoine P., Rolin S., Van Assel S., Geuskens M., Jauniaux J.C., Dinsart C., Huet G., Pays E. A gene from the VSG expression site encodes one of several transmembrane adenylate cyclases located on the flagellum of *Trypanosoma brucei.* Mol Cell Biol; 12; 1992; 1218-1225.

[36] Berberof M., Pays A., Pays E. A similar gene is shared by both the VSG and procyclin gene transcription units of *Trypanosoma brucei.* Mol Cell Biol; 11; 1991; 1473-1479.

[37] Carruthers V.B., Navarro M., Cross G.A.M. Targeted disruption of expression site-associated gene-1 in bloodstream-form *Trypanosoma brucei.* Mol Biochem Parasitol; 81; 1996; 65-79.

[38] Munoz-Jordan J.L., Davies K.P., Cross G.A.M. Stable expression of mosaic coats of variant surface glycoproteins in *Trypanosoma brucei.* Science; 272; 1996; 1795-1797.

[39] Borst P., Gommers-Ampt J.H., Ligtenberg M.J., Rudenko G., Kieft R., Taylor M., Blundell P., Van Leeuwen F. Control of antigenic variation in African trypanosomes. Cold Spring Harbor Symp Quant Biol; 58; 1993; 105-114.

[40] Cross G.A.M. Antigenic variation in trypanosomes : secrets surface slowly. Bioessays; 18; 1996; 283-291.

[41] Pays E, Vanhamme L. Developmental regulation of gene expression in African trypanosomes. In : Smith DF, Parsons M, editors. Molecular Biology of Parasitic Protozoa. IRL Press, Oxford, 1996 : 88–114.

[42] Barry J.D. The relative significance of mechanisms of antigenic variation in African trypanosomes. Parasitol Today; 13; 1997; 212-218.

[43] Horn D., Cross G.A.M. Analysis of *Trypanosoma brucei vsg* expression site switching in vitro. Mol Biochem Parasitol; 84; 1997; 189-201.

[44] Gommers-Ampt J.H., Van Leeuwen F., de Beer A.L.J., Vliegenthart J.F.G., Dizdaroglu M., Kowalak J.A., Crain P.F., Borst P. β-D-Glucosyl-hydroxymethyluracil : a novel modified base present in the DNA of the parasitic protozoan *Trypanosoma brucei.* Cell; 75; 1993; 1129-1136.

[45] Van Leeuwen F., Wijsman E.R., Kuyl-Yeheskiely E., Van der Marel G.A., Van Boom J.H., Borst P. The telomeric GGGTTA repeats of *Trypanosoma brucei* contain the hypermodified base J in both strands. Nucleic Acids Res; 24; 1996; 2476-2482.

[46] Horn D., Cross G.A.M. A developmentally regulated position effect at a telomeric locus in *Trypanosoma brucei.* Cell; 83; 1995; 555-561.

[47] Chung H.M., Lee M.G.S., Van der Ploeg L.H.T. RNA polymerase I-mediated protein-coding gene expression in *Trypanosoma brucei.* Parasitol Today; 8; 1992; 414-418.

[48] Gottschling D.E., Aparicio O.M., Billington B.L., Zakian V.A. Position effect at *Saccharomyces cerevisiae* telomeres : reversible repression of pol II transcription. Cell; 63; 1990; 751-762.

[49] Le Ray D., Barry J.D., Vickerman K. Antigenic heterogeneity of metacyclic forms of *Trypanosoma brucei.* Nature; 273; 1978; 300-302.

[50] ten Asbroek A.L.M.A., Ouellette M., Borst P. Targeted insertion of the neomycin phosphotransferase gene into the tubulin gene cluster of *Trypanosoma brucei.* Nature; 348; 1990; 174-175.

[51] Lee M.G.S., Van der Ploeg L.H.T. Homologous recombination and stable transfection in the parasitic protozoan *Trypanosoma brucei.* Science; 250; 1990; 1583-1587.

[52] Eid J., Sollner-Webb B. Stable integrative transformation of *Trypanosoma brucei* that occurs exclusively by homologous recombination. Proc Natl Acad Sci USA; 88; 1991; 2118-2121.

[53] Blundell P.A., Rudenko G., Borst P. Targeting of exogenous DNA into *Trypanosoma brucei* requires a high degree of homology between donor and target DNA. Mol Biochem Parasitol; 76; 1996; 215-229.

[54] Pays E., Lheureux M., Steinert M. The expression-linked copy of the surface antigen gene in *Trypanosoma* is probably the one transcribed. Nature; 292; 1981; 265-267.

[55] Pays E. Gene conversion in trypanosome antigenic variation. Prog Nucleic Acid Res Mol Biol; 32; 1985; 1-26.

[56] McCulloch R., Rudenko G., Borst P. Gene conversions mediating antigenic variation in *Trypanosoma brucei* can occur in variant surface glycoprotein expression sites lacking 70-base-pair repeat sequences. Mol Cell Biol; 17; 1997; 833-843. .

[57] Pays E. Pseudogenes, chimeric genes and the timing of antigen variation in African trypanosomes. Trends Genet; 5; 1989; 389-391.

[58] Barbet A.F., Kamper S.M. The importance of mosaic genes to trypanosome survival. Parasitol Today; 9; 1993; 63-66.

[59] Pays E., Guyaux M., Aerts D., Van Meirvenne N., Steinert M. Telomeric reciprocal recombination as a possible mechanism for antigenic variation in trypanosomes. Nature; 316; 1985; 562-564.

[60] Rudenko G., McCulloch R., Dirks-Mulder A., Borst P. Telomere exchange can be an important mechanism of variant surface glycoprotein gene switching in *Trypanosoma brucei*. Mol Biochem Parasitol; 80; 1996; 65-75.

[61] Laurent M., Pays E., Van der Werf A., Aerts D., Magnus E., Van Meirvenne N., Steinert M. Translocation alters the activation rate of a trypanosome surface antigen gene. Nucleic Acids Res; 12; 1984; 8319-8328.

[62] Van der Werf A., Van Assel S., Aerts D., Steinert M., Pays E. Telomere interactions may condition the programming of antigen expression in *Trypanosoma brucei*. EMBO J; 9; 1990; 1035-1040.

[63] Fang G., Cech T.R. The b subunit of *Oxytricha* telomere-binding protein promotes G-quartet formation by telomeric DNA. Cell; 44; 1993; 875-885.

[64] Thon G., Baltz T., Eisen H. Antigenic diversity by the recombination of pseudogenes. Genes Dev; 3; 1989; 1247-1254.

[65] Thon G., Baltz T., Giroud C., Eisen H. Trypanosome variable surface glycoproteins: composite genes and order of expression. Genes Dev; 9; 1990; 1374-1383.

[66] Paindavoine P., Pays E., Laurent M., Geltmeyer Y., Le Ray D., Mehlitz D., Steinert M. The use of DNA hybridization and numerical taxonomy in determining relationships between *Trypanosoma brucei* stocks and subspecies. Parasitology; 92; 1986; 31-50.

[67] Dero B., Zampetti-Bosseler F., Pays E., Steinert M. The genome and the antigen gene repertoire of *Trypanosoma brucei gambiense* are smaller than those of *T. b. brucei*. Mol Biochem Parasitol; 26; 1987; 247-256.

[68] Gibson W. Will the real *Trypanosoma b. gambiense* please stand up. Parasitol Today; 2; 1986; 255-257.

[69] Lu Y., Hall T., Gay L.S., Donelson J.E. Point mutations are associated with a gene duplication leading to the bloodstream reexpression of a trypanosome metacyclic VSG. Cell; 72; 1993; 397-406.

[70] Graham V.S., Barry J.D. Is point mutation a mechanism for antigenic variation in *Trypanosoma brucei*. Mol Biochem Parasitol; 79; 1996; 35-45.

[71] Baltz T., Giroud C., Bringaud F., Eisen H., Jacquemot C., Roth C.W. Exposed epitopes on a *Trypanosoma equiperdum* variant surface glycoprotein altered by point mutations. EMBO J; 10; 1991; 1653-1659.

[72] Jenni L., Marti S., Schweizer J., Betschart B., Le Page R.W.F., Wells J.M., Tait A., Paindavoine P., Pays E., Steinert M. Hybrid formation between trypanosomes during cyclical transmission. Nature; 322; 1986; 173-175.

[73] Paindavoine P., Zampetti-Bosseler F., Pays E., Schweizer J., Guyaux M., Jenni L., Steinert M. Trypanosome hybrids generated in tsetse flies by nuclear fusion. EMBO J; 5; 1986; 3631-3636.

[74] Swindle J, Tait A. Trypanosomatid genetics. In: Smith DF, Parsons M, editors. Molecular Biology of Parasitic Protozoa. IRL Press, Oxford, 1996: 6–34.

[75] Roditi I., Pearson T.W. The procyclin coat of African trypanosomes. Parasitol Today; 6; 1990; 79-82.

[76] Stebeck C.E., Pearson T.W. Mini-review: Major surface glycoproteins of procyclic stage African trypanosomes. Exp Parasitol; 78; 1994; 432-436.

[77] Richardson J.P., Beecroft R.P., Tolson D.L., Liu M.K., Pearson T.W. Procyclin: An unusual immunodominant glycoprotein surface antigen from procyclic stage of African trypanosomes. Mol Biochem Parasitol; 31; 1988; 203-216.

[78] McConville M.J. Glycosyl-phosphatidylinositols and the surface architecture of parasitic protozoa. In: Smith DF, Parsons M, editors. Molecular Biology of Parasitic Protozoa. IRL Press, Oxford, 1996: 205–228.

[79] Ferguson M.A.J., Murray P., Rutherford H., McConville M.J. A simple purification of procyclic acid repetitive proteins and demonstration of a sialated glycosyl-phosphatidylinositol membrane anchor. Biochem J; 290; 1993; 51-55.

[80] Paturiaux-Hanocq F., Zitmann N., Hanocq-Quertier J., Vanhamme L., Rolin S., Geuskens M., Ferguson M., Pays E. Expression of a variant surface glycoprotein of *Trypanosoma gambiense* in procyclic forms of *Trypanosoma brucei* shows that the cell-type dictates the nature of the glycosyl-phosphatidylinositol membrane anchor attached to the glycoprotein. Biochem J; 324; 1997; 885-895.

[81] Clayton C.E., Fueri J.P., Itzakhi J.E., Bellofatto V., Sherman D.R., Wisdom G.S., Vijayasarathy S., Mowatt M.R. Transcription of the procyclic acidic repetitive protein genes of *Trypanosoma brucei*. Mol Cell Biol; 10; 1990; 3036-3047.

[82] Rudenko G., Le Blancq S., Smith J., Lee M.G.S., Rattray A., Van der Ploeg L.H.T. Procyclic acidic repetitive (PARP) genes located in an unusually small α-amanitin-resistant

transcription unit : PARP promoter activity assayed by transient DNA transfection in *Trypanosoma brucei*. Mol Cell Biol; 10; 1990; 3492-3504.

[83] Koenig E., Delius H., Carrington M., Williams R.O., Roditi I. Duplication and transcription of procyclin genes in *Trypanosoma brucei*. Nucleic Acids Res; 17; 1989; 8727-8739.

[84] Berberof M., Pays A., Lips S., Tebabi P., Pays E. Characterization of a transcription terminator of the procyclin PARP A unit of *Trypanosoma brucei*. Mol Cell Biol; 16; 1996; 914-924.

[85] Koenig-Martin E., Yamage M., Roditi I. *Trypanosoma brucei :* a procyclin-associated gene encodes a polypeptide related to ESAG 6 and 7 proteins. Mol Biochem Parasitol; 55; 1992; 135-146.

[86] Bayne R.A.L., Kilbride E.A., Lainson F.A., Tetley L., Barry J.D. A major surface antigen of procyclic stage *Trypanosoma congolense*. Mol Biochem Parasitol; 61; 1993; 295-310.

[87] Beecroft R.P., Roditi I., Pearson T.W. Identification and characterization of an acidic major surface glycoprotein from procyclic stage *Trypanosoma congolense*. Mol Biochem Parasitol; 61; 1997; 285-294.

[88] Seyfang A., Mecke D., Duszenko M. Degradation, recycling and shedding of *Trypanosoma brucei* variant surface glycoprotein. J Protozool; 37; 1990; 546-552.

[89] Roditi I., Schwarz H., Pearson T.W., Beecroft R.P., Liu M.K., Richardson J.P., Buhring H.J., Pleiss J., Bulow R., Williams R.O., Overath P. Procyclin gene expression and loss of the variant surface glycoprotein during differentiation of *Trypanosoma brucei*. J Cell Biol; 108; 1989; 737-746.

[90] Balber A.E. The pellicle and the membrane of the flagellum, flagellar adhesion zone, and flagellar pocket : functionally discrete surface domains of the bloodstream form of African trypanosomes. Crit Rev Immunol; 10; 1990; 177-201.

[91] Overath P., Chaudri M., Steverding D., Ziegelbauer K. Invariant surface proteins in *Trypanosoma brucei*. Parasitol Today; 10; 1994; 53-58.

[92] Overath P., Stierhof Y.D., Wiese M. Endocytosis and secretion in trypanosomatid parasites — tumultuous traffic in a pocket. Trends Cell Biol; 7; 1997; 27-33.

[93] Langreth S.G., Balber A.E. Protein uptake and digestion in bloodstream and culture forms of *Trypanosoma brucei*. J Protozool; 22; 1975; 40-53.

[94] Schell D., Evers R., Preis D., Ziegelbauer K., Kiefer H., Lottspeich F., Cornelissen A.W.C.A., Overath P. A transferrin-binding protein of *Trypanosoma brucei* is encoded by one of the genes in the variant surface glycoprotein gene expression site. EMBO J; 10; 1991; 1061-1066.

[95] Salmon D, Hanocq-Quertier J, Paturiaux-Hanocq F, Nolan D, Pays A, Tebabi P, Michel A, Pays E, Characterization of the ligand binding site of the transferrin receptor in Trypanosoma brucei demonstrates structural homology with the variant surface glycoprotein. EMBO J ; 16 ; 1997 ; 7272-7278.

[96] Coppens I., Baudhuin P., Opperdoes F.R., Courtoy P.J. Receptor for the low-density lipoproteins on the hemoflagellate *Trypanosoma brucei*. Purification and involvement in growth of the parasite. Proc Natl Acad Sci USA; 85; 1988; 6753-6757.

[97] Coppens I., Bastin P., Courtoy P.J., Baudhuin P., Opperdoes F.R. A rapid method purifies a glycoprotein of M_r 145 000 as the LDL receptor of *Trypanosoma brucei* brucei. Biochem Biophys Res Commun; 178; 1991; 185-191.

[98] Lee M.G.S., Bihain B.E., Russell D.G., Deckelbaum R.J., Van der Ploeg L.H.T. Characterization of a cDNA encoding a cysteine-rich cell surface protein located in the flagellar pocket of the protozoan *Trypanosoma brucei*. Mol Cell Biol; 10; 1990; 4506-4517.

[99] Bastin P., Stephan A., Raper J., Saint-Remy J.-M., Opperdoes F.R., Courtoy P. An Mr 145 kDa low-density lipoprotein (LDL)-binding protein is conserved throughout the Kinetoplastida order. Mol Biochem Parasitol; 76; 1996; 43-56.

[100] Bastin P., Coppens I., Saint-Remy J.M., Baudhuin P., Opperdoes F.R., Courtoy P.J. Identification of a specific epitope on the extracellular domain of the LDL-receptor of *Trypanosoma brucei brucei*. Mol Biochem Parasitol; 63; 1994; 193-202.

[101] Hajduk S.L., Hager K.M., Esko J.D. Human high density lipoprotein killing of African trypanosomes. Annu Rev Microbiol; 48; 1994; 139-162.

[102] Hager K.M., Hajduk S.L. Mechanism of resistance of African trypanosomes to cytotoxic human HDL. Nature; 385; 1997; 823-826.

[103] De Greef C., Hamers R. The serum resistance-associated (SRA) gene of *Trypanosoma brucei rhodesiense* encodes a variant surface glycoprotein-like protein. Mol Biochem Parasitol; 68; 1994; 277-284.

[104] Alexandre S., Paindavoine P., Tebabi P., Pays A., Halleux S., Steinert M., Pays E. Differential expression of a family of putative adenylate/guanylate cyclase genes in *T. brucei*. Mol Biochem Parasitol; 43; 1990; 279-288.

[105] Alexandre S., Paindavoine P., Hanocq-Quertier J., Paturiaux-Hanocq F., Pays E. Families of adenylate cyclase genes in *Trypanosoma brucei*. Mol Biochem Parasitol; 77; 1996; 173-182.

[106] Sanchez M.A., Zeoli D., Klamo E.M., Kavanaugh M.P., Landfear S.M. A family of putative receptor-adenylate cyclases from *Leishmania donovani.* J Biol Chem; 270; 1995; 17551-17558.

[107] Pitt G., Milona N., Borleis J., Lin K., Reed R., Devreotes P. Structurally distinct and stage-specific adenylyl cyclase genes play different roles in *Dictyostelium* development. Cell; 69; 1992; 305-315.

[108] Rolin S., Halleux S., Van Sande J., Dumont J., Pays E., Steinert M. Stage-specific adenylate cyclase activity in *T. brucei.* Exp Parasitol; 71; 1990; 350-352.

[109] Rolin S., Paindavoine P., Hanocq-Quertier J., Hanocq F., Claes Y., Le Ray D., Overath P., Pays E. Transient adenylate cyclase activation accompanies differentiation of *Trypanosoma brucei* from bloodstream to procyclic forms. Mol Biochem Parasitol; 61; 1993; 115-126.

[110] Voorheis H.P., Martin B.R. Characteristics of the calcium-mediated mechanism activating adenylate cyclase in *T. brucei.* Eur J Biochem; 116; 1981; 471-477.

[111] Voorheis H.P., Martin B.R. Local anaesthetics including benzyl alcohol activate adenylate cyclase in *T. brucei* by a calcium-dependent mechanism. Eur J Biochem; 123; 1982; 371-376.

[112] Hide G., Gray A., Harrison C.M., Tait A. Identification of an epidermal growth factor receptor homologue in trypanosomes. Mol Biochem Parasitol; 36; 1989; 51-59.

[113] Lucas R., Magez S., De Leys R., Fransen L., Scheerlinck J.P., Rampelberg M., Sablon E., De Baetselier P. Mapping the lectin-like activity of tumor necrosis factor. Science; 263; 1994; 814-817.

[114] Olsson T., Bakhiet M., Hojeberg B., Ljungdahl A., Edlund C., Andersson G., Ekre H.P., Fung Leung W.P., Mak T., Wigzell H., Fiszer U., Kristensson K. CD8 is critically involved in lymphocyte activation by a *T. brucei brucei*-released molecule. Cell; 72; 1993; 715-727.

[115] Lucas R., Magez S., Songa B., Darji A., Hamers R., De Baetselier P. A role for TNF during African trypanosomiasis : involvement in parasite control, immunosuppression and pathology. Res Immunol; 144; 1993; 370-376.

[116] Magez S., Geuskens M., Beschin A., Del Favero H., Verschueren H., Lucas R., Pays E., De Baetselier P. Specific uptake of Tumor Necrosis Factor- α is involved in growth control of *Trypanosoma brucei.* J Cell Biol; 137; 1997; 715-727.

[117] Tachado S., Schofield L. Glycosylphosphatidylinositol toxin of *Trypanosoma brucei* regulates IL-1 α and TNF- α expression in macrophages by protein tyrosine kinase mediated signal transduction. Biochem Biophys Res Commun; 205; 1994; 984-991.

[118] Van Meirvenne N., Janssens P.G., Magnus E. Antigenic variation in syringe-passaged populations of *Trypanosoma brucei.* 1. Rationalization of the experimental approach. Ann Soc Belg Med Trop; 55; 1975; 1-23.

[119] Steverding D., Stierhof Y.D., Fuchs H., Tauber R., Overath P. Transferrin-binding complex is the receptor for transferrin uptake in *Trypanosoma brucei.* J Cell Biol; 131; 1995; 1173-1182.

[120] Borst P, Bitter W, Blundell P, Cross M, McCulloch R, Rudenko G, Taylor MC, Van Leeuwen F. The expression sites for variant surface glycoproteins of *Trypanosoma brucei.* In : Hide G, Mottram JC, Coombs GH, Holmes PH, editors. Trypanosomiasis and Leishmaniasis : Biology and Control. British Society for Parasitology/CAB International, Oxford, 1996 : 109–131.

[121] Van Meirvenne N., Magnus E., Janssens P.G. The effect of normal human serum on trypanosomes of distinct antigenic types (ETat 1 to 12) isolated from a strain of *Trypanosoma brucei rhodesiense.* Ann Soc Belg Med Trop; 56; 1976; 55-63.

[122] Eisenthal R., Game S., Holman G.D. Specificity and kinetics of hexose transport in *Trypanosoma brucei.* Biochim Biophys Acta; 985; 1989; 81-89.

[123] Bringaud F., Baltz T. A potential hexose transporter gene expredominantly in the bloodstream form of *Trypanosoma brucei.* Mol Biochem Parasitol; 52; 1992; 111-122.

[124] Bringaud F., Baltz T. Differential regulation of two distinct families of glucose transporter genes in *Trypanosoma brucei.* Mol Cell Biol; 13; 1993; 1146-1154.

[125] Barrett M.P., Tetaud E., Seyfang A., Bringaud F., Baltz T. Functional expression and characterization of the *Trypanosoma brucei* procyclic glucose transporter. Biochem J; 312; 1995; 687-691.

[126] Jackson D.G., Voorheis H.P. Changes in the pattern of cell surface proteins during transformation of bloodstream forms of *Trypanosoma brucei* in vitro. Biochem Soc Trans; 18; 1990; 1032-1033.

[127] Jackson D.G., Windle H.J., Voorheis H.P. The identification, purification and characterization of two invariant surface glycoproteins located beneath the surface barrier of bloodstream forms of *Trypanosoma brucei.* J Biol Chem; 268; 1993; 8085-8095.

[128] Nolan DP, Jackson DG, Windle HJ, Pays A, Geuskens M, Michel A, Voorheis HP, Pays E. Characterization of a novel, stage-specific, invariant surface protein in *Trypanosoma*

brucei containing an internal, serine-rich, repetitive motif. J Biol Chem ; 272 ; 1997 ; 29212-292221.

[129] Ziegelbauer K., Overath P. Identification of invariant surface glycoproteins in the bloodstream stage of *Trypanosoma brucei*. J Biol Chem; 267; 1992; 10791-10796.

[130] Ziegelbauer K., Multhaup G., Overath P. Molecular characterization of two invariant surface glycoproteins specific for the bloodstream stage of *Trypanosoma brucei*. J Biol Chem; 267; 1993; 10797-10803.

[131] Ziegelbauer K., Rudenko G., Kieft R., Overath P. Genomic organization of an invariant surface glycoprotein gene family of *Trypanosoma brucei*. Mol Biochem Parasitol; 69; 1995; 53-63.

[132] Ziegelbauer K., Stahl B., Karas M., Stierhof Y.D., Overath P. Proteolytic release of cell surface proteins during differentiation of *Trypanosoma brucei*. Biochemistry; 32; 1993; 3737-3742.

[133] Brickman M.J., Balber A.E. *Trypanosoma brucei rhodesiense*: membrane glycoproteins localized primarily in endosomes and lysosomes of bloodstream forms. Exp Parasitol; 76; 1993; 329-344.

[134] Brickman M.J., Balber A.E. Transport of a lysosomal membrane glycoprotein from the golgi to endosomes and lysosomes via the cell surface in African trypanosomes. J Cell Sci; 107; 1994; 3191-3200.

[135] Lee M.G.-S., Russel D.G., D'Alesandro P.A., Van der Ploeg L.H.T. Identification of membrane-associated proteins in *Trypanosoma brucei* encoding an internal EAR-LRAEE amino acid repeat. J Biol Chem; 269; 1994; 8408-8415.

[136] Gardiner P.R., Finerty J.F., Dwyer D.M. Iodination and identification of surface membrane antigens in procyclic *Trypanosoma rhodesiense*. J Immunol; 136; 1983; 2259-2264.

[137] Stebeck C.E., Beecroft R.P., Singh B.N., Jardim A., Olafson R.W., Tuckey C., Prenevost K.D., Pearson T.W. Kinetoplastid membrane protein-11 (KMP-11) is differentially expressed during the life cycle of African trypanosomes and is found in a wide variety of kinetoplastid parasites. Mol Biochem Parasitol; 71; 1995; 1-13.

[138] Jackson D.G., Smith D.K., Luo C., Elliot J.F. Cloning of a novel surface antigen from the insect stages of *Trypanosoma brucei* by expression in COS cells. J Biol Chem; 268; 1993; 1894-1900.

[139] Carter N.S., Fairlamb A.H. Arsenical-resistant trypanosomes lack an unusual adenosine transporter. Nature; 361; 1993; 173-176.

[140] Carter N.S., Berger B.J., Fairlamb A.H. Uptake of diamidine drugs by the P2 nucleoside transporter in merlarsen-sensitive and resistant *Trypanosoma brucei brucei*. J Biol Chem; 270; 1995; 28153-28157.

[141] Rifkin M.R., Fairlamb A.H. Transport of ethanolamine and its incorporation into variant surface glycoprotein of bloodstream forms of *Trypanosoma brucei*. Mol Biochem Parasitol; 15; 1985; 245-256.

[142] Rifkin M.R., Strobos C.A., Fairlamb A.H. Specificity of ethanolamine transport and its further metabolism in *Trypanosoma brucei*. J Biol Chem; 270; 1995; 16160-16166.

[143] Steiger R.F., Opperdoes F.R., Bontemps J. Subcellular fractionation of *Trypanosoma brucei* bloodstream forms with special reference to hydrolases. Eur J Biochem; 105; 1980; 163-175.

[144] McLaughlin J. Subcellular distribution of particle-associated antigens in *Trypanosoma rhodesiense*. J Immunol; 128; 1982; 2656-2663.

[145] McLaughlin J. The association of distinct acid phosphatases with the flagellar pocket and surface membrane fractions isolated from *Trypanosoma rhodesiense*. Mol Cell Biochem; 70; 1986; 177-184.

[146] Walter R.D., Opperdoes F.R. Subcellular distribution of adenylate cyclase, cyclic-AMP phosphodiesterase, protein kinases and phosphoprotein phosphatases in *Trypanosoma brucei*. Mol Biochem Parasitol; 6; 1982; 287-295.

[147] McLaughlin J. *Trypanosoma rhodesiense*: Antigenicity and immunogenicity of flagellar pocket membrane components. Exp Parasitol; 64; 1987; 1-11.

[148] Olenick J.G., Wolff R., Nauman R.K., McLaughlin J. A flagellar pocket membrane fraction from *Trypanosoma brucei rhodesiense*: Immunogold localization and nonvariant immunoprotection. Infect Immun; 56; 1988; 92-98.

[149] Voorheis H.P., Gale J.S., Owen M.J., Edwards W. The isolation and partial characterization of the plasma membrane from *Trypanosoma brucei*. Biochem J; 180; 1977; 11-24.

[150] Siddiqui A.A., Zhou Y., Podesta R.B., Clarke M.W. Isolation of a highly enriched plasma membrane fraction of *Trypanosoma brucei* by free-flow electrophoresis. Mol Biochem Parasitol; 40; 1990; 95-104.

[151] Nolan D.P., Voorheis H.P. Bioenergetic studies of bloodstream forms of *Trypanosoma brucei*: electrical and H^+ gradients. Biochem Soc Trans; 18; 1990; 735-739.

[152] Nolan DP, Voorheis HP. Factors that determine the plasma membrane potential in bloodstream forms of *Trypanosoma brucei*. Eur J Biochem 1997 (in press).

[153] Nolan DP, Voorheis HP. Transformation of *Trypanosoma brucei* from its bloodstream form into its procyclic form is accompanied by a change in the ionic conductance of the

plasma membrane. In : Keeling D, Benham C, editors. Ion Transport. Academic Press, London, UK, 1989 : 355.

[154] Nolan D.P., Voorheis H.P. The distribution of permeant ions demonstrates the presence of at least two electrical gradients in bloodstream forms of *Trypanosoma brucei.* Eur J Biochem; 202; 1991; 411-420.

[155] Benaim G., Lopez-Estrano C., Docampo R., Moreno S.N. A calmodulin-stimulated Ca^{2+} pump in plasma membrane vesicles from *Trypanosoma brucei;* selective inhibition by pentamidine. Biochem J; 296; 1993; 759-763.

[156] Nolan D., Revelard P., Pays E. Overexpression and characterization and of a Ca^{2+} ATPase of the endoplasmic reticulum of *Trypanosoma brucei.* J Biol Chem; 269; 1994; 26045-26051.

[157] Pays E. Genome organization and control of gene expression in trypanosomatids. In : Broda PM, Oliver SG, Sims P, editors. The Eukaryotic Microbial Genome. Cambridge University Press, Cambridge, 1993 : 99–132.

[158] Zomerdijk J.C.B.M., Kieft R., Duyndam M., Shiels P.G., Borst P. Efficient production of functional mRNA mediated by RNA polymerase I in *Trypanosoma brucei.* Nature; 353; 1991; 772-775.

[159] Zomerdijk J.C.B.M., Kieft R., Shiels P.G., Borst P. Alpha-amanitin-resistant transcription units in trypanosomes : a comparison of promoter sequences for a VSG gene expression site and for the ribosomal RNA genes. Nucleic Acids Res; 19; 1991; 5153-5158.

[160] Brown S.D., Huang J., Van der Ploeg L.H.T. The promoter for the procyclic acidic repetitive protein (PARP) genes of *Trypanosoma brucei* shares features with RNA polymerase I promoters. Mol Cell Biol; 12; 1992; 2644-2652.

[161] Janz L., Clayton C. The PARP and rRNA promoters of *Trypanosoma brucei* are composed of dissimilar sequence elements that are functionally interchangeable. Mol Cell Biol; 14; 1994; 5804-5811.

[162] Vanhamme L., Pays A., Tebabi P., Alexandre S., Pays E. Specific binding of proteins to the noncoding strand of a crucial element of the variant surface glycoprotein, procyclin, and ribosomal promoters of *Trypanosoma brucei.* Mol Cell Biol; 15; 1995; 5598-5606.

[163] Rudenko G., Blundell P.A., Dirks-Mulder A., Kieft R., Borst P. A ribosomal DNA promoter replacing the promoter of a telomeric VSG gene expression site can be efficiently switched on and off in *T. brucei.* Cell; 83; 1995; 547-553.

[164] Ben Amar M.F., Jefferies D., Pays A., Bakalara N., Kendall G., Pays E. The actin gene promoter of *Trypanosoma brucei.* Nucleic Acids Res; 19; 1991; 5857-5862.

[165] Lee M.G.S. An RNA polymerase II promoter in the hsp70 locus of *Trypanosoma brucei.* Mol Cell Biol; 16; 1996; 1220-1230.

[166] Vanhamme L., Pays E. Control of gene expression in trypanosomes. Microbiol Rev; 59; 1995; 223-240.

[167] Graham S.V. Mechanisms of stage-regulated gene expression in Kinetoplastida. Parasitol Today; 11; 1995; 217-223.

[168] Pays E., Coquelet H., Pays A., Tebabi P., Steinert M. *Trypanosoma brucei :* post-transcriptional control of the variable surface glycoprotein gene expression site. Mol Cell Biol; 9; 1989; 4018-4021.

[169] Pays E., Coquelet H., Tebabi P., Pays A., Jefferies D., Steinert M., Koenig E., Williams R.O., Roditi I. *T. brucei :* constitutive activity of the VSG and procyclin gene promoters. EMBO J; 9; 1990; 3145-3151.

[170] Rudenko G., Blundell P.A., Taylor M.C., Kieft R., Borst P. VSG gene expression site control in insect form *Trypanosoma brucei.* EMBO J; 13; 1994; 5470-5482.

[171] Jefferies D., Tebabi P., Pays E. Transient activity assays of the *Trypanosoma brucei* VSG gene promoter : control of gene expression at the post-transcriptional level. Mol Cell Biol; 11; 1991; 338-343.

[172] Zomerdijk J.C.B.M., Ouellette M., ten Asbroek A.L.M.A., Kieft R., Bommer A.M.M., Clayton C.E., Borst P. The promoter for a variant surface glycoprotein gene expression site in *Trypanosoma brucei.* EMBO J; 9; 1990; 2791-2801.

[173] Biebinger S., Rettenmaier S., Flaspohler J., Hartmann C., Pena-Diaz J., Wirtz L.E., Hotz H.R., Barry J.D., Clayton C. The PARP promoter of *Trypanosoma brucei* is developmentally regulated in a chromosomal context. Nucleic Acids Res; 24; 1996; 1202-1211.

[174] Jefferies D., Tebabi P., Le Ray D., Pays E. The ble resistance gene as a new selectable marker for *Trypanosoma brucei :* fly transmission of stable procyclic transformants to produce antibiotic resistant bloodstream forms. Nucleic Acids Res; 21; 1993; 191-195.

[175] Berberof M., Vanhamme L., Pays A., Tebabi P., Jefferies D., Welburn S., Pays E. The 3'-terminal region of the mRNAs for VSG and procyclin can confer stage-specificity to gene expression in *Trypanosoma brucei.* EMBO J; 14; 1995; 2925-2934.

[176] Urmenyi T.P., Van der Ploeg L.H.T. PARP promoter-mediated activation of a VSG expression site promoter in insect form *Trypanosoma brucei.* Nucleic Acids Res; 23; 1995; 1010-1018.

[177] Qi C.C., Urmenyi T., Gottesdiener K.M. Analysis of a hybrid PARP/VSG ES promoter in procyclic trypanosomes. Mol Biochem Parasitol; 77; 1996; 147-159.

[178] Vanhamme L., Berberof M., Le Ray D., Pays E. Stimuli of differentiation regulate RNA elongation in the transcription units for the major stage-specific antigens of *Trypanosoma brucei*. Nucleic Acids Res; 23; 1995; 1862-1869.

[179] Ullu E, Tschudi C, Gunzl A. Trans-splicing in trypanosomatid protozoa. In : Smith DF, Parsons M, editors. Molecular biology of parasitic protozoa. IRL Press, Oxford, 1996 : 115–133.

[180] Hug M., Carruthers V., Sherman D., Hartmann C., Cross G.A.M., Clayton C.E. A possible role for the 3'-untranslated region in developmental regulation in *Trypanosoma brucei*. Mol Biochem Parasitol; 61; 1993; 87-96.

[181] Clayton C., Hotz H.R. Post-transcriptional control of PARP gene expression. Mol Biochem Parasitol; 77; 1996; 1-6.

[182] Ehlers B., Czichos J., Overath P. RNA turnover in *Trypanosoma brucei*. Mol Cell Biol; 7; 1987; 1242-1249.

[183] Dorn P.L., Aman R.A., Boothroyd J.C. Inhibition of protein synthesis results in super-induction of procyclin (PARP) RNA levels. Mol Biochem Parasitol; 44; 1991; 133-140.

[184] Graham S.V., Barry J.D. Polysomal, procyclin mRNAs accumulate in bloodstream forms of monomorphic and pleomorphic trypanosomes treated with protein synthesis inhibitors. Mol Biochem Parasitol; 80; 1996; 179-191.

[185] Hehl A., Vassella E., Braun R., Roditi I. A conserved stem-loop structure in the 3' untranslated region of procyclin mRNAs regulates expression in *Trypanosoma brucei*. Proc Natl Acad Sci USA; 91; 1994; 370-374.

[186] Pays E., Hanocq-Quertier J., Hanocq F., Van Assel S., Nolan D., Rolin S. Abrupt RNA changes precede the first cell division during the differentiation of *Trypanosoma brucei* bloodstream forms into procyclic forms in vitro. Mol Biochem Parasitol; 61; 1993; 107-114.

[187] Pays E, Rolin S, Magez S. Cell signalling in trypanosomatids. In : Hide G, Mottram JC, Coombs GH, Holmes PH, editors. Trypanosomiasis and Leishmaniasis : Biology and Control. British Society for Parasitology/CAB International, Oxford, 1986 : 199–225.

[188] Darji A., Lucas R., Magez S., Torreele E., Palacios J., Sileghem M., Bajyana Songa E., Hamers R., De Baetselier P. Mechanisms underlying trypanosome-elicited immunosuppression. Ann Soc Belg Med Trop; 72; 1992; 27-38.

[189] Tachado S.D., Schofield L. Signal transduction in macrophages by glycosylphosphatidylinositols of *Plasmodium*, *Trypanosoma*, and *Leishmania* : activation of protein tyrosine kinases and protein kinase C by inositolglycan and diacylglycerol moieties. Proc Natl Acad Sci USA; 94; 1997; 4022-4027.

[190] Borst P. Transferrin receptor, antigenic variation and the prospect of a trypanosome vaccine. Trends Genet; 7; 1991; 307-309.

[191] Mkunza F., Olaho W.M., Powell C.N. Partial protection against natural trypanosomiasis after vaccination with a flagellar pocket antigen from *Trypanosoma brucei rhodesiense*. Vaccine; 13; 1995; 151-154.

[192] Carrington M., Boothroyd J. Implications of conserved structural motifs in disparate trypanosome surface proteins. Mol Biochem Parasitol; 81; 1996; 119-126.

2

The molecular phylogeny of trypanosomes : evidence for an early divergence of the Salivaria

Jochen Haag,
Colm O'hUigin,
Peter Overatha

*Max-Planck-Institut für Biologie,
D 72076 Tübingen, Germany.*

Abstract

Chronic infections with trypanosomes dwelling extracellularly in the blood and tissues of their hosts are observed in all vertebrate classes. We present here a molecular phylogenetic reconstruction of trypanosome evolution based on nucleotide sequences of small subunit rRNA genes. The evolutionary tree suggests an ancient split into one branch containing all Salivarian trypanosomes and a branch containing all non-Salivarian lineages. The latter branch splits into a clade containing bird, reptilian and Stercorarian trypanosomes infecting mammals and a clade with a branch of fish trypanosomes and a branch of reptilian/amphibian lineages. The branching order of the non-Salivarian trypanosomes supports host-parasite cospeciation scenarios, but also suggests host switches, e.g. between bird and reptilian trypanosomes. The tree is discussed in relation to the modes of adaptation that allow trypanosomes to infect immunocompetent vertebrates. Most importantly, the early divergence of the Salivarian lineages suggests that the presence of a dense proteinaceous surface coat that is subject to antigenic variation is a unique invention of this group of parasites.

Keywords : Salivaria; Trypanosomes; Molecular phylogeny

1 • Introduction

Antigenic variation as it occurs in the African trypanosomes is a paradigmatic mechanism for evasion of the hosts' immune response [1–3]. The question of how this complex mechanism arose during the course of evolution of the genus *Trypanosoma* is difficult to approach experimentally. One possibility would be to look for characteristic features of antigenic variation in vertebrate trypanosomes. At present, the genes coding for the variant surface proteins (*vsg* genes) coding for the coat covering the parasites are the only players known in this system. The extensive variability of this large gene family both within a species and between species that are known to undergo antigenic variation [4, 5], makes a search for *vsg* genes in presumably more distant relatives of the African trypanosomes a questionable undertaking. Although less direct, a phylogenetic tree of trypanosomes based on conserved genes may be informative both for inferences about the origin of antigenic variation and about other features of *Trypanosoma*. In this paper, we present a phylogenetic reconstruction of trypanosome phylogeny based on the genes coding for the small subunit ribosomal RNA (SSU rRNA). The tree will be discussed with particular reference to the modes of adaptation invented by trypanosomes in coping with their hosts' immune response.

2 • Trypanosomes and their phylogeny

The genus *Trypanosoma* (Family : Trypanosomatidae ; Order : Kinetoplastida) comprises unicellular flagellates that are parasites of all vertebrate classes. The characteristic morphological forms of trypanosomes are the trypomastigotes observed in the blood and tissues of vertebrate hosts, and the epimastigotes which are found in the invertebrate vector. The vectors can be haematophagous arthropods (insects or arachnids) for mammalian, avian as well as some amphibian and reptilian trypanosomes. Fish and certain amphibian and reptilian trypanosomes are transmitted by leeches. Infective stages which develop from epimastigotes in the vector are designated metacyclic forms ; they have a trypomastigote morphology [6].

Some representative vertebrate trypanosomes, their hosts and vectors are listed in Table 1.

The mammalian trypanosomes are divided in the Salivaria and the Stercoraria according to their mode of transmission, predominantly inoculative by tsetse flies or contaminative by a variety of blood-sucking insects, respectively. All Salivaria are considered to evade the humoral immune response of their hosts by the expression of antigenically distinct and highly abundant VSGs, which cover the parasites as an ultrastructurally clearly delineated coat [1–3]. In a given cell and at a given time, only one of several hundred *vsg* genes is expressed. Although the coat proteins are highly immunogenic, the infection is chronic because a trypanosome clone can form antigenically different VSG coats by the differential activation of previously inactive *vsg* genes and the parasite is, therefore, always one step ahead of the host's immune response. The Stercorarian rat trypanosome, *T. lewisi*, causes a transient infection, which is terminated by

T A B L E   1

Trypanosome species [a]

Species	Vertebrate hosts	Vectors	Mode of transmission	Course of infection	Type of immunity	References
Mammalian trypanosomes						
Salivaria						
T. brucei	Game and domestic mammals	Tsetse flies	Inoculative	Chronic	Antibody-mediated	[1, 6]
T. equiperdum	Equines	—	Coitus	Chronic	Antibody-mediated	
T. evansi		Horse flies, tsetse flies, vampire bats	Mechanical	Chronic	Antibody-mediated	
T. congolense		Tsetse flies	Inoculative	Chronic	Antibody-mediated	
T. simiae	Pigs	Tsetse flies	Inoculative	Chronic	Antibody-mediated	
T. vivax		Tsetse flies, horse flies	Inoculative/mechanical	Chronic	Antibody mediated	
Stercoraria						
T. lewisi	Rat	Rat flea	Contaminative	Transient	Antibody-mediated	[7, 8]
T. musculi	Mouse	Mouse flea	Contaminative	Chronic	Antibody-mediated	
T. cruzi	Man, rodents, marsupials	Triatomine bugs	Contaminative	Chronic	Cell-mediated and humoral	[9]
Avian trypanosomes *T. avium* *T. bennetti* *T. sp. N355*	Birds	Culicine mosquitos, simulid flies, hypoboscid flies, dermanysid mites	Contaminative or by ingestion	Chronic	Antibody-mediated ?	[10]
Amphibian trypanosome *T. mega* *T. rotatorium*	Frogs, toads, newts, salamanders	Leeches, sandflies, mosquitos	Inoculative (leeches) or contaminative (sandflies)	Chronic	?	[11]
Reptilian trypanosomes	Lizards, turtles, crocodiles, snakes	Leeches, sandflies	Inoculative (leeches) or contaminative (sandflies)	Chronic	?	[12]
T. varani						
T. scelopori						
T. grayi		Tsetse flies				
T. therezieni						
Fish trypanosomes *T. carassii* *T. boissoni* *T. triglae*	Bony and cartilaginous fishes	Leeches	Inoculative	Chronic	Antibody-mediated ?	[13–16]

[a] Most of the information listed in this table can be found in [6].

the production of antibodies resulting in an apparently sterile immunity [8]. Although the course of infection in the mouse trypanosome, *T. musculi,* is very similar, and a mouse that has controlled the initial, acute phase is permanently resistant to reinfection, some parasites may remain cloistered in the vasa recta of the kidney [17]. There is no indication that these rodent parasites change their surface by antigenic variation. *T. cruzi,* the etiological agent of Chagas' disease, is characterized by amastigotes replicating in the cytoplasm of mammalian cells such as macrophages or muscle cells, and by extracellular, non-dividing trypomastigotes in the blood [9]. The surface of both amastigotes and trypomastigotes is dominated by carbohydrate-rich mucin-like molecules ([18]; I. Almeida, personal communication), which gives a fuzzy ultrastructural appearance. Both antibodies and macrophage activating factors secreted by helper T cells are instrumental for controlling the acute phase of the infection. The subsequent life-long chronic phase is ascribed to the persistence of parasites inside host cells rather than to antigenic variation of the type observed for the Salivaria [9]. Much less is known about the numerous trypanosomes described in the other four vertebrate classes. They are considered to be blood parasites causing chronic infections. In avian [10] and fish trypanosomes [13–16], there is evidence for an antibody-mediated immune response but the mechanisms that enable them to persist in their immunocompetent hosts have not been investigated.

In the 1960s, several authors formulated hypotheses on the evolution of the genus *Trypanosoma.* Baker [19] suggested a phylogeny in which an ancestral trypanosomatid gave rise to one branch containing insect-transmitted lineages (trypanosomes of crocodiles, birds and mammals excluding the Salivaria) and a branch containing leech-transmitted species (trypanosomes of fish, amphibia and aquatic reptiles). The African trypanosomes were considered to be derived from the leech-aquatic vertebrate lineage, a view subsequently shared by Woo [20]. In this scenario, the Salivarian and the Stercorarian trypanosomes (Table 1) were not expected to be closely related. In contrast, Hoare [21] proposed that the Salivaria originated recently from Stercorarian trypanosomes.

Between 1988 and 1995, work by several groups has led to a proposal for the phylogeny of the Kinetoplastida from a comparison of small (SSU) and large subunit (LSU) rRNA gene sequences [22–28]. All but two [27, 28] of these studies suggested that trypanosomes are paraphyletic and that *T. brucei,* the only representative of the Salivaria included in the analysis, constitutes an early diverging branch. The other vertebrate trypanosomes formed a monophyletic group. In contrast, comparison of amino acid sequences of glyceraldehyde-3-

phosphate dehydrogenase [29] or gene sequences coding for several other proteins [30, 31] suggested monophyly of the Stercorarian *T. cruzi* and the Salivarian *T. brucei.*

The phylogenetic reconstructions of the Kinetoplastida were mainly interpreted with respect to the origin of parasitism, i.e. the acquisition or loss of a digenetic life style, or the evolution of RNA editing of mitochondrial genes. We are interested in the different modes of adaptation that allow trypanosomes to infect and persist in vertebrates. Inferences about the evolutionary origin of these mechanisms require knowledge about the phylogenetic relationship of trypanosomes. This prompted us to extend the existing data set for SSU rRNA gene sequences of the Kinetoplastida [32, 33] by sequencing the genes for 11 species representative for parasites of different vertebrate classes.

3 • Molecular phylogeny of SSU rRNA genes

3.1 Rate variation

Phylogenetic tree reconstructions are vulnerable to artefacts where one or more lineages show an accelerated evolutionary rate for the gene under study. Both the tree topology and molecular clock based dates will be affected. In particular, the tree topology is affected where rapidly evolving lineages tend to be displaced towards the root of the tree and to group together (so called long branch attraction). Evidence has been presented that SSU rRNA genes may behave as erratic molecular clocks [34, 35]. Previous studies have not addressed the question of rate variation extensively which may explain some of the anomalous topologies found. Our approach is to identify possible irregularities in the tree represented by such long branches and to verify topologies in their absence.

To determine how much variation in substitution rates in the SSU rRNA sequences occurs among the lineages examined here, we measure the relative distance from outgroups to the species or individual isolates within the lineage (Table 2). We use the term OTU (operational taxonomic unit) for convenience to cover all sequence sources, whether from different isolates or species. *Trypanoplasma borelli* and *Bodo caudatus,* representatives of the Bodonina, the sister suborder of the Trypanosomatina, are used to measure relative distances to all OTUs. For a given OTU, *Bodo caudatus* gives generally higher substitutional distances than *Trypanoplasma borelli,* presumably implying a faster substitution rate in *Bodo caudatus.* Among the OTUs tested, the largest distances to both outgroups are found in

	N	GC%	T. borrelli	B. caudatus	C. fasciculata	*Leptomonas* sp.	L. tarentolae	E. monterogei
T. lewisi	1788	48.60	9.5	11.8	4.7	5.0	4.7	4.9
T. musculi	1788	48.60	9.5	11.8	4.7	5.0	4.7	4.9
T. cruzi	1789	48.24	10.1	11.9	5.8	5.9	5.8	6.0
T. varani	1786	49.16	9.9	12.2	5.1	5.1	5.2	5.5
T. scelopori	1787	49.22	10.0	11.9	5.9	6.1	6.2	6.4
T. bennetti	1787	49.24	10.3	12.0	6.0	6.1	6.2	6.3
T. grayi	1787	48.85	9.1	11.4	4.8	5.1	4.7	4.9
T. sp. N335	1787	48.74	9.7	11.8	4.6	4.9	4.6	4.8
T. avium	1786	48.88	9.9	12.0	5.0	5.2	4.9	5.2
T. boissoni	1788	48.60	10.8	12.2	5.5	5.8	5.8	6.1
T. triglae	1788	48.71	10.8	12.2	5.6	6.0	6.0	6.2
T. carassii	1787	48.18	10.5	12.0	5.9	6.1	6.1	6.3
T. mega	1790	48.83	9.7	11.4	4.6	4.8	4.7	4.9
T. therezieni	1787	48.52	10.0	11.7	4.7	5.0	4.9	5.0
T. rotatorium	1786	48.49	10.4	12.0	5.4	5.3	5.4	5.3
T. equiperdum	1788	50.89	10.9	13.4	8.2	8.8	8.7	8.6
T. brucei	1788	50.95	10.9	13.4	8.2	8.8	8.7	8.7
T. simiae (KETRI)	1779	51.60	12.1	13.0	8.9	9.5	9.0	9.2
T. simiae (CP11)	1777	51.60	12.1	13.0	8.7	9.4	8.9	9.0
T. congo (Tsavo)	1779	52.00	12.0	13.3	9.0	9.5	9.2	9.2
T. congo (Kilifi)	1784	51.35	11.9	13.7	8.5	9.0	9.0	9.2
T. congo (River)	1784	51.79	11.7	13.7	8.5	9.0	8.9	9.1
T. congo (IL1180)	1786	51.34	11.5	13.6	8.4	9.0	8.8	9.0
T. congo (68Q)	1786	51.46	11.5	13.6	8.4	9.0	8.8	9.0
T. vivax	1781	55.31	15.5	15.4	13.0	13.4	13.0	13.2
B. culicis	1786	51.90	12.9	13.9	—	—	—	—
C. oncopelti	1774	48.93	12.1	13.4	—	—	—	—
P. serpens	1759	49.23	10.6	12.7	—	—	—	—
H. muscarum	1784	48.60	10.8	11.8	—	—	—	—
C. fasciculata	1789	48.80	9.9	12.2	—	—	—	—
Leptomonas sp.	1789	48.52	10.1	11.7	—	—	—	—
L. tarentolae	1789	48.57	10.1	12.2	—	—	—	—
E. monterogei	1788	48.55	10.5	12.4	—	—	—	—
B. caudatus	1782	48.32	9.3	—	—	—	—	—
T. borreli	1784	47.42	—	9.3	—	—	—	—

TABLE 2

Number of aligned nucleotides (N), G + C content (GC%) and substitutional distance (%) for SSU rRNA estimated using Kimura's two parameter method between outgroups *Trypanoplasma borreli* (*T. borreli*) and *Bodo caudatus* (*B. caudatus*), putative outgroups (*C. fasciculata*, *Leptomonas* sp., *L. tarentolae*, *E. monterogei*) and other kinetoplastid species comparisons involving *T. vivax* (15.5 and 15.4%, respectively). The other Salivarian trypanosomes give values ranging from 10.9 to 12.1% to *Trypanoplasma borelli* and 13.0 to 13.7% to *Bodo caudatus*. The Salivarian trypanosomes generally are more distant from both outgroups than are other trypanosomes, which range from 9.1 to 10.8% to *Trypanoplasma borelli* and 11.4 to 12.2% to *Bodo caudatus*. Both *Blastocrithidia culicis* (12.9 and 13.9%, respectively) and *Crithidia oncopelti* (12.1 and 13.4%, respectively) show distances to *Trypanoplasma borelli* and *Bodo caudatus*, which are comparable to those found in Salivarian trypanosomes. The other non-trypanosomes (*Herpetomonas muscarum, Phytomonas serpens, Crithidia fasciculata, Leptomonas* sp., *Leishmania tarentolae* and *Endotrypanum monterogei*) show distances in the ranges 9.9–10.8% to *Trypanoplasma borelli* and 11.7–12.7% to *Bodo caudatus*, values comparable to those found with non-Salivarian trypanosomes.

The undisputed outgroups are distant from the trypanosomes so that much of the distance measured consists of changes incurred in the outgroup lineage. Consequently, they lack resolving power in determining the extent of rate changes. A more closely related outgroup will resolve rate differences within the trypanosomes more successfully. If the trypanosomes are taken to be monophyletic (vide infra), then distances measured to the comparatively slowly evolving *Crithidia fasciculata, Leptomonas* sp., *Leishmania tarentolae* and *Endotrypanum monterogei* groups will resolve changes incurred along the lineage leading to trypanosomes in greater detail. The tendencies seen in comparisons with *Trypanoplasma borelli* and *Bodo caudatus* are clearly observed using the closer «outgroups» (Table 2). While *T. vivax* shows distances of 13–13.4%, the other Salivarian trypanosomes show distances which range from 8.2 to 9.5%. Salivarian trypanosomes show in turn greater distances to the selected outgroups than to other trypanosomes which range from 4.6 to 6.3%. This suggests that the lineage leading to *T. vivax* may have undergone three times as many substitutions as lineages leading to some non-Salivarian trypanosomes since the existence of their last shared common ancestor. Under such conditions of rate variation, the phylogenetic reconstructions need to be approached with considerable caution particularly regarding the position of the rapidly evolving Salivaria.

Hasegawa and Hashimoto [36] indicated that large differences in GC content will adversely affect phylogenetic reconstruction. For the species used here, the GC content does not vary substantially but divides the OTUs into at least three groups. Firstly, in the range 48.2–49.3% lie all but the Salivarian trypanosomes and *Trypanoplasma borelli*. Secondly, all Salivaria except *T. vivax* have GC contents ranging from 50.9–52%. Finally, *T. vivax* is alone in hav-

FIGURE 1

Neighbor-joining tree of SSU rRNA sequences. Trypanosome strains and DNAs : *T. therezieni* (isolated from *Chamaeleo brevicornis* in Madagascar by Brygoo in 1963), *T. musculi* LUM 343 (isolated from *Mus musculus* by Krampitt in 1962) and *T. sp.* N335 (isolated from the Java sparrow, *Padda oryzivora,* by LeRay in 1969) were obtained by D. LeRay, Antwerp. *T. equiperdum* STIB 818 (isolated in China) was provided by R. Brun, Basel. Procyclic forms of *T. simiae* CP11 [37] were a gift from T.W. Pearson, Victoria, Canada. *T. congolense* 68 Q was provided by L. Jenni, Basel. *T. lewisi* (ATCC 30085, isolated from a rat, *Rattus norvegicus),* *T. mega* (ATCC 30038, isolated from a toad, *Bufo regularis)* and *T. bennetti* strain KT-2 (ATCC 50102, isolated from an American kestrel, *Falco sparverius)* were obtained from the American Type Culture Collection. Genomic DNA of *T. grayi* ANR4 and *T. varani* V54 was a gift from W. Gibson, Leicester. *T. grayi* was isolated from *Glossina gambiensis* by J. McNamara; it develops in the hindgut of *Glossina* and has been shown to infect crocodiles ([38, 39] and W. Gibson, personal communication). *T. varani* V54 was isolated from the monitor lizard, *Varanus exanthematicus,* by Ranque in 1973 [40]; this trypanosome can infect sandflies ([38, 41] and W. Gibson, personal communication). Growth of trypanosomes : *T. mega* and *T. bennetti* were grown in diphasic blood agar medium (ATCC culture medium 1011). *T. simiae* was maintained in culture as described [42]. *T. therezieni* and *T. sp.* N335 were cultivated in semi-defined medium 79 [43] at 27 °C. *T. equiperdum, T. evansi, T. congolense* and *T. musculi* were isolated from the blood of infected mice by isopycnic Percoll centrifugation [44] and DEAE cellulose chromatography [45]. Likewise, *T. lewisi* was purified from the blood of infected rats. Because *T. lewisi* and *T. musculi* have a greater negative surface charge than the Salivarian trypanosomes, an improved yield for these trypanosomes

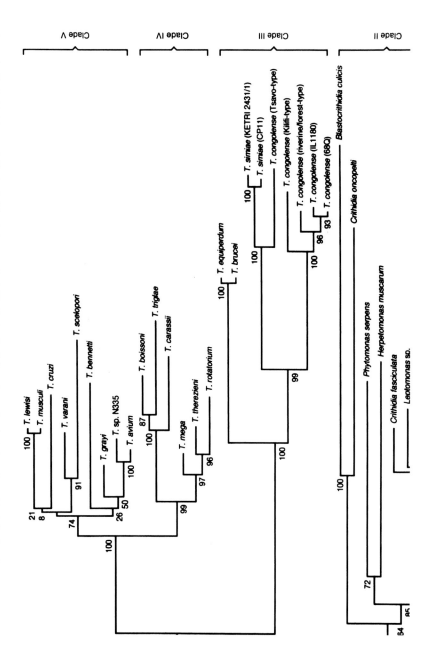

ing a GC content of 55.4%. A strong correlation is seen between GC content and substitutional distances to outgroups, reaching a coefficient of 0.97 when *Crithidia fasciculata* is used as outgroup. While the variables are clearly related, the shift in GC content does not of itself explain the higher substitution rate and the nature of the correlation remains unclear.

3.2 Tree topology

Fig. 1 shows a neighbor joining tree constructed using all OTUs except the Salivarian trypanosome, *T. vivax*. The *T. vivax* sequence groups with other Salivarian trypanosomes in all tree construction methods used. However, because of its elevated substitution rate it tends toward outgroup status, pulling its relatives with it. Therefore, *T. vivax* is omitted from Fig. 1 in order to obtain a better resolution. Over similar time periods other lineages do not appear to evolve as rapidly as *T. vivax*. Nevertheless, trees were made where each rapidly evolving lineage was omitted. None of these omissions change the topology significantly.

At least five major clades can be distinguished in the tree of the Kinetoplastida. The first clade (Clade I in Fig. 1) consists of *Trypanoplasma borelli* and *Bodo caudatus*. As expected, this outgroup is separated from all trypanosomatid lineages with 100% bootstrap support. The family Trypanosomatidae is divided into two major clades. Firstly, one clade (Clade II) groups a branch containing *Crithidia oncopelti* and *Blastocrithidia culicis* with another containing *Phytomonas serpens*, *Herpetomonas muscarum*, *Crithidia fasciculata*, *Leptomonas* sp., *Leishmania tarentolae* and *Endotrypanum monterogei*. The sequences of the last four species group together tightly with 100% bootstrap support. Secondly, all members of the genus *Trypanosoma* group together, divided into three major clades (Table 1). All the Salivarian trypanosomes form one major clade (Clade III). This clade is strongly supported by bootstrap values of 100% and is recovered in all tree making methods. The remaining 14 sequences form a single group (100% bootstrap support) which can be divided into two further clades containing on the one hand *T. boissoni*, *T. triglae*, *T. carassii*, *T. mega*, *T. therezieni* and *T. rotatorium* (99% bootstrap support, Clade IV; for hosts see Table 1) and on the other hand *T. lewisi*, *T. musculi*, *T. cruzi*, *T. varani*, *T. scelopori*, *T. bennetti*, *T. grayi*, *T.* sp. N335 and *T. avium* (74% bootstrap support, Clade V). Less clear is the exact branching order between Clade II, III and the other two trypanosome Clades IV and V. Fig. 1 puts the major trypanosome clades together, supporting monophyly, but with poor bootstrap support (42%).

The five major clades of the Kinetoplastida which are seen in neighbor-joining trees are also recovered in parsimony analysis. Within each clade, the branching order varies only slightly between the methods. The unweighted pair group method with arithmetic averages (UPGMA) is thought to be less robust than either neighbor-joining or parsimony under conditions of rate variation. Nevertheless, four of the five clades are recovered in UPGMA trees, the exception being that Clades IV and V fuse.

FIGURE 1 (FOLLOWING)

was obtained by increasing the ionic strength of the buffer used for the DEAE cellulose column [46]. PCR amplification and DNA sequencing: Genomic DNA was isolated by the procedure of Medina-Acosta and Cross [47]. The entire SSU rRNA genes were amplified using oligonucleotide primers ssu/U1 (5'-TGATTCT-GCCAGTAGTCATA-3') and ssu/L1 (5'-CTACAGCTACCTTGTTACGA-3'), which are situated at the conserved 5'- and 3'-termini of the rRNA coding region, respectively. PCR amplification was performed using 100 ng genomic DNA. PCR products were separated on 0.7% agarose gels, bands corresponding to the amplified fragments were excised and the DNA was isolated using the QIAquick Gel Extraction Kit (Qiagen). Both strands of the isolated SSU rRNA genes were directly sequenced by the dideoxynucleotide chain-termination method using a set of fluorescein-labeled sequencing primers annealing to regions conserved among all kinetoplastids. Primer sequences are available on request. Sequencing was performed on a Pharmacia ALF DNA Sequencer. The SSU-rRNA sequences from all other species were taken from the GenBank™. Alignments and tree-making: Alignments were based on those of Maslov et al. [32] and optimized by eye following inclusion of new sequences. This was performed using the lineup protocol of the GCG package [48]. The tree is based on Kimura's two parameter distances [49] and constructed with the neighbor-joining algorithm of Saitou and Nei [50] using the MEGA program [51]. A total of 1808 conserved sites were used in the constructions. Trees were made using both distance (neighbor-joining and UPGMA) and character methods (maximum parsimony employing the heuristic algorithm of MEGA). Where particular OTUs were thought to evolve rapidly, trees were constructed both with and without these OTUs.

The tree presented here gives the most comprehensive coverage to date of the genus *Trypanosoma* (34 species or isolates including 24 trypanosome sequences). Our tree differs from the bulk of those based on SSU rRNA presented up to 1996 [23–26, 32] which suggested that the genus *Trypanosoma* is paraphyletic, encompassing *Leishmania, Crithidia* and their relatives. The widespread finding of trypanosome paraphyly using SSU rRNA can for the most part be ascribed to variable substitution rates within the genus and to fewer species being available for the early studies. Subsequent studies on SSU rRNA [33, 34] where inclusion of additional sequences correct for artefacts of rate change, have pointed towards monophyly of *Trypanosoma,* in agreement with data from other genes [29–31]. Given the difficulties of phylogenetic reconstruction in the Kinetoplastida and the problems in deciding even whether *Trypanosoma* is mono- or paraphyletic, it is not surprising that some details may vary between trees depending on the species used and the method of phylogenetic reconstruction. Using a maximum likelihood approach, Lukes et al. [33] show the trypanosomes to be monophyletic. However within the genus *Trypanosoma,* they obtain a picture where Clades III, IV and V are indistinct. Their likelihood tree has fewer species (16 species or isolates including 11 trypanosomes) than presented here and the fusion of trypanosome clades is probably due to the limited choice of species. The large array of species (38 species or isolates including 14 trypanosome sequences) used by Philippe [34] in a recent parsimony study fall into the five clades determined here and the relationships among all 13 shared trypanosome species are topologically identical to those shown in Fig. 1. Thus, we have reasonable confidence in the presence of at least five distinct groups and the subdivision of the trypanosomes into three groups.

The evidence presented here indicates that in trypanosomes, particularly in the Salivaria, the SSU rRNA has undergone changes in substitution rates resulting in several fold rate differences between Clade V and Clades III and IV. Others [34] have arrived at similar conclusions using different outgroup species. Phylogenetic reconstruction may fail where substitution rates differ widely among taxa. The consistency of findings using several tree making methods and consistency with authors using different data sets [33, 34] does not of itself show that the phylogenetic reconstruction has been successful. Thus, we have sought corroborative evidence in other genetic loci for the phylogeny of the trypanosomes. This work (Haag et al., in preparation) indicates that essential elements of the topology and distances in the rRNA tree are correct. Therefore, we have greater confidence in drawing certain conclusions from the rRNA tree.

3.3   Dating the splits

To date the times of genesis of the major clades we take two approaches. Firstly, data are available on the rate of evolutionary change of rRNA genes in other species. Ochman and Wilson give an estimate of 2% substitution per 100 million years (MY) in a study of bacterial sequences [52]. More recently, Escalante and Ayala [53] give an estimate of 0.85% per 100 MY for metazoans. The second estimate of the rate is more appropriate to this data set given the close relationship of the taxa. Using this rate, we obtain a time of divergence of Clades IV and V, the two non-Salivarian trypanosome groups at about 150 MY. The time of divergence of the Salivarian trypanosomes from the other trypanosomes is about 300 MY. Since we are using a rate determined for a large group and applying it to a phylogeny with some rate variation apparent, we are cautious about these date estimates. Nevertheless, there is a second way to estimate divergence times using the phylogeny of Fig. 1. If parasites have cospeciated with their hosts (vide infra) we can expect that most divergences between parasites will reflect the divergence times of their hosts. We have taken the divergence of bird trypanosomes (*T. avium*) from the rodent trypanosomes (*T. lewisi* and *T. musculi*) as reflecting the divergence times of their hosts. Using a divergence date for this split of 220 MY, we obtain an estimate for the divergence date of Clades IV and V at about 250 MY. The time of divergence of the Salivarian trypanosomes from the other trypanosomes is about 500 MY. We can repeat this exercise using the split of the fish trypanosomes, *T. carassii* and *T. boissoni*, from higher vertebrate trypanosomes (*T. avium, T. lewisi, T. musculi*). Taking the divergence of fish from higher vertebrates at 400 MY before present, we obtain dates of 130 MY before present for the split of Clades IV and V and 260 MY before present for the split of Clade III from Clades IV/V. Similar estimates, 140 and 280 MY, respectively, are obtained for these splits when we use the estimate of Lake et al. [22] for the divergence of trypanosomes from *Crithidia fasciculata* at 264 MY before present. Taking the average of these dates, we arrive at an estimate for the split of Clade III from Clades IV/V at 335 MY and for Clades IV and V at 170 MY before present. These datings must be considered preliminary considering the variation in the substitution rates observed for the rRNA gene sequences. They clearly require confirmation by the analysis of other genes.

4 • Biological implications of the tree

4.1 Pro and contra trypanosome-vertebrate co-speciation

Considering that blood sucking arthropods can mediate transfer of trypanosomes by several modes (mechanical, inoculative, contaminative or by vector ingestion) it is probable that ongoing host switches between terrestrial vertebrates may occur. If such host switching proves commonplace or is evolutionary successful it might scramble any phylogenetic signal coming from cospeciation events in phylogenetic trees as has been previously argued for trypanosomes [32, 33]. On the other hand, host switching may be rare or be inviable in the longer evolutionary term. In this case, cospeciation will be the primary determinant of relationships among parasites. Tentative evidence favouring the cospeciation scenario in trypanosomes has been presented before [34].

Implicit in our divergence dating using host divergence times is the belief that cospeciation is indeed an important determinant of phylogenetic relationships among the trypanosomes. We have two main grounds for this belief. Firstly, there is a reasonable concordance between dates based on putative cospeciation events and those determined using the molecular clock of SSU rRNA (this study) or protein genes (J. Haag, in preparation). Secondly, the tree of trypanosomes (Fig. 1) shows a substantial degree of concordance with that of their various hosts and little evidence of substantial scrambling through host switching. Thus, all bird trypanosomes fall in a single clade, as do fish, amphibian and mammalian (excluding Salivarian) trypanosomes. Some exceptions to cospeciation scenarios which occur may be explained by ancient divergences giving rise to two lineages of trypanosomes as is apparently the case for the Salivarian and Stercorarian trypanosomes both of which infect mammals. Other exceptions, possibly due to host switching, are discussed below.

Clade V suggests an early divergence of bird (*T.* sp. N335, *T. avium* and *T. bennetti*) and Stercorarian trypanosomes (*T. lewisi, T. musculi* and *T. cruzi*). The appearance of a crocodile trypanosome, *T. grayi*, infecting tsetse flies [38, 39] within the avian group is unexpected, but could be due to an incorrect species identification because *T. grayi* is easily confused with bird trypanosomes [54]. Additionally, the closer relationship of the lizard trypanosomes *T. varani* [40] and *T. sclepori* [33] to mammalian rather than to bird trypanosomes is inconsistent with the accepted phylogeny of their vertebrate hosts. As already mentioned, the fact that blood-sucking arthropods can mediate transfer of trypanosomes by several modes suggests the occurrence of host switches between terrestrial vertebrates. In fact, there are reports about an albeit transient infection of *Glossina* by a bird trypanosome [54] and the infection of crocodiles by *T. brucei* [20].

Analysis of Clade IV also shows the limits of cospeciation scenarios for trypanosome diversification [33]. Although, this clade clearly separates into a fish and an amphibian/reptile branch, the branching order of the fish trypanosomes does not correspond to the divergence of their hosts because the elasmobranch trypanosome, *T. boissoni*, is more closely related to a teleost trypanosome, *T. triglae*, than the latter to another teleost trypanosome, *T. carassi*. Similarly, the frog trypanosome, *T. rotatorium*, is more closely related to *T. therezieni*, a chameleon parasite, than to another anuran trypanosome, *T. mega*, isolated from a toad. As noted above, loose specificity of leeches for fish or leeches and arthropods for amphibia and reptilia, may facilitate host switching of the parasites.

All our estimates point to an old split between the Salivaria and the rest of the trypanosomes. Our tree does not provide evidence that they diverged recently from lineages grouped either in Clade II or Clades IV/V as suggested earlier by several authors [19–21]. The large evolutionary distance of the Salivarian *T. brucei* (Clade III) and the Stercorarian *T. cruzi* (Clade V) tallies, for example, with major differences in their genome organization [55, 56] and differences in the extent of editing of transcripts of the mitochondrial maxicircle DNA [25]. The tree does not support the suggestion that the Salivarian trypanosomes have arisen at the time of the appearance of placental mammals < 85 MY ago nor of their common vector, the tsetse fly about 30–60 MY ago or even its ancestor, the protoglossina, 140 MY ago [57].

The distinctiveness of the Salivaria as a monophyletic clade is supported with 100% bootstrap values. The initial branching of *T. vivax* (subgenus *Duttonella;* not shown in Fig. 1, see above) is followed by a split between the subgenus *Trypanozoon* (*T. brucei* and its close relative *T. equiperdum)* and representatives of the subgenus *Nannomonas* (*T. congolense* and *T. simiae*). While four *T. congolense* sequences form a tight cluster, one unexpectedly groups with two *T. simiae* sequences. In general, relationships among the Salivaria are in accordance with their accepted classification [6]; the divergence of *T. vivax* appears to be the most ancient (predicted in [21]) followed by *T. brucei* and *T. congolense*.

4.2   Surface structure and immune evasion

Our results suggest that the specific features of antigenic variation observed in the Salivaria is a unique invention. In *T. brucei,* about 8% of the genome is required to specify about 1000 *vsg* genes [58]. Conceivably, the diversification of such a large repertoire can only occur under a strong selective pressure such as the specific humoral immune response of a vertebrate. While the VSG may have had its origin in an ancient invertebrate trypanosome, the expansion of the gene pool for different surface coats as well as the formation of the complex machinery required for switching *vsgs* may have required cycling of trypanosomes between vector and host over extended evolutionary times.

The separation of the Salivaria from the rest of the trypanosomes is in agreement with the available evidence that none of the members of Clades III–V have a VSG-like surface coat and none show antigenic variation. The surface coat of the bloodstream stages of the Salivaria is a sharply delineated, continuous structure as shown by electron microscopy [59]. The fuzzy, filamentous surface revealed by several of the non-Salivarian species (*T. lewisi, T. cruzi, T. carassii*) suggests the presence of carbohydrate-rich components, i.e. glycoproteins and glycolipids [59–61]. A carbohydrate-dominated surface may provide the primary shield against attack by the innate immune system, in particular the alternative complement pathway. Unless the parasites have an intracellular stage instrumental for immune evasion (*T. cruzi*), the effectiveness of the antibody response may determine whether immunity will be sterile (*T. lewisi*) or only partial leading to a latent state (*T. carassii, T. avium*). The phylogenetic tree provides a basis for the choice of trypanosome species for the further analysis of hemoflagellate immune evasion mechanisms, which may be more diverse than presently believed.

Acknowledgements

We thank D. LeRay, Yves Claes, W. Gibson, R. Brun and T. Pearson for trypanosome strains and samples of DNA. D. Maslov for 55U-rRNA alignments, Christoph Geserick and Jens Ruoff for help with DNA sequencing and J. Klein for critical comments on the manuscript. We also acknowledge helpful discussions with Manolo Gouy.

REFERENCES

[1] Vickerman K, Myler PJ, Stuart KD. African Trypanosomiasis. In : Warren KS, editor. Immunology and Molecular Biology of Parasitic Infections. Boston : Blackwell, 1993 : 170–212.

[2] Cross G.A.M. Antigenic variation in trypanosomes : Secrets surface slowly. Bioessays; 18; 1996; 283-291.

[3] Borst P., Rudenko G., Taylor M.C., Blundell P.A., van Leeuwen F., Bitter W., Cross M., McCullock R. Antigenic variation in trypanosomes. Arch Med Res; 27; 1996; 379-388.

[4] Carrington M., Miller N., Blum M., Roditi I., Wiley D., Turner M. Variant specific glycoprotein of *Trypanosoma brucei* consists of two domains each having an independently conserved pattern of cysteine residues. J Mol Biol; 221; 1991; 823-836.

[5] Urakawa T., Eshita Y., Majiwa P.A.O. The primary structure of *Trypanosoma (Nannomonas) congolense* variant surface glycoproteins. Exp Parasitol; 85; 1997; 215-224.

[6] Molyneux DH, Ashford RW. The Biology of *Trypanosoma* and *Leishmania*. Parasites of Man and Domestic Animals. London : Taylor and Francis, 1983.

[7] Viens P. Immunology of non-pathogenic trypanosomes of rodents. In : Tizard I, editor. Immunology and Pathogenesis of Trypanosomiasis. Boca Raton (FL) : CRC Press, 1985 : 201–223.

[8] Albright J.W., Albright J.F. Rodent trypanosomes : Their conflict with the immune system of the host. Parasitol Today; 7; 1991; 137-140.

[9] Takle GB, Snary D. South American trypanosomiasis (Chagas' disease). In : Warren KS, editor. Immunology and Molecular Biology of Parasitic Infections. Boston : Blackwell, 1993 : 213–236.

[10] Apanius V. Avian trypanosomes as models of hemoflagellate evolution. Parasitol Today; 7; 1991; 87-90.

[11] Bardsley J.E., Harmsen R. The trypanosomes of anura. Adv Parasitol; 11; 1973; 1-73.

[12] Telford SR Jr. Kinetoplastid hemoflagellates of reptiles. In : Kreier JP, editor. Parasitic Protozoa, vol. 10. New York : Academic Press, 1995 : 161–223.

[13] Lom J, Dyková I. Protozoan Parasites of Fishes. Amsterdam : Elsevier, 1992.

[14] Lom J. Biology of the trypanosomes and trypanoplasms of fish. In : Lumsden WHR, Evans DA, editors. Biology of the Kinetoplastida, vol. II. New York : Academic Press, 1979 : 269–337.

[15] Woo P.T.K. Immune response of fish to parasitic protozoa. Parasitol Today; 3; 1987; 186-188.

[16] Woo PTK. Flagellate parasites of fish. In : Kreier JP, editor. Parasitic Protozoa, vol. 8. New York : Academic Press, 1994 : 1–80.

[17] Viens P., Targett G.A.T., Wilson V.C.L.C., Edwards C.I. The persistence of *Trypanosoma (Herpetosoma) musculi* in the kidneys of immune CBA mice. Trans R Soc Trop Med Hyg; 66; 1972; 669-670.

[18] Almeida I.C., Ferguson M.A.J., Schenkman S., Travassos L.R. Lytic anti- α-galactosyl antibodies from patients with chronic Chagas' disease recognize novel O-linked oligosaccharides on mucin-like glycosylphosphatidylinositol-anchored glycoproteins of *Trypanosoma cruzi*. Biochem J; 304; 1994; 793-802.

[19] Baker J.R. Speculations on the evolution of the family trypanosomatidae Doflein, 1901. Exp Parasitol; 13; 1963; 219-233.

[20] Woo P.T.K. Origin of mammalian trypanosomes which develop in the anterior-station of blood-sucking arthropods. Nature; 228; 1970; 1059-1062.

[21] Hoare C.A. Evolutionary trends in mammalian trypanosomes. Adv Parasitol; 5; 1967; 47-91.

[22] Lake J.A., de la Cruz V.F., Ferreira P.C.G., Morel C., Simpson L. Evolution of parasitism : Kinetoplastid protozoan history reconstructed from mitochondrial rRNA gene sequences. Proc Natl Acad Sci USA; 85; 1988; 4779-4783.

[23] Gomez E., Valdes A.M., Pinero D., Hernandez R. What is a genus in the Trypanosomatidae family ? Phylogenetic analysis of two small rRNA sequences. Mol Biol Evol; 8; 1991; 254-259.

[24] Fernandes A.P., Nelson K., Beverley S.M. Evolution of nuclear ribosomal RNAs in kinetoplastid protozoa : Perspectives on the age and origins of parasitism. Proc Natl Acad Sci USA; 90; 1993; 11608-11612.

[25] Maslov D.A., Avila H.A., Lake J.A., Simpson L. Evolution of RNA editing in kinetoplastid protozoa. Nature; 368; 1994; 345-348.

[26] Landweber L.F., Gilbert W. Phylogenetic analysis of RNA editing : A primitive genetic phenomenon. Proc Natl Acad Sci USA; 91; 1994; 918-921.

[27] Marche S., Roth C., Philippe H., Dollet M., Baltz T. Characterization and detection of plant trypanosomatids by sequence analysis of the small subunit ribosomal RNA gene. Mol Biochem Parasitol; 71; 1995; 15-26.

[28] Berchthold M., Philippe H., Breunig A., Brugerolle G. The phylogenetic position of *Dimastigella trypanoformis* within the parasitic kinetoplastids. Parasitol Res; 80; 1994; 672-679.

[29] Wiemer E.A.C., Hannaert V., van den Ijssel P.R.L.A., van Roy J., Opperdoes F.R., Michels P.A.M. Molecular analysis of glyceraldehyde-3-phosphate dehydrogenase in *Trypanoplasma borreli*: An evolutionary scenario of subcellular compartmentation in Kinetoplastida. J Mol Evol; 40; 1995; 443-454.

[30] Hashimoto T., Nakamura Y., Kamaishi T., Adachi J., Nakamura F., Okamoto K., Hasegawa M. Phylogenetic place of kinetoplastid protozoa inferred from a protein phylogeny of elongation factor 1 α. Mol Biochem Parasitol; 70; 1995; 181-185.

[31] Alvarez F., Cortinas M.N., Musto H. The analysis of protein coding genes suggest monophyly of *Trypanosoma*. Mol Phylogenet Evol; 5; 1996; 333-343.

[32] Maslov D.A., Lukes J., Jirku M., Simpson L. Phylogeny of trypanosomes inferred from the small and large subunit rRNAs : Implications for the evolution of parasitism in the trypanosomatid protozoa. Mol Biochem Parasitol; 75; 1996; 197-205.

[33] Lukes J., Jirku M., Dolezel D., Kral'ová I., Hollar L., Maslov D.A. Analysis of ribosomal RNA genes suggests that trypanosomes are monophyletic. J Mol Evol; 44; 1997; 521-527.

[34] Philippe H. Molecular phylogeny of kinetoplastids. In : Coombs GH, Vickerman K, Sleigh MA, Warran A, editors. Evolutionary Relationships among Protozoa. Systematics Association, Chapman and Hall, 1998 (in press).

[35] Friedrich M., Tautz D. An episodic change of rDNA nucleotide substitution rate has occurred during the emergence of the insect order Diptera. Mol Biol Evol; 14; 1997; 644-653.

[36] Hasegawa M., Hashimoto T. Ribosomal RNA trees misleading. Nature; 361; 1993; 23.

[37] Zweygarth E., Röttcher D. The occurrence of *Trypanosoma (Nannomonas) simiae* in the cerebrospinal fluid of domestic pigs. Parasitol Res; 73; 1987; 479-480.

[38] Dirie M.F., Wallbanks K.R., Molyneux D.H., McNamara J. Comparison of *Trypanosoma grayi*-like isolates from West and East Africa. Ann Trop Med Parasitol; 85; 1991; 49-52.

[39] McNamara J.J., Snow W.F. Improved identification of *Nannomonas* infections in tsetse flies from The Gambia. Acta Trop; 48; 1991; 127-136.

[40] Ranque P. Etudes morphologique et biologique de quelques trypanosomides recoltes au Senegal. PhD dissertation. Aix-Marseille : University of Aix-Marseille II, 1973.

[41] Minter-Goedbloed E., Leake C.J., Minter D.M., McNamara J., Kimber C., Bastien P., Evans D.A., Le Ray D. *Trypanosoma varani* and *Trypanosoma grayi*-like trypanosomes : Development in vitro and in insect hosts. Parasitol Res; 79; 1993; 329-333.

[42] Stebeck C.E., Beecroft R.P., Singh B.N., Jardim A., Olafson R.W., Tuckey C., Prenevost K.D., Pearson T.W. Kinetoplastid membrane protein 11 (KMP-11) is differentially expressed during the life cycle of African trypanosomes and is found in a wide variety of kinetoplastid parasites. Mol Biochem Parasitol; 71; 1995; 1-13.

[43] Brun R., Schönenberger M. Cultivation and in vitro cloning of procyclic culture forms of *Trypanosoma brucei* in a semi-defined medium. Acta Trop; 36; 1979; 289-292.

[44] Grab D.J., Bwayo J.J. Isopycnic isolation of African trypanosomes on Percoll gradients formed in situ. Acta Trop; 39; 1982; 363-366.

[45] Lanham S.M., Godfrey D.G. Isolation of salivarian trypanosomes from man and other mammals using DEAE-cellulose. Exp Parasitol; 28; 1970; 521-534.

[46] Darling T., Balber A.E., Blum J.J. A comparative study of D-lactate, L-lactate and glycerol formation by four species of *Leishmania* and by *Trypanosoma lewisi* and *Trypanosoma gambiense*. Mol Biochem Parasitol; 30; 1988; 253-258.

[47] Medina-Acosta E., Cross G.A.M. Rapid isolation of DNA from trypanosomatid protozoa using a simple «mini-prep» procedure. Mol Biochem Parasitol; 59; 1993; 327-330.

[48] Devereux J., Haeberli P., Smithies O. A comprehensive set of sequence analysis programs for the VAX. Nucleic Acids Res; 12; 1984; 387-395.

[49] Kimura M. A simple method for estimating evolutionary rates of base substitutions through comparative studies of nucleotide sequences. J Mol Evol; 16; 1980; 111-120.

[50] Saitou N., Nei M. The neighbor-joining method. A new method for reconstructing phylogenetic trees. Mol Biol Evol; 4; 1987; 406-425.

[51] Kumar S, Tamura K, Nei M. MEGA, Molecular Evolutionary Genetics Analysis. Pennsylvania State University Press, University Park, Version 1.01, 1993.

[52] Ochman H., Wilson A.C. Evolution in bacteria : Evidence for a universal substitution rate in cellular genomes. J Mol Evol; 26; 1987; 74-86.

[53] Escalante A.A., Ayala F.J. Evolutionary origin of *Plasmodium* and other Apicomplexa based on rRNA genes. Proc Natl Acad Sci USA; 92; 1995; 5793-5797.

[54] Molyneux D.H. Experimental infections of avian trypanosomes in *Glossina*. Ann Trop Med Parasitol; 67; 1973; 223-228.

[55] Donelson J.E. Genome research and evolution of trypanosomes. Curr Opin Genet Dev; 6; 1996; 699-703.

[56] Musto H., Rodriguez-Maseda H., Bernardi G. The nuclear genomes of African and American trypanosomes are strikingly different. Gene; 141; 1994; 63-69.

[57] Lambrecht F.L. Palaeoecology of tsetse flies and sleeping sickness in Africa. Proc Am Philos Soc; 124; 1980; 367-385.

[58] Van der Ploeg L.H.T., Valerio D., De Lange T., Bernards A., Borst P., Grosveld F.G. An analysis of cosmid clones of nuclear DNA from *Trypanosoma brucei* shows that the genes for variant surface glycoproteins are clustered in the genome. Nucleic Acids Res; 10; 1982; 5905-5923.

[59] Vickerman K. On the surface coat and flagellar adhesion in trypanosomes. J Cell Sci; 5; 1969; 163-193.

[60] Brener Z. Biology of *Trypanosoma cruzi*. Ann Rev Microbiol; 27; 1973; 347-382.

[61] Paulin J.J., Lom J., Nohynkova E. The fine structure of *Trypanosoma danilewskyi*: II. Structure and cytochemical properties of the cell surface. Protistologica; 16; 1980; 375-383.

3

Abstract

During infection of a mammalian host, African trypanosomes are in constant contact with the host's immune system. These protozoan parasites are infamous for their ability to evade the immune responses by periodically switching their major variant surface glycoprotein (VSG), a phenomenon called antigenic variation. Antigenic variation, however, is likely to be only one of several mechanisms enabling these organisms to thrive in the face of the immune defenses. The ability to grow in high levels of interferon-gamma (IFN-γ) and to avoid complement-mediated destruction may also facilitate the parasite's survival. In this review we summarize (i) the activation of trypanosome genes for three different VSGs during antigenic variation, (ii) the secretion of a trypanosome protein that induces host CD8$^+$ T cells to produce IFN-γ, and (iii) the evidence for trypanosome protein similar to a surface protease of *Leishmania* that plays a role in resistance to complement-mediated lysis.

Keywords : Trypanosomes; Recombinant cloning; VSG genes; T cell; Leishmania

Multiple mechanisms of immune evasion by African trypanosomes[1]

John E. Donelson,
Kent L. Hill,
Najib M.A. El-Sayed

Department of Biochemistry, University of Iowa, Iowa City, Iowa 52242, USA

1 • Introduction

The molecular mechanisms used by African trypanosomes to evade the immune responses of their mammalian hosts have been an object of interest and investigation for most of this century. As early as 1907, the Italian scientist, A. Massaglia, concluded that African trypanosomes in the bloodstream «escape destruction because they become used or habituated to the action of antibodies» (quoted in [1]), a remarkable deduction given the understanding of immunology at the time. The discovery in 1976 that different populations of trypanosomes in the mammalian bloodstream possess different proteins

1. *Abbreviations* : BC, basic copy; EC, expression copy; ELC, expression linked extra copy; ESAG, expression site-associated gene; GP63, glycoprotein of 63 kilodaltons; IFN-γ, interferon gamma; MVAT, metacyclic variant antigen type; TLTF, T lymphocyte triggering factor; VSG, variant surface glycoprotein.

on their surface [2] drew attention to the phenomenon of antigenic variation in African trypanosomes, the process whereby these organisms periodically change the major protein on their surface enabling them to potentially keep one step ahead of the immune system's response. The first recombinant cloning of the trypanosome genes for these variant surface glycoproteins (VSGs) in 1979–1980 [3, 4] ushered in the use of molecular biology techniques to study the events at the DNA and RNA level in trypanosomes that are responsible for antigenic variation.

The 1980's and 1990's have seen the publication of a large amount of data documenting that bloodstream African trypanosomes switch from the expression of one VSG to another and that this switch is sometimes associated with duplicative transpositions or other rearrangements of VSG genes within the trypanosome genome (reviewed by several articles in this book). The intricacies of these VSG gene switching events and the success in elucidating their molecular mechanisms have focused attention on antigenic variation as the dominant immune defense mechanism of these parasites. However, antigenic variation is not the sole determinant of the amazingly successful ability of this parasite to evade the immune defenses. It is not known to be directly responsible for the resistance of African trypanosomes to complement-mediated lysis or for the elevated level of interferon-gamma (IFN-γ) and the profound suppression of many immune responses that occur in the infected host. Thus, antigenic variation appears to be but one of several mechanisms that African trypanosomes use to evade the immune system of their mammalian hosts.

2 • Immunology of African trypanosome infections

The immune responses and pathogenesis that occur in a mammalian host infected with African trypanosomes are complex and poorly understood. From an immune perspective, a trypanosome is a package of thousands of invariant antigens surrounded by 10 million copies of a single VSG [5]. As bloodstream trypanosomes are lysed and destroyed during an infection, the immune system is continually assaulted by massive amounts of the invariant antigens and the different VSGs, but the immune responses against these antigens are not successful in clearing the infection because the invariant proteins are inaccessible inside the living trypanosomes and the readily accessible VSGs periodically switch. Thus, many of the immune events that occur during an African trypanosome infection are likely the result of the perpetual presence of ever-changing VSGs mixed with many invariant antigens, a situation similar to that of successive infections by related but non-identical organisms (reviewed by [6]).

The immune responses to an African trypanosome infection are dominated by two overwhelming phenomena : a massive non-specific polyclonal activation of B cells and a generalized suppression of some humoral (B cell) and cellular (T cell) immune functions [69]. The polyclonal B cell activation results in a large production of IgM, the first class of antibodies to be generated by the appearance of new foreign antigens. This activation is not triggered entirely by the continually changing epitopes of the different VSGs, however, since the newly synthesized antibodies do not react solely with the VSGs and other trypanosome antigens. They frequently are heterospecific in their reactivity and can be autoantibodies directed against the proteins and nucleic acids of the host. It has been proposed that an unknown non-VSG molecule of trypanosomes [6, 7], or perhaps even the VSGs themselves [8], serve as the mitogen causing this massive non-specific expansion of B cells and the subsequent increase in immunoglobulin concentration. The greatly elevated levels of IgM and resultant antigen–antibody complexes in turn cause hyperplasia of the reticuloendothelial system, especially the spleen and lymph nodes, and are likely to be responsible for many of the pathogenic characteristics of the infection.

The other striking immune feature of African trypanosome infections, a dramatic suppression of immune responses other than the initial B cell activation, results in an increased susceptibility to opportunistic infections. This generalized immune suppression has been reported to affect a large variety of both B cell and T cell functions and seems to inhibit many secondary immune events (reviewed in [6]). For example, the enormous IgM production is not followed by the normally concomitant increase in IgG and the other antibody classes, and T cell proliferation is severely suppressed. However, the concentration of IFN-γ is greatly increased in experimental animals infected with *Trypanosoma brucei*. Macrophage activity is enhanced, perhaps by the increase in IFN-γ, and the elimination of trypanosomes by antibodies is thought to be mediated by opsonization and destruction by liver macrophages, rather than by complement-mediated lysis [9, 10]. The levels of some cytokines such as IL-2 decrease during trypanosome infections which may contribute to the lack of T cell proliferation. Although the co-existence of massive polyclonal B cell expansion and profound immunosuppression appears to be a paradox, both phenomena obviously generate an environment conducive to perpetuation of the infection.

This review summarizes recent progress in our laboratory on three of the above issues related to the general question of how African trypanosomes in the mammalian bloodstream avoid destruction by the immune system : (a) characterizations of the duplication and transcription of VSG genes involved in antigenic variation; (b) elucidation of a trypanosome protein that induces host CD8+ T cells to produce IFN-γ; and (c) identification of a protease that the trypanosome may utilize to evade complement-mediated lysis.

3 • The expression of three telomere-linked VSG genes

The final developmental stage of African trypanosomes in the tsetse fly is a quiescent form of the parasites in the insect's salivary glands called the metacyclic stage. Metacyclic trypanosomes can express only one of 10–15 different VSGs on their surface [11–13], in contrast to bloodstream trypanosomes which sequentially express hundreds of different VSGs. The metacyclic VSGs are used to define the metacyclic variant antigen types (MVATs) of the parasite. After metacyclic parasites enter the mammalian bloodstream, they continue to express one of the MVAT VSGs for 5–7 days and then change to the expression of a bloodstream VSG followed by the periodic VSG switching. Late in the infection MVAT VSGs are occasionally re-expressed as bloodstream VSGs.

The expressed genes for both bloodstream and metacyclic VSGs are invariably located near chromosomal telomeres. Only a few expressed bloodstream VSG genes have been examined in detail, but all have been found to be transcribed from telomere-linked expression sites that typically consume 45–60 kb and contain (in a 5' to 3' direction) a promoter, seven or more expression site-associated genes (ESAGs), a variable number of 70–76-bp repeats, and the VSG gene followed by subtelomeric and telomeric DNA repeats (see other chapters for reviews). Transcription of these bloodstream VSG gene expression sites generate polycistronic precursor RNAs containing eight or more protein-coding regions that are subsequently processed into mature, monocistronic mRNAs. Likewise, only a few telomere-linked expression sites for VSG genes expressed during the metacyclic stage have been characterized in detail, but these MVAT VSG gene expression sites are much smaller in size than those for bloodstream VSG genes. These telomere-linked MVAT VSG expression sites lack many or all of the ESAGs, do not contain the multiple 70–76-bp repeats and are transcribed into monocistronic precursor RNAs from a proximal promoter located within 2 kb of the VSG gene [14, 15].

Several years ago our laboratory began to investigate bloodstream trypanosome clones that re-express VSGs normally present during the metacyclic stage. Our goal was to elucidate the molecular mechanisms responsible for the activation of these MVAT VSG genes in bloodstream trypanosomes. For these investigations we have focused on trypanosome clones that initially appeared to have on their surface one of three metacyclic VSGs named MVAT4, MVAT5 and MVAT7. Bloodstream trypanosomes expressing one of these MVAT VSGs were initially identified in immunofluorescence assays of bloodstream trypanosome populations using monoclonal antibodies specific for each of these three MVAT VSGs [16]. When a trypanosome population containing a few organisms that reacted with these monoclonal antibodies was found, the parasites were serially diluted to either one or a few organisms that were used to infect immunocompromised mice and the new population assayed with the monoclonal antibodies again. This process of dilution and subsequent growth in immunocompromised mice was repeated several times until a pure population (> 99%) of bloodstream trypanosomes was obtained that expressed the VSG recognized by the MVAT monoclonal antibodies. These bloodstream trypanosome clones expressing either the MVAT4, MVAT5 or MVAT7 VSG became the basis of our subsequent studies. DNA and RNA were isolated from each of these three sets of trypanosome clones for construction of genomic DNA and cDNA libraries. In addition, the same libraries were prepared from a bloodstream trypanosome clone of the same serodeme, called the WRATat 1.1 clone, which expresses an unrelated bloodstream VSG gene. The MVAT VSG chromosomal genes and their corresponding cDNAs were isolated from these libraries, and used for sequencing studies and as probes in Southern and Northern blots to

FIGURE 1

Summary of the duplicative gene transpositions (MVAT 5 and MVAT 7) and the in situ gene activation (MVAT4) associated with the re-expression in bloodstream trypanosomes of the MVAT5, MVAT7 and MVAT4 VSG genes. Rectangles are VSG genes (1.5 kb in length) or ESAG I family members. Black circles are telomeres. Black flags are the active promoters in the bloodstream re-expressor trypanosomes. White flags are promoters not active in bloodstream re-expressor trypanosomes but thought to be active in metacyclic trypanosomes. BC and ELC are the loci containing the basic copy and expression linked copy, respectively, of the VSG gene. Zigzag lines in the MVAT5 ELC denotes 70–76-bp repeats. The BC locus of the MVAT4 VSG gene is also shown as an expressed copy *(EC)* locus since there is no duplication event to create an ELC. Crossed lines between the BC and ELC loci are the 5' boundaries of the duplicative gene transposition. Wavy lines with an arrowhead are precursor RNAs derived from their respective promoters. Adapted from reference [19].

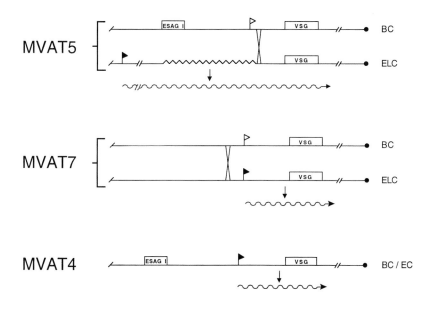

determine the positions and organization of these genes in their expressed and non-expressed states.

We found that in WRATat 1.1 trypanosomes each of the three MVAT VSGs is encoded by a silent, single copy gene already located near a telomere [indicated in Fig. 1 as the basic copy (BC) MVAT VSG genes]. In Southern blots probed with unique portions of each of the three MVAT VSG cDNAs, no other isogene that cross-hybridizes under high hybridization stringency was found to occur in the WRATat 1.1 genome, either at a chromosome-interior location or near a telomere, suggesting that these MVAT VSG genes are not closely related members of isogene families as are some bloodstream VSG genes. Consistent with this observation is the finding that none of these three telomere-linked, basic copy MVAT VSG genes is preceded by a long stretch of 70–76-bp repeats which are thought to be involved in some bloodstream VSG gene duplications and rearrangements [17]. Two of these three basic copy MVAT VSG genes, however, are preceded by a member of the ESAG I family located 5–7 kb upstream. An ESAG I is not located within 5–7 kb upstream of the other basic copy MVAT VSG gene, although it is not known if it might be positioned still further upstream. Members of the other ESAG families found in bloodstream VSG gene expression sites have not been detected in the vicinity of the MVAT VSG genes.

Each of these three basic copy MVAT VSG genes is, however, preceded about 2 kb upstream by a 70-bp sequence that acts as a promoter when placed in front of a reporter gene on a plasmid used in transient transfections of trypanosomes [14, 18, 19]. These promoter sequences are likely to be activated during the metacyclic stage of the life cycle, although we have not conclusively proven this possibility. These three MVAT VSG gene promoters possess 42% positional identity (Fig. 2) and we have conducted limited mutagenesis studies to demonstrate that specific nucleotides shared within the 70-bp are crucial for the promoter activity.

We have also determined at least 5 kb of sequence upstream of each of the three basic copy MVAT VSG genes and find that, other than the aforementioned ESAG I, the only regions of similarity among these three upstream regions are the 70-bp promoter sequences. A comparison of these three MVAT promoter sequences with the sequences previously determined for the promoters of three bloodstream VSG promoters [20–22] revealed that relatively few nucleotides are shared among all six promoters. The longest stretch of identity among all six promoters is three adjacent nucleotides and only about one in five positions in the 70-bp are shared by the same nucleotide in all six promoters (see Fig. 6 of [19]). Thus, there is still

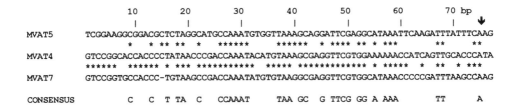

```
              10        20        30        40        50        60        70 bp
               |         |         |         |         |         |         |     ↓
MVAT5    TCGGAAGGCGGACGCTCTAGGCATGCCAAATGTGGTTAAAGCAGGATTCGAGGCATAAATTCAAGATTTATTTCAAG
              *    *  ** **   *    ******    ******  *  **** **  *  ***      **      **
MVAT4    GTCCGGCACCACCCCTATAACCCGACCAAATACATGTAAAGCGAGGTTCGTGGAAAAAACCATCAGTTGCACCCATA
          ******  ****** *  ***  ***********   *****  **************  *  *****   *  **   *  ***
MVAT7    GTCCGGTGCCACCC-TGTAAGCCGACCAAATATGTGTAAGGCGAGGTTCGTGGCATAAACCCCCGATTTAAGCCAAG

CONSENSUS        C   C  T TA  C    CCAAAT     TAA GC   G TTCG GG A AAA       TT       A
```

much to be learned about the sequences that serve as the promoters at VSG expression sites.

Our early analyses of the bloodstream trypanosome clones re-expressing these three MVAT VSGs revealed that indeed the silent, basic copy MVAT VSG gene served as the donor gene for the bloodstream re-expression event. However, each of the three basic copy MVAT VSG genes was found to be re-expressed in bloodstream trypanosomes via a different molecular mechanism. Each of these three mechanisms is discussed in turn.

3.1   Re-expression of MVAT5 VSG

Southern blots of genomic DNA from three independently derived bloodstream trypanosome clones re-expressing the MVAT5 VSG demonstrated that in each case the telomere-linked, basic copy VSG gene is duplicated and the duplicated copy is located adjacent to another telomere. The upstream (5') boundary of the duplicated segment occurs 844-bp in front of the start codon of the VSG gene in two of the three cases, and only 234-bp in front of the start codon in the other case [16, 23]. Thus, none of these three duplications of the basic copy MVAT5 VSG gene includes the promoter sequence located about 2 kb upstream of the gene (Fig. 1). The downstream (3') boundaries of these three independent gene duplications could not be identified from Southern blots but they must be located more than 300-bp downstream of the VSG gene stop codon, and it is possible that the duplicated segments extend all the way down to the telomere itself, although this possibility has not been confirmed.

In each of the three cases the upstream (5') boundary of the newly duplicated segment containing the MVAT5 VSG gene is positioned immediately 3' of a region of at least 20 kb that possesses tandem 70–76-bp repeats (jagged line in Fig. 1). Thus, it is likely that these repeats participated in the recombination events that led to the translocation of the duplicated segment into the expression site despite the fact that the basic copy MVAT5 VSG donor gene is not preceded by a sequence resembling a consensus of the 70–76-bp repeat.

FIGURE 2

Sequence alignment of the promoters located about 2 kb upstream of the basic copy genes for the MVAT5, MVAT7 and MVAT4 VSGs. The sequences correspond to the flags shown in Fig. 2. Asterisks indicate nucleotide identity. The arrow indicates transcription start sites mapped in the MVAT7 and MVAT4 re-expressor trypanosomes. CONSENSUS shows those 42% of the positions that are identical in the three promoters. Adapted from reference [19].

We have been unable to identify genomic DNA clones containing the region located upstream of the tandem 70–76-bp repeats. Probably, the 20 kb of 70–76-bp repeats is unstable in recombinant DNA clones. Thus, we do not know if the three independent duplications were translocated into the same expression site or if they went to different expression sites. The results of Southern blots are consistent with the same expression site being used for each of the three duplications, but since the restriction sites preceding the 70–76-bp repeats are more than 20 kb upstream of the probe sequence, it is difficult to deduce an accurate restriction map. Nuclear RNA run-on assays and UV-irradiation inactivation experiments demonstrated that, in each of the three cases, the promoter for the expression site lies far upstream of the expressed MVAT5 VSG gene and almost surely is located upstream of the 70–76-bp repeats. Thus, the duplicative activation of the basic copy MVAT5 VSG gene in bloodstream trypanosomes is similar to that described for several bloodstream VSG genes, i.e. the duplicated gene is inserted immediately downstream of 70–76-bp repeats of an expression site and the transcription unit begins many kb upstream of the VSG gene itself. The monocistronic MVAT5 VSG mRNA is then derived from this large precursor RNA.

Although most features of these MVAT5 VSG gene duplications and expression are similar to those of a «conventional» bloodstream VSG gene duplication/expression, one common feature of the three independent MVAT5 VSG gene duplications is decidedly unconventional. In each of the three duplications, the duplicated gene of about 1500-bp is not a faithful copy of the MVAT5 VSG donor gene [16, 23]. Point mutations distinguishing the duplicated gene from the donor gene are distributed throughout the coding region, with the greatest concentration of mutations occurring in the middle half of the gene. These point changes were first detected on Southern blots in which restriction enzymes that cleave in the coding region of the basic copy gene were found to not cleave in the duplicated gene. The presence of the mutations was subsequently confirmed by sequence determinations of multiple cDNA and genomic DNA clones derived from the bloodstream trypanosome re-expressor clones. Fig. 3 summarizes the distribution of the mutations in the three duplicated gene copies. One duplicated gene copy *(Rx 1)* has 35 point mutations,

FIGURE 3

Distribution of point mutations in the duplicated VSG gene of three independent bloodstream trypanosome clones re-expressing the basic copy MVAT5 VSG gene [23]. The large rectangle represents the 518 codons of the basic copy *(BC)* MVAT5 VSG donor gene. The duplicated VSG gene in MVAT5 trypanosome re-expressor clones 1, 2 and 3 *(Rx 1, Rx 2 and Rx 3)* contains 35, 11 and 28 point mutations, respectively, when compared to the BC donor gene. Vertical lines represent the point mutations that cause an amino acid change; black dots are the point mutations that do not cause an amino acid change.

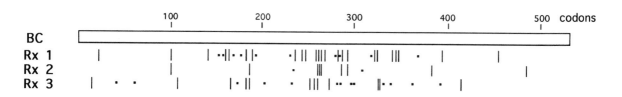

another (*Rx 2*) has 11 and the third (*Rx 3)* has 28 point changes, all relative to the original basic copy MVAT5 donor gene. The sequence of this donor gene is unchanged in each of these three trypanosome re-expressor clones and in the WRATat 1.1 trypanosome clone expressing an unrelated bloodstream VSG. Thus, the mechanism responsible for the mutations does not introduce changes into the donor gene of the duplication. Likewise, the region of the duplicated segment located upstream of the MVAT5 VSG gene (844-bp in the *Rx 1* and *Rx 2* duplications, and 234-bp in the *Rx 3* duplication) does not possess any mutations relative to the corresponding region preceding the donor gene. Since mutations would be expected to occur in this upstream region of the duplicated segment if they were introduced in a completely random manner during the duplicative transposition event, the events responsible for them must be confined to the coding region, or perhaps to the region between the spliced leader and the polyadenylation addition sites. Another clue that the mutations are not introduced randomly during the duplication event is the fact that in the sense strand of the coding region, 54% of the mutations are purine transitions and only 7% are pyrimidine transitions (out of the 74 total mutations in the three duplications). If the mutations were introduced randomly by, for example, a DNA polymerase involved in the duplication, both strands would be expected to have an equal distribution of purine and pyrimidine transitions.

Despite the indications that the mutations are not randomly generated, the molecular mechanism responsible for them remains unclear. We have discussed some of the possible alternatives previously [23, 24], so will not repeat them here except to note that the data on the mutations are consistent with, but do not prove, the existence of an RNA intermediate in the events leading to expression of the duplicated MVAT5 VSG genes. This possibility might account for the strand bias of the mutations and their locations between the spliced leader and polyadenylation addition sites in the duplicated segment. Also supporting this possibility is the presence in the trypanosome genome of more than 400 copies of a retrotransposon-like element called *ingi,* each of which contains a reverse transcriptase gene whose sequence varies slightly from one *ingi* to another [25–28]. If some of these *ingi* elements encode a reverse transcriptase with a very low proof-reading activity, point mutations could be introduced during the reverse transcription of an mRNA whose DNA product could become integrated into the genome at a VSG gene expression site.

Finally, about two-thirds of the point mutations lead to changes in the encoded amino acids (Fig. 3). The observation that most of these mutations are located in the middle of the gene may suggest that mutations which change the amino acids in the N- and C-termini interfere with the ability of the VSG to fold or target properly and result in death of the organism. Monoclonal antibodies directed against the VSG from each of the MVAT5 re-expressor clones can distinguish among the three VSGs, indicating that at least some of the mutations alter the epitopes of these closely related VSGs [23]. Thus, the introduction of point mutations in duplicated VSG genes is a way for the trypanosome to expand its repertoire of immunologically distinct VSGs.

3.2   Re-expression of MVAT7 VSG

Southern blots of genomic DNA from a bloodstream trypanosome clone re-expressing the MVAT7 VSG revealed that this telomere-linked, basic copy MVAT7 VSG gene is also duplicated and inserted near another telomere prior to its expression in bloodstream trypanosomes, similar to that of the MVAT5 VSG gene (Fig. 1). In this MVAT7 case, however, sequence determinations of the duplicated gene and its corresponding cDNA revealed that the sequence of duplicated gene is an exact replica of the basic copy donor gene [19]. No mutations occurred during the duplication. It is not clear why the duplication of one telomere-linked, basic copy MVAT VSG gene would not involve mutations (MVAT7), whereas three independent duplications of another telomere-linked, basic copy MVAT VSG gene would each have mutations (MVAT5), unless the duplication of these two donor genes occurs via different molecular mechanisms. In the original isolation of bloodstream trypanosomes re-expressing MVAT VSGs, the few parasites re-expressing the MVAT7 VSG were detected about as frequently as the few organisms re-expressing the MVAT5 VSG, so duplications of both donor genes likely occur at about the same low rate.

In addition to these mutations, several other differences exist between the duplications of the basic copy MVAT7 and MVAT5 VSG genes. First, the 5' boundary of the duplicated MVAT7 VSG gene occurs about 3 kb upstream of the start codon, which is more than 2 kb further upstream than the 5' boundaries of the duplicated MVAT5 VSG genes. Secondly, the 70–76-bp repeats in the bloodstream MVAT5 VSG expression site are not present in the expression site of the re-expressed MVAT7 VSG gene. Likewise, no members of the ESAG I family have been found upstream of the either the MVAT7 VSG donor gene or its expressed duplicated copy. Thirdly, and most interestingly, the MVAT7 duplicated segment includes the promoter sequence preceding the MVAT7 VSG donor gene (Fig. 1). Thus, this promoter is co-duplicated with its MVAT VSG gene. Primer extension experiments and nuclear RNA run on assays demonstrate that this promoter is used for the transcription of the expressed MVAT7 VSG gene and that the region immediately preceding it in the expression site is not transcribed. Therefore, the co-duplicated promoter is the promoter that is activated at the expression site, in contrast to the MVAT5 VSG gene duplications in which the duplicated gene is subsequently transcribed from a far upstream promoter already present in the expression site.

3.3   Re-expression of MVAT4 VSG

Southern blots of genomic DNA from a bloodstream trypanosome clone re-expressing the MVAT4 VSG indicated that the single telomere-linked, basic copy MVAT4 VSG gene was not duplicated or otherwise rearranged prior to its re-expression in the bloodstream. Likewise, careful quantification of the radioactive signals of slot blots containing genomic DNAs from several trypanosome clones probed with the MVAT4 VSG cDNA failed to provide evidence for a gene duplication [14]. Thus, the bloodstream re-expression of the MVAT4 VSG gene is an example of the in situ activation of a VSG gene already located near a telomere (Fig. 1). Primer extension experiments and nuclear run on assays indicate that the bloodstream transcription of this gene is initiated at the sequence about 2 kb upstream of the gene that was shown via transient transfections with a reporter gene to possess promoter activity. The 2 kb region between this promoter and the VSG start codon does not possess an open translation reading frame of any significant length and precursor RNA derived from this promoter sequence does not have a spliced leader at its 5' end. Thus, this precursor RNA is a monocistronic RNA that is processed via 3' polyadenylation and 5' spliced leader addition to a site about 20 nucleotides in front of the VSG start codon to yield the MVAT4 mRNA.

Fig. 1 shows that an ESAG I is located about 3 kb upstream of this MVAT4 promoter sequence (5 kb upstream of the VSG gene). However, when ESAG I cDNAs from a cDNA library of this MVAT4 re-expressor trypanosome clone were isolated and examined, none was found to have exactly the same sequence as this specific ESAG I family member [29]. Of the 25 ESAG I cDNA clones from this library whose sequences were determined, at least 20 different ESAG I members were identified, none of which are identical to the ESAG I gene preceding the MVAT4 promoter. Furthermore, nuclear RNA run on assays in the presence of α-amanitin demonstrated that these expressed ESAG I members are transcribed by an RNA polymerase II (α-amanitin sensitive) activity, rather than the α-amanitin resistant activity known to transcribe VSG genes, including the re-expressed MVAT4 VSG gene [29]. Thus, although ESAG families were first identified as genes whose expression is associated with that of telomere-linked VSG genes (hence, the name of expression site associated genes), in this bloodstream trypanosome clone re-expressing the MVAT4 VSG, the expressed ESAG I family members are not transcribed by the same RNA polymerase as the VSG gene, nor are these expressed ESAG I members in the vicinity of the VSG gene.

To summarize the information available on the re-expression of the MVAT4, MVAT5 and MVAT7 VSGs in bloodstream trypanosomes, the activation of these three basic copy VSG genes share some common features and differ in other respects. For example, the MVAT4 and MVAT7 VSG genes are both transcribed into monocistronic precursor RNAs whose transcription is initiated from the same promoters thought to be used in the metacyclic expression of these genes. Interestingly, these two promoters are much more similar in sequence to each other than either is to the MVAT5 promoter (Fig. 2). In contrast, the basic copy MVAT5 VSG gene is not re-expressed from its own promoter. It is re-expressed via duplication to a «conventional» bloodstream expression site, containing 70–76-bp repeats, in which transcription initiation occurs far upstream to generate a large precursor RNA that is cleaved into individual mRNAs. On the other hand, the MVAT5 and MVAT7 VSG genes are similar in that they are both re-expressed in the bloodstream via duplicative transposition, whereas the MVAT4 VSG gene is re-expressed via in situ activation (Fig. 1). Finally, MVAT5 VSG gene duplications are associated with mutations in the VSG coding region (Fig. 3), whereas the MVAT7 VSG gene duplication generates a faithful copy of the donor gene.

4 • A trypanosome protein that triggers IFN-γ production

One of the hallmarks of an African trypanosome infection is an elevated level of IFN-γ in the bloodstream. When rodents are experimentally infected with African trypanosomes, IFN-γ production in the spleen increases markedly within a few hours [6]. However, in rodents depleted of CD8+ T cells by injection of anti-CD8 antisera or in knockout animals possessing a deletion in the CD8 gene, the trypanosomes do not induce as much IFN-γ, the parasitemia is decreased and the infected animals survive longer [30]. In contrast, in rodents depleted of CD4+ T cells, trypanosomes induce about the same level of IFN-γ as they do in wild type animals of the same strain. These results are consistent with the possibility that a constituent(s) of bloodstream trypanosomes stimulates, either directly or indirectly, the production of IFN-γ from CD8+ T cells but not from CD4+ T cells. Several years ago bloodstream trypanosomes were shown to release a protein that possesses this property, i.e. its presence induces CD8+, but not CD4+, T cells to secrete IFN-γ [31–33]. This protein, named T lymphocyte triggering factor or TLTF, was subsequently shown to bind directly to the CD8 molecule on T cells [30]. IFN-γ, in turn, induces the production of a mitogen-activated protein (MAP) kinase in African trypanosomes [34] which might be a factor contributing to proliferation of trypanosomes in the bloodstream. Consistent with this possibility, a monoclonal antibody directed against TLTF reduces parasite levels in, and increases survival of, mice infected with African trypanosomes [35, 36].

In collaboration with Moiz Bakhiet, Tomas Olsson, Krister Kristensson and their colleagues, who first identified and characterized TLTF, we immunoscreened a trypanosome cDNA library with antisera directed against affinity purified TLTF. A partial length cDNA clone whose protein product reacted with the antisera was used to identify full length cDNAs containing the 5' spliced leader and 3' poly(A). The corresponding full length recombinant protein was produced in *Escherichia coli* as a fusion protein using two different expression plasmids in which the partner protein was either thioredoxin or glutathione-*S*-transferase [37]. Both versions of the fusion protein were used to raise antisera and to test for TLTF activity. In blind assays the antisera against the recombinant fusion proteins were found to inhibit the ability of native TLTF to induce the production of IFN-γ from CD8+ T cells. Likewise, the recombinant fusion proteins themselves were shown to possess the TLTF activity of inducing CD8+ T cells to produce IFN-γ, whereas unrelated fusion proteins produced from the same expression plasmids did not have this activity. These results are consistent with the interpretation that the cDNA encodes TLTF.

The protein sequence deduced from the TLTF cDNA is 453 amino acids in length. It bears no obvious similarity to IGIF (IFN-γ inducing factor), a protein recently identified in mouse liver that induces IFN-γ production by CD4+ T cells [38]. The lack of similarity between these two proteins could be because one targets CD8+ T cells and the other acts on CD4+ T cells. However, TLTF is similar in sequence to two mammalian sequences that have been deposited in GenBank without further characterization. One is a mouse protein of 489 amino acids designated as a growth arrest-specific protein. The other protein is encoded by a randomly sequenced human cDNA from a fetal lung cDNA library. In each case TLTF displays about 35% identity and 58% similarity to the mammalian protein [37]. Although the properties and functions of these mouse and human proteins are unknown, it is tempting to speculate that they may possess an activity towards CD8+ cells that resembles that of TLTF. If so, then TLTF, a trypanosome-encoded protein, mimics the activity of an immunomodulatory protein of its host. In recognition of this possibility, we have suggested that TLTF is an example of a group of proteins that we have designated as trypanokines, i.e. factors secreted by trypanosomes that modulate the cytokine network of the host immune system for the benefit of the parasite [37]. Another potential trypanokine is a secreted cysteine protease [39, 40] since cysteine proteases of other microorganisms have been shown to modulate cytokine activity [41, 42].

For TLTF to gain access to host T lymphocytes, it must first be delivered to the exterior of the trypanosome cell. However, the deduced TLTF amino acid sequence does not contain a hydrophobic region that might serve as a signal for membrane transport. Since it specifically lacks a classical N-terminal hydrophobic signal sequence similar to those found in most secreted eukaryotic proteins [43], we decided to investigate how TLTF is targeted for export from the trypanosome cell. For these experiments the luciferase gene in the trypanosome expression plasmid pHD1 [44] was replaced with a mutated version of the gene for the green fluorescent protein (GFP) of *Aquorea victoria* that gives 30–100-times more fluorescence than wild type GFP [45]. Trypanosomes transiently transfected with this plasmid display a bright green fluorescence several hours after electroporation (Fig. 4, left).

The fluorescence is distributed uniformly throughout the trypanosome cell including the nucleus and the flagellum. Thus, the amino acid sequence of GFP itself does not restrict it from, nor direct it to, any specific compartment within the trypanosome.

When the TLTF coding sequence is placed either in front of, or behind, the GFP gene to generate a TLTF-GFP fusion protein and the resultant plasmid is transiently transfected into trypanosomes, the result shown in the right panel of Fig. 4 is obtained. The green fluorescence is now confined to vesicles in the cytoplasm of the trypanosome, most of which are located near a region of the trypanosome called the flagellar pocket. This surface pocket of trypanosomes has long been thought to be the site of endocytosis and secretion for the

FIGURE 4

Targeting of a fusion protein of TLTF and the green fluorescent protein (GFP) to vesicles localized near the trypanosome flagellar pocket. The trypanosomes were transiently transfected with an expression plasmid containing the GFP gene alone (left panel) or a plasmid encoding a TLTF-GFP fusion protein (right panel). The trypanosome on the right was stained with ethidium bromide to reveal the nucleus (large red area) and the kinetoplast (small red area). The kinetoplast serves as a marker for the subcellular location of the flagellar pocket.

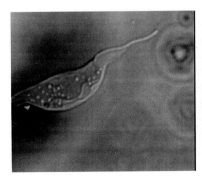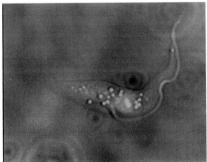

organism. It is derived from a specialized invagination of the cell membrane that forms at the location where the flagellum emerges from the cell. Thus, since TLTF is a secreted protein, it is reasonable to find that vesicles containing the TLTF-GFP fusion protein would congregate around the flagellar pocket. The fact that the same vesicular localization of the fluorescence is obtained when TLTF is positioned either in front of or behind GFP indicates that the location of the fusion protein is not an artifact of the relative order of the TLTF and GFP sequences. Thus, TLTF appears to be a member of the group of secreted eukaryotic proteins for which the amino acid sequence provides no indication of the targeting signal. Interestingly, some of the other secreted proteins in this group are mammalian immunoregulatory proteins such as IL-1b and adult T cell leukemia-derived factor (ADF) [46, 47].

Many questions remain about TLTF. Is there a unique secretory pathway for TLTF in trypanosomes ? What is the sequence in TLTF that targets it to the cytoplasmic vesicles ? How do TLTF and CD8[+] cells interact ? What is the signaling pathway within CD8[+] T cells that stimulates INF-g production ? Does vaccination with recombinant TLTF reduce susceptibility to trypanosome infection ? These questions are currently being addressed experimentally.

5 • A trypanosome protein similar to the metalloprotease GP63 of *Leishmania*

While conducting a preliminary project to determine the efficiency of sequencing random fragments of trypanosome genomic DNA for discovering new trypanosome genes, we identified a fragment that potentially encodes a protein with substantial similarity to a surface protease called GP63 that occurs in all *Leishmania* species investigated [48]. This fragment was used to screen trypanosome cDNA and genomic DNA libraries, and to probe Southern blots of trypanosome genomic DNA. These experiments revealed that African trypanosomes possess several non-identical, tandemly arrayed genes encoding GP63-like proteins [70]

GP63s and their genes in different *Leishmania* species have studied extensively [49–52]. These studies have included characterizations of the zinc protease activity and its substrate specificity, elucidation of the post-translation modifications of this glycosylphosphatidylinositol (GPI)-anchored protein, and determination of the chromosomal organization and differential expression of the multicopy GP63 genes. Depending on the *Leishmania* species, the infective metacyclic promastigote form of *Leishmania* can have as many as one-half million GP63 molecules on its surface [50, 53]. These *Leishmania* GP63s have

FIGURE 5

Comparison of the amino acid sequences of a GP63-like protein from *Trypanosoma brucei rhodesiense* (Tbr GP63-1) and a GP63 expressed in stationary promastigotes of *Leishmania chagasi* (Lc GP63-S1) [68]. Asterisks indicate positions of identity. Dashes are gaps introduced to maximize alignment. Shaded boxes show 19 cysteines and open boxes show ten prolines whose positions are conserved in the two proteins. The large open box labeled Zn is the protease active site of the Leishmania GP63s. The over-line indicates a highly acidic, serine-rich region of the trypanosome GP63, which is not present in the *Leishmania* GP63 shown but does occur some of the other *Leishmania* GP63s whose genes have been sequenced.

been hypothesized to have a number of different functions, several of which involve the interaction between the infective promastigote and host macrophages. GP63s have been reported to participate in the entry of promastigotes into macrophages [54–56] and to contribute to the survival of the amastigote form of *Leishmania* inside the macrophage [57]. The protease activity of GP63 on the surface of the promastigotes has also been shown to contribute to the resistance of promastigotes to complement-mediated lysis [58]. Finally, immunization with recombinant GP63 has been found to partially protect experimental animals against *Leishmania* infections [59–62]. A GP63-like protein has also been reported in another trypanosomatid, *Crithidia fasciculata* [63] but it has not been as extensively studied in this organism, which is not known to infect mammals. Since African trypanosomes do not have an intracellular stage in their mammalian host as does *Leishmania,* we examined the properties of the trypanosome genes for the GP63-like proteins further.

Determination of the complete coding sequences of a trypanosome cDNA and two chromosomal genes demonstrated that about 40% of the amino acids in the middle one-half of the trypanosome protein are identical to corresponding positions of the *Leishmania* and *Crithidia* GP63s (Fig. 5).

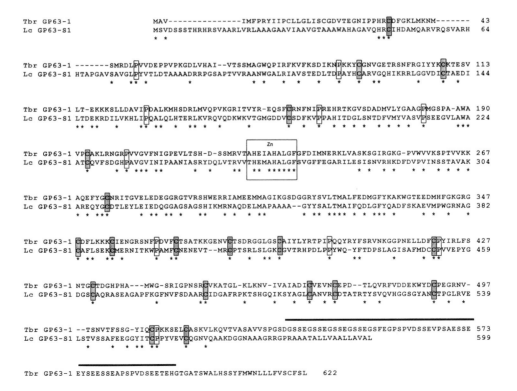

The positions of 19 cysteines and ten prolines are conserved throughout the full length of these GP63 sequences. Since cysteines participate in potential disulfide linkages and prolines disrupt secondary structure, the conservation of these amino acid positions suggests that the trypanosome protein has a tertiary structure similar to that of GP63s of these other organisms. The longest stretch of amino acid identity of the trypanosome protein with the *Leishmania* and *Crithidia* GP63s is in the region known to be the catalytic site of the zinc protease activity of *Leishmania* GP63. Two histidines and one glutamic acid in this region, which are conserved in the trypanosome protein, have been shown to be essential for the protease activity [64]. These amino acid similarities of the trypanosome protein and the *Leishmania* and *Crithidia* GP63s indicates that it shares structural properties and likely protease activity with GP63s of these other organisms.

Nuclear RNA run on assays indicate that the trypanosome GP63 genes are transcribed to an equal extent in bloodstream and procyclic organisms, whereas Northern blots show that their mRNAs accumulate to a 50-fold higher steady state level in bloodstream trypanosomes than in procyclic organisms. In bloodstream trypanosomes the ratio of mRNAs for GP63 and the VSG is about 1 : 150, as determined by cDNA library screenings. Since the VSG mRNA represents about 5% of the total mRNA population of bloodstream trypanosomes, about 0.03% of the mRNA encodes GP63.

The function of GP63 in bloodstream trypanosomes has not been determined yet. However, one attractive possibility is that the surface protease activity of GP63 might contribute to evasion of complement-mediated lysis of bloodstream trypanosomes, a function consistent with one of its proposed roles in *Leishmania* [58]. Bloodstream trypanosomes are known to activate the alternative pathway of complement in human serum, but appear not to lyse because the complement cascade does not go beyond the association of C3 convertase with the parasite surface [65]. Procyclic trypanosomes, on the other hand, have a much lower amount of GP63 and are highly susceptible to complement-mediated cytolysis [66]. This model for resistance to complement-mediated lysis by African trypanosomes can be tested by comparing the susceptibility to complement of bloodstream and procyclic trypanosomes transfected with plasmids over expressing GP63 versus that of untransfected organisms. In addition, it will be interesting to see if GP63 is highly expressed during the metacyclic stage of the African trypanosome life cycle, the stage that encounters the complement system first upon infection from the tsetse fly. In this respect, a preliminary report has occurred of a membrane-bound metalloprotease in infective metacyclic trypomastigotes of *Trypanosoma cruzi* [67], an intracellular parasite that causes

Chagas disease in Latin America and must also evade the complement system after transmission from the insect.

Acknowledgements

The research in our laboratory was supported by NIH grants AI32135 and AI40591. KLH was supported by NIH grants AI09872 and AI07511.

REFERENCES

[1] Ross R, Thomson D A case of sleeping sickness studied by precise enumerative methods : further observations. Proc R Soc London; 83; 1910; 187-205.

[2] Bridgen PJ, Cross GAM, Bridgen J N-terminal amino acid sequences of variant-specific surface antigens from *Trypanosoma brucei.* Nature; 263; 1976; 613-614.

[3] Williams RO, Young JR, Majiwa PAO Genomic rearrangements correlated with antigenic variation in in *Trypanosoma brucei.* Nature; 282; 1979; 847-849.

[4] Hoeijmakers JH, Frasch AC, Bernards A, Borst P, Cross GA Novel expression-linked copies of the genes for variant surface antigen in trypanosomes. Nature; 284; 1980; 78-80.

[5] Vickerman K Developmental cycles and biology of pathogenic trypanosomes. Br Med Bull; 41; 1985; 105-114.

[6] Sileghem M, Flynn JN, Darji A, De Baetselier P, Naessens J. African Trypanosomiasis. In : Kierszenbaum F, editor. Parasite Infections and the Immune System. San Diego : Academic Press, 1994 : 1–51.

[7] Urquhart GM, Murray M, Murray PK, Jennings FW, Bate E Immunosuppression in *Trypanosoma brucei* infections in rates and mice. Trans R Soc Trop Med Hyg; 67; 1973; 528-535.

[8] Diffley P Trypanosomal surface coat variant antigen causes polyclonal lymphocyte activation. J Immunol; 131; 1983; 1983-1986.

[9] Jokiranta TS, Jokipii L, Meri S Complement resistance of parasites. Scand J Immunol; 42; 1995; 9-20.

[10] Dempsey WA, Mansfield JM Lymphocyte function in experimental African trypanosomiasis. V. Role of antibody and the mononuclear phagocyte system in variant-specific immunity. J Immunol; 130; 1983; 405-411.

[11] Esser KM, Schoenbechler MJ, Gingrich JB *Trypanosoma rhodesiense* blood forms express all antigen specificities relevant to protection against metacyclic (insect form) challenge. J Immunol; 129; 1982; 1715-1718.

[12] Crowe JS, Barry JD, Luckins AG, Ross CA, Vickerman K All metacyclic variable antigen types of *Trypanosoma congolense* identified using monoclonal antibodies. Nature; 306; 1983; 389-391.

[13] Turner CM, Barry JD, Maudlin I, Vickerman K An estimate of the size of the metacyclic variable antigen repertoire of *Trypanosoma brucei rhodesiense.* Parasitology; 97; 1988; 269-276.

[14] Alarcon CM, Son HJ, Hall T, Donelson JE A monocistronic transcript for a trypanosome variant surface glycoprotein. Mol Cell Biol; 14; 1994; 5579-5591.

[15] Graham SV, Barry JD Transcriptional regulation of metacyclic variant surface glycoprotein gene expression during the life cycle of *Trypanosoma brucei.* Mol Cell Biol; 15; 1995; 5945-5956.

[16] Lu Y, Hall T, Gay LS, Donelson JE Point mutations are associated with a gene duplication leading to the bloodstream reexpression of a trypanosome metacyclic VSG. Cell; 72; 1993; 397-406.

[17] McCulloch R, Rudenko G, Borst P Gene conversions mediating antigenic variation in *Trypanosoma brucei* can occur in variant surface glycoprotein expression sites lacking 70-base-pair repeat sequences. Mol Cell Biol; 17; 1997; 833-843.

[18] Nagoshi Lu Y, Alarcon CM, Donelson JE The putative promoter for a metacyclic VSG gene in African trypanosomes. Mol Biochem Parasitol; 72; 1995; 33-45.

[19] Kim KS, Donelson JE Co-duplication of a variant surface glycoprotein gene and its promoter to an expression site in African trypanosomes. J Biol Chem; 272; 1997; 24637-24645.

[20] Pays E, Coquelet H, Tebabi P, Pays A, Jefferies D, Steinert M, Koenig E, Williams RO, Roditi I *Trypanosoma brucei :* constitutive activity of the VSG and procyclin gene promoters. EMBO J; 9; 1990; 3145-3151.

[21] Gottesdiener K, Chung H-M, Brown SD, Lee MG-S, Van der Ploeg LHT Characterization of VSG gene expression site promoters and promoter-associated DNA rearrangement events. Mol Cell Biol; 11; 1991; 2467-2480.

[22] Zomerdijk JCBM, Kieft R, Shiels PG, Borst P Alpha-amanitin-resistant transcription units in trypanosomes : a comparison of promoter sequences for a VSG gene expression site and for the ribosomal RNA genes. Nucleic Acids Res; 19; 1991; 5153-5158.

[23] Lu Y, Alarcon CM, Hall T, Reddy LV, Donelson JE A strand bias occurs in point mutations associated with VSG gene conversion in *Trypanosoma rhodesiense*. Mol Cell Biol; 14; 1994; 3971-3980.

[24] Donelson JE Mechanisms of antigenic variation in *Borrelia hermsii* and African trypanosomes. J Biol Chem; 270; 1995; 7783-7786.

[25] Kimmel BE, Ole-MoiYoi OK, Young JR Ingi, a 5.2 kb dispersed sequence element from *Trypanosoma brucei* that carries half of a smaller mobile element at either end and has homology with mammalian lines. Mol Cell Biol; 7; 1987; 1465-1475.

[26] Lodes MJ, Smiley BL, Stadnyk AW, Bennett JL, Myler PJ, Stuart K Expression of a retroposon-like sequence upstream of the putative *Trypanosoma brucei* variant surface glycoprotein gene expression site promoter. Mol Cell Biol; 13; 1993; 7036-7044.

[27] Aksoy S, Lalor TM, Martin J, Van der Ploeg LH, Richards FF Multiple copies of a retroposon interrupt spliced leader RNA genes in the African trypanosome, *Trypanosoma gambiense*. EMBO J; 6; 1987; 3819-3826.

[28] Pays E, Murphy NB DNA-binding fingers encoded by a trypanosome retroposon. J Mol Biol; 197; 1987; 147-148.

[29] Morgan RW, El-Sayed NMA, Kepa JK, Pedram M, Donelson JE Differential expression of the expression site-associated gene I family in African trypanosomes. J Biol Chem; 271; 1996; 9771-9777.

[30] Olsson T, Bakhiet M, Hojeberg B, Ljungdahl A, Edlund C, Andersson G, Ekre H-P, Fung-Leung W-P, Mak T, Wigzell H, Fiszer U, Kristensson K CD8 is critically involved in lymphocyte activation by a *T. brucei brucei*-released molecule. Cell; 72; 1993; 715-727.

[31] Bakhiet M, Olsson T, Van der Meide P, Kristensson K Depletion of CD8+ T cells suppresses growth of *Trypanosoma brucei brucei* and interferon-gamma production in infected rats. Clin Exp Immunol; 81; 1990; 195-199.

[32] Olsson T, Bakhiet M, Kristensson K Interactions between *Trypanosoma brucei* and CD8+ T cells. Parasitol Today; 8; 1992; 237-239.

[33] Olsson T, Bakhiet M, Edlund C, Hojeberg B, Van der Meide PH, Kristensson K Bidirectional activating signals between *Trypanosoma brucei* and CD8+ T cells : a trypanosome-released factor triggers interferon-γ production that stimulates parasite growth. Eur J Immunol; 21; 1991; 2447-2454.

[34] Hua SB, Wang CC Interferon-gamma activation of a mitogen-activated protein kinase, KFR1, in the bloodstream form of *Trypanosoma brucei*. J Biol Chem; 272; 1997; 10797-10803.

[35] Bakhiet M, Olsson T, Edlund C, Hojeberg B, Holmberg K, Lorentzen J, Kristensson K A *Trypanosoma brucei brucei*-derived factor that triggers CD8+ lymphocytes to interferon-γ secretion : Purification, characterization and protective effects in vivo by treatment with a monoclonal antibody against the factor. Scand J Immunol; 37; 1993; 165-178.

[36] Bakhiet M, Olsson T, Mhlanga J, Buscher P, Lycke N, Van der Meide PH, Kristensson K Human and rodent interferon-γ as a growth factor for *Trypanosoma brucei*. Eur J Immunol; 26; 1996; 1359-1364.

[37] Vaidya T, Bakhiet M, Hill KL, Olsson T, Kristensson K, Donelson JE The gene for a trypanosome triggering factor from African trypanosomes. J Exp Med; 186; 1997; 433-438.

[38] Okamura H, Tsutsul H, Komatsu T, Yutsudo M, Hakura A, Tanimoto T, Torigoe K, Okura T, Nukada Y, Hattori K, Akita K, Namba M, Tanabe F, Konishi K, Fukuda S, Kurimoto M Cloning of a new cytokine that induces IFN-γ production by T cells. Nature; 378; 1995; 88-91.

[39] McKerrow JH The proteases and pathogenicity of parasitic protozoa. Annu Rev Microbiol; 47; 1993; 821-853.

[40] Lonsdale-Eccles JD, Mpimbaza WN, Nkhungulu RM, Olobo J, Smith L, Tosomba OM, Grab DJ Trypanosomatid cysteine protease activity may be enhanced by a kininogen-like moiety from host serum. Biochem J; 305; 1995; 549-556.

[41] Kapur V, Majesky MW, Li L-L, Black RA, Musser JM Cleavage of interleukin 1 β (IL-1 β) precursor to produce active IL-1b by a conserved extracellular cysteine protease from *Streptococcus pyogenes*. Proc Natl Acad Sci USA; 90; 1993; 7676-7680.

[42] LaMarre J, Wollenberg GK, Gonias SL, Hayes MA Cytokine binding and clearance properties of proteinase-activated α2-macroglobulins. Lab Invest; 65; 1991; 3-14.

[43] Schatz G, Dobberstein B Common principles of protein translocation across membranes. Science; 271; 1996; 1519-1526.

[44] Hug M, Carruthers VB, Hartmann C, Sherman DS, Cross GAM, Clayton C A possible role for the 3'-untranslated region in developmental regulation in *Trypanosoma brucei.* Mol Biochem Parasitol; 61; 1993; 87-96.

[45] Cormack BP, Valdivia RH, Falkow S FACS-optimized mutants of the green fluorescent protein (GFP). Gene; 173; 1996; 33-38.

[46] Muesch A, Hartmann E, Rohde K, Rubartelli A, Sitia R, Rapoport TA A novel pathway for secretory proteins ? TIBS; 15; 1990; 86-88.

[47] Tagaya Y, Maeda Y, Mitsui A, Kondo N, Matsui H, Hamuro J, Brown N, Arai K, Yokota T, Wakasugi H, Yodoi J ATL-derived factor (ADF), an IL-2 receptor/Tac inducer homologous to thioredoxin; possible involvement of dithiol-reduction in the IL-2 receptor induction. EMBO J; 8; 1989; 757-764.

[48] El-Sayed NMA, Donelson JE A survey of *Trypanosoma brucei rhodesiense* genome using shotgun sequencing. Mol Biochem Parasitol; 84; 1997; 167-178.

[49] Bordier C The promastigote surface protease of *Leishmania.* Parasitol Today; 3; 1987; 151-153.

[50] Bouvier J, Schneider P, Etges R Leishmanolysin: Surface metalloproteinase of *Leishmania.* Methods Enzymol; 248; 1995; 614-633.

[51] Chang K-P, Chaudhuri G Molecular determinants of *Leishmania* virulence. Annu Rev Microbiol; 44; 1990; 499-529.

[52] Roberts SC, Swihart KG, Agey MW, Ramamoorthy R, Wilson ME, Donelson JE Sequence diversity and organization of the *msp* gene family encoding gp63 of *Leishmania chagasi.* Mol Biochem Parasitol; 62; 1993; 157-172.

[53] Medina-Acosta E, Beverley SM, Russell DG Evolution and expression of the *Leishmania* surface proteinase (gp63) gene locus. Infect Agents Dis; 2; 1993; 25-34.

[54] Chang C-S, Chang K-P Monoclonal antibody affinity purification of a leishmania membrane glycoprotein and its inhibition of *Leishmania*-macrophage binding. Proc Natl Acad Sci USA; 83; 1986; 100-104.

[55] Liu X, Chang K-P Extrachromosomal genetic complementation of surface metalloproteinase (gp63)-deficient *Leishmania* increases their binding to macrophages. Proc Natl Acad Sci USA; 89; 1992; 4991-4995.

[56] Soteriadou KP, Remoundos MS, Katsikas MD, Tzinia AK, Tsikaris V, Sakarellos D, Tzartos SJ The Ser-Arg-Tyr-Asp region of the major surface glycoprotein of *Leishmania* minics the Arg-Gly-Asp-Ser cell attachment region of fibronectin. J Biol Chem; 267; 1992; 13980-13985.

[57] McGwire B, Chang K-P Genetic rescue of surface metalloproteinase (gp63)-deficiency in *Leishmania amazonensis* variants increases their infection of macrophages at the early phase. Mol Biochem Parasitol; 66; 1994; 345-347.

[58] Brittingham A, Morrison CJ, McMaster WR, McGwire BS, Chang K-P, Mosser DM Role of the *Leishmania* surface protease gp63 in complement fixation, cell adhesion, and resistance to complement-mediated lysis. J Immunol; 155; 1995; 3102-3111.

[59] Olobo JO, Anjili CO, Gicheru MM, Mbati PA, Kariuki TM, Githure JI, Koech DK, McMaster WR Vaccination of vervet monkeys against cutaneous leishmaniosis using recombinant *Leishmania* 'major surface glycoprotein' (gp63). Vet Parasitol; 60; 1995; 199-212.

[60] Gheorghiu M, Dellagi K, Gicquel B Recombinant BCG expressing the leishmania surface antigen Gp63 induces protective immunity against *Leishmania major* infection in BALB/c mice. Microbiology; 141 (Pt 7); 1995; 1585-1592.

[61] Xu D, McSorley SJ, Chatfield SN, Dougan G, Liew FY Protection against *Leishmania major* infection in genetically susceptible BALB/c mice by gp63 delivered orally in attenuated *Salmonella typhimurium* (AroA- AroD-). Immunology; 85; 1995; 1-7.

[62] Connell ND, Medina-Acosta E, McMaster WR, Bloom B, Russell DG Effective immunization against cutaneous leishmaniasis with recombinant bacille Calmette-Guerin expressing the *Leishmania* surface proteinase gp63. Proc Natl Acad Sci USA; 90; 1993; 11473-11477.

[63] Inverso JA, Medina-Acosta E, O'Connor J, Russell DG, Cross GAM *Crithidia fasciculata* contains a transcribed leishmanial surface proteinase (gp63) gene homologue. Mol Biochem Parasitol; 57; 1993; 47-54.

[64] McGwire BS, Chang K-P Posttranslational regulation of a *Leishmania* HEXXH metalloprotease (gp63). J Biol Chem; 271; 1996; 7903-7909.

[65] Devine DV, Falk RJ, Balber AE Restriction of the alternative pathway of human complement by intact *Trypanosoma brucei* subsp. *gambiense.* Infect Immun; 52; 1986; 223-229.

[66] Mosser DM, Roberts JF *Trypanosoma brucei:* Recognition in vitro of two developmental forms by murine macrophages. Exp Parasitol; 54; 1982; 310-316.

[67] Salles JM, Thomas N, Carreira Fragoso MA, Goldenberg S Purification of a metalloproteinase constitutively expressed during *Trypanosoma cruzi* metacyclogenesis. Mem Inst Oswaldo Cruz; 91; 1996; 269.

[68] Ramamoorthy R, Donelson JE, Maybodi M, Panitz S, Paetz KE, Wilson ME Three distinct RNA species code for the major surface protease (gp63) of *Leishmania donovani chagasi.* J Biol Chem; 267; 1992; 1888-1895.

[69] Pepin J, Donelson JE. Human African trypanosomiasis. In: Guerrant RL, Krogstad DJ, Maguire JH, Walker KH, Weller P, editors. Tropical Infectious Diseases: Principles, Pathogens and Practice. New York: Churchill Livingstone (in press).

[70] El-Sayed NMA, Donelson JE African trypanosomes have differentially expressed genes encoding homologues of the *Leishmania* GP63 surface protease. J Biol Chem; 272; 1997; 26742-26748.

Control of VSG gene expression sites in Trypanosoma brucei

Piet Borst,
Wilbert Bitter,
Patricia A. Blundell,
Inês Chaves,
Mike Cross,
Herlinde Gerrits,
Fred van Leeuwen,
Richard McCulloch,
Martin Taylor,
Gloria Rudenko

Division of Molecular Biology, The Netherlands Cancer Institute, Plesmanlaan 121, 1066 CX Amsterdam, The Netherlands.

Abstract

Antigenic variation in African trypanosomes continues to be one of the most elaborate and intriguing strategies ever devised by a protozoan parasite to avoid complete destruction by the immune defense of its mammalian host. Here we review some of the recent advances in our understanding of this strategy, concentrating on (unpublished) work from our laboratory. © Francqui Foundation, Published by Elsevier Science B.V. All rights reserved.

Keywords: Expression site; *Trypanosoma brucei*; Modified base; J; Transferrin receptor; Antigenic variation.

1 • Basic features of antigenic variation in African trypanosomes

Fig. 1 specifies what is required to make a success of antigenic variation. We briefly discuss some of these points where new evidence is available.

The basic features of surface coat switching in *T. brucei* have been amply reviewed in recent years [1-10] and are summarized in Fig. 2.

As most of the genes for Variant Surface Glycoproteins (VSGs) are located in a chromosome-internal position [11], switching mechanism A [12] is the main route for switching the VSG gene in the actively transcribed telomeric VSG gene expression site (ES). The presence of some 100 mini-chromosomes [13], which carry a VSG gene at least at one end, in addition to some 25 larger chromosomes [14] also provides a substantial repertoire of telomeric VSG genes that can enter the active ES by

FIGURE 1

What is required to make a success of antigenic variation?

1.   A large repertoire of surface antigens.

2.   A mechanism for switching the surface antigen expressed in a subfraction
     of the trypanosome population, before antibodies hit the trypanosomes.

3.   The ability to express surface antigens in a defined order to avoid
     population heterogeneity.

4.   The ability to combine antigenic variation with substrate uptake (relatively
     invariant receptors and translocators).

5.   The ability to survive in multiple hosts (in the cases where the parasite has
     managed to colonize multiple hosts with a competent immune system).

mechanisms B or C. Mechanism C, discovered by Etienne Pays and co-workers [15], initially appeared to be used only rarely, but recent work shows that this is not always so [16].

How chromosome-internal genes enter an active expression site has long been a matter of speculation [1, 6, 17]. It is clear that this process depends on relatively short imperfect sequences. On the 5' side these sequences consist of a short array of 70 bp repeats. Long arrays of these repeats are present in the expression site in front of the active VSG gene (Fig. 3). At the 3' end the cross-over between incoming gene and the gene residing in the ES may occur anywhere in the 3'-UTR of the VSG gene or behind this [18]. One would expect the 70 bp repeats to be essential for the entry of most chromosome-internal genes into the ES. It has also been speculated that the 70 bp repeats are required as a target for a nuclease that initiates the duplicative transposition of VSG genes into an active ES (reviewed in [1, 6]). McCulloch et al. [19] have shown, however, that telomere gene

FIGURE 2

The major mechanisms of VSG gene switching in *T. brucei* (from Borst et al., 1997 [5]). The thick lines represent the so-called 221 VSG expression site, with the flag indicating a promoter, the black filled box the 221 VSG gene, and the white box another telomeric VSG gene (VSG gene X). V, Y and Z are other chromosome-internal VSG genes. The hygromycin resistance gene introduced behind the promoter of the 221 expression site (see Fig. 1) is indicated by a diagonally striped box. The dashed line with an arrow indicates transcription. The figure illustrates how the different mechanisms can be distinguished, by using an expression site marked with a resistance gene. In mechanisms A–C, the Hygro gene is actively transcribed following the switch, whereas it is silent in mechanism D. In mechanisms A and B the single copy 221 VSG gene is lost. Whether A or B occurred can be derived from knowing the original location of the new VSG gene. In C, the 221 VSG gene moves to another chromosome.

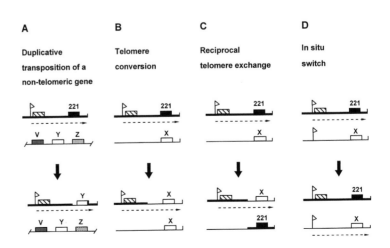

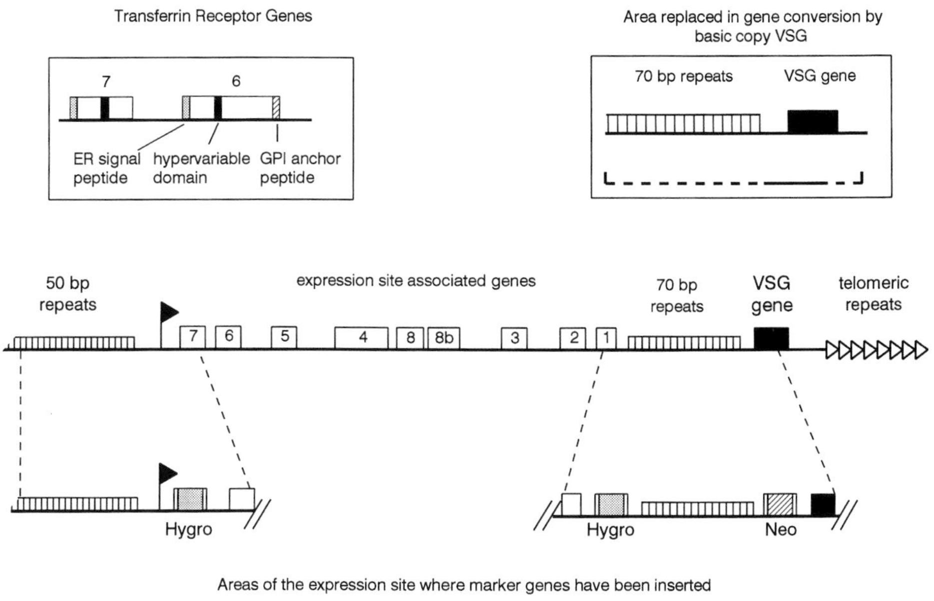

Areas of the expression site where marker genes have been inserted

conversion (mechanism B in Fig. 2) can still occur when the 70 bp repeats are deleted from the active ES.

In principle the trypanosome would be able to express its whole repertoire of VSG genes in a single ES using mechanisms A–C in Fig. 2. In practice, there are multiple ESs, allowing in situ switches (mechanism D). Hybridization experiments indicate that there are about 20 ESs, at least six of which are functional (and the others may be as well).

2 ● Why multiple expression sites ?

The multiplicity of ESs requires complex controls to ensure that only one out of 20 ESs is active at a time. Initially, it was unclear why the trypanosome would make the management of its coat repertoire more complex than strictly necessary. In the past two years we have found, however, that a plausible raison d'être for multiple ESs does not so much reside in the additional opportunities these provide for switching coat, but in the ability to switch the expression site associated genes (ESAGs) co-expressed with the VSG gene in each ES (Fig. 3).

Pioneering work by the Overath laboratory, extended by several other laboratories (reviewed by [2, 5, 20]), has shown that ESAGs 6 and 7 encode two sub-units for a heterodimeric transferrin-receptor

FIGURE 3

Schematic representation of a VSG gene expression site, modeled after [55, 56]. The flag indicates the promoter, the numbers in the boxes indicate the ESAGs. The enlargements show features of ESAG 6 and 7, which encode subunits of the transferrin receptor, and the area of the expression site replaced during gene conversion of a basic copy VSG gene. Positions of marker insertion or DNA replacements are indicated below the expression site.

(Tf-R), located in the flagellar pocket. Receptor subunits encoded by the different ESs differ in an interesting fashion in their sequence, suggesting that multiple ESs exist to allow antigenic variation of receptors [21]. More recent work has shown, however, that receptor variability may primarily be required to allow *T. brucei* to cope with the diversity of Tfs in a range of mammalian hosts [2].

The sequence of Tf has evolved rapidly in mammalian evolution and, for instance, human and bovine Tfs differ by 30% in amino acid sequence [22]. One cannot expect a single receptor to tightly bind ligands that vary so much in structure and, indeed, we have found that Tf-Rs encoded by different ESs markedly differ in their affinity for Tfs from different mammals [2]. A striking example is the very low affinity of the Tf-R encoded in the 221 ES for canine Tf. Variants expressing this ES grow fine in bovine and murine serum (and bind the corresponding Tfs with high affinity), but hardly at all in canine serum. Prolonged growth of trypanosomes in canine serum leads to selection of normally growing trypanosomes that have activated the V02 ES, which encodes a Tf-R with substantial affinity for canine Tf. Sluggish growth of VAT 221a in canine serum (and switching to the VO2 ES) can be completely prevented by adding 0.1 μg bovine Tf ml$^-$, which is less than 0.01% of the normal Tf concentration in serum [22a].

We think that our results on the Tf-R strongly support the idea that the multiplicity of ESs serves to allow *T. brucei* to colonize a large range of mammals, each with its unique plasma composition in which the trypanosome has to survive. The ancestral trypanosome may have had a single ES in which ESAGs were gradually collected to allow an efficient activation of a series of genes required for survival in a small set of mammalian hosts. Duplication of this ES would have allowed the second set of ESAGs to evolve and adapt to new hosts. The implication of this hypothesis is that the other ESAGs might also be selected for inclusion in the ES because they are involved in functions that need to be varied depending on the host. This remains to be verified.

3 • Control of expression sites; general considerations

The increase in host range, provided by the multiplicity of ESs, is bought at a price. The trypanosome now needs mechanisms to keep all but one of the 20 or so ESs silent and to switch between ESs. Some of the mechanisms that have been considered are summarized in Fig. 4. Two major models can be distinguished : one in which there is cross-talk between sites and one in which sites are activated and inactivated independently. Several arguments have led to a consensus that cross-talk does not occur : The most important argument is that experimental evidence was obtained for the simultaneous activity of two ESs in a single trypanosome [23, 24]. Although this evidence seemed conclusive in 1985, we have second thoughts in 1997 and we return to these doubts below. A second argument was that the control of the ES promoter appears to have a major negative component. In a plasmid in transient transfection assays the promoter appears to be fully activated [25-27] and even when the promoter is stably inserted in other locations of the genome than its normal position, the promoter may be active [28, 29].

Hence, most efforts in the past 10 years went into the analysis of mechanisms of ES control based on independent (in)activation of ESs (see Fig. 4). Control by DNA rearrangements close to the promoter, e.g. by promoter inversion, was ruled out at an early stage [25], but it has been more difficult to rule out that DNA rearrangements far upstream of the promoter contribute to control [30-32]. With the introduction of selectable markers into ESs [28, 33, 34], it became easier to select for in situ switches (mechanism D in Fig. 2) and check for DNA rearrangements more systematically. Navarro and Cross [35] found no systematic major alterations associated with switching in the large block of 50 bp repeats [25, 32] upstream of the ES promoter (see Fig. 3) and this is in agreement with our unpublished results. Although minor alterations in the 50 bp repeats or major rearrangements even further upstream (an area not yet checked) cannot be excluded as the cause of ES promoter (in)activation, we consider this option now unattractive.

4 ● Does the expression site have to move to the nucleolus to be transcribed ?

There is considerable evidence that the ES is transcribed by an RNA polymerase resembling polymerase I [36-[38] (reviewed by Van der Ploeg and Lee, 1997 [39]), the polymerase that normally restricts its activity to the large rRNA genes. As transcribed rRNA genes are usually located in the nucleolus of eukaryotes, it is conceivable that the ES has to move to the nucleolus to be transcribed, as suggested by Van der Ploeg [40]. If there is only a single ES attachment site per nucleolus for which the multiple ESs compete, this would also provide an explanation for mutually exclusive expression of different ESs.

How are VSG gene expression sites switched on and off?

A. Cross-talk between sites

B. Independent activation/inactivation of sites

  1. By DNA rearrangements
    - close to the promoter
    - far from the promoter

  2. Without DNA rearrangements
    - by telomere attachment
    - by telomere modification
    - by telomere-related semi-stable position
      effects, as observed in yeast

To test this idea, Zomerdijk [41] used fluorescent in situ hybridization (FISH) to determine the intra-nuclear location of nascent RNA derived from the active ES. He found no co-localization, but some investigators were not convinced by his results, because these were based on hybridization with repetitive probes. In the past year we have reinvestigated this issue, using an ES containing unique marker genes. This has confirmed that the active ES is not in the nucleolus, whereas marker genes located in the rRNA gene array and driven by a ribosomal DNA promoter do localize to the nucleolus (unpublished results). Although this does not exclude that the active ES is in a specialized nuclear sub-compartment, we are confident that the active compartment is not the nucleolus.

5 • Is the activity of the expression site promoter controlled by DNA modification ?

An unusual form of DNA modification in *T. brucei* was independently discovered by Pays et al. [42] and Bernards et al. [43]. This modification affected *Pst* I and *Pvu* II sites in and around telomeric VSG genes in inactive ESs, but not in the active one. Modification was absent in chromosome-internal VSG genes and undetectable in DNA from insect-form trypanosomes. This appeared to link modification to the inactivation of ESs and raised the possibility that the activity of ESs might be controlled by a competition between transcription initiation and modification [43].

The identification of a novel modified DNA base in *T. brucei*, β-glucosyl-hydroxymethyluracil or J for short [44, 45], has opened the way for a critical test of the relation between modification and expression site control. We have raised antibodies against J that allow immunoprecipitation of J-containing DNA fragments. These have

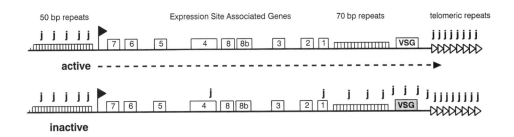

made it possible to locate J more precisely in the *T. brucei* genome and to detect smaller amounts of J in other organisms.

The anti-J antibodies precipitate silent VSG gene fragments known to contain modified *Pst* I and *Pvu* II sites. We have also shown, using specific oligonucleotides containing J, that substitution of the T in one strand of a *Pvu* II recognition site blocks cleavage by the enzyme. As no other modified nucleotides have been detected in *T. brucei,* we think that the presence of J can fully account for the modified restriction endonuclease sites detected in silent telomeric VSG genes by Bernards et al. [43] and Pays et al. [42]. However, the distribution of J in telomeric DNA is more complex than could have been anticipated from modified restriction endonuclease sites, as illustrated by the summary of our data presented in Fig. 5. The bulk of J is in sequences that cannot be probed with restriction endonucleases, the $(GGGTTA)_n$ repeats present at the ends of trypanosome telomeres [46], and the 50 bp repeats upstream of the ES promoter area. An unexpected result is that these repeats retain their J when the ES is activated. When an ES is silenced, substitution of T by J spreads over most of the ES. The highest concentrations of J are found in and around the VSG gene and in the 70 bp repeats upstream of the VSG gene, but significant amounts of J are also found in the ESAGs and in the promoter area. No J has been detected at all in chromosome-internal silent VSG genes or in (transcribed) house-keeping genes.

Although these results are compatible with the model of Bernards et al. [43] for control of telomeric silencing by DNA modification, other results make us less enthusiastic about this model. First, we have found that J is not restricted to *Kinetoplastida* that undergo antigenic variation, but is also present in *Trypanosoma cruzi, Leishmania, Crithidia* and even in the distant bodonid/crypotobiid *Trypanoplasma borreli,* a fish parasite. Secondly, we have succeeded in increasing or decreasing the level of J in the trypanosome genome 10-fold (by growing trypanosomes in nucleoside analogues) and this did not grossly affect the rate of expression site switching. Finally, our recent work has shown that the modifying enzyme responsible for the first step in J bio-

FIGURE 5

DNA modification due to J in and around telomeric VSG expression sites. Model of the distribution of J in active and inactive VSG expression sites (see Fig. 3). The ES promoter is indicated by a flag, transcription by a dashed line. The degree of modification was determined by anti-J immunoprecipitation of sonicated DNA fragments combined with dot-blot hybridizations. For ESAGs and 70 bp repeats the cumulative signal of all copies in the genome was analyzed. Telomeric repeats, 50 bp repeats, VSG genes and promoter regions were also studied in individual expression sites by Southern-blot hybridizations. The absence of J in actively transcribed VSG genes suggests that J is most likely also absent from active ESAGs and transcribed 70 bp repeats, but this has not been tested directly. No immunoprecipitation of the inactive 221 ES promoter itself was detected with restriction fragments containing part of the *HYG* gene inserted directly downstream of the promoter.

synthesis can recognize a remarkably diverse number of sequences, but only if these occur in a certain context, i.e. in or near repetitive sequences that are not transcribed [46]. This suggests that modification requires a specific chromatin structure or sub-nuclear location of the DNA, which must be imposed before DNA modification.

Although these results do not disprove the model of Bernards et al. [43], they indicate that J may stabilize transcriptional repression, rather than initiate it, and that J may have wider functions than in antigenic variation. An obvious possibility is that J helps to repress recombination between repeated sequences located on different chromosomes. A tight link between transcriptional repression and absence of recombination has been demonstrated in fission yeast [47]. If modified DNA acts as a less effective donor for gene conversion than unmodified DNA, this could also help chromosome-internal VSG genes to compete against telomeric VSG genes for entry into the active ES. It should also be noted that the presence of J in ribosomal repeats (our unpublished results) correlates with observations in *Saccharomyces,* showing that proteins involved in telomeric silencing and in transcriptional, repression of silent mating type loci are also involved in the normal function of the nucleolus (see Kennedy et al., 1997 [48], for a recent discussion). Obviously, these speculations can only be critically tested when the level of J in the genome can be drastically modified. This will probably require identification and disruption of genes involved in J biosynthesis.

6 • Sequences required for the control of expression sites

The last mechanism mentioned in Fig. 4 is telomeric silencing, as first proposed by Gottschling et al. [49] and invoked both by the Cross group [34, 50] and our group [5, 21, 33]. Telomeric silencing in yeast depends on a specific chromatin state, initiated by RAP1 binding to telomeric repeats, which recruits the SIR2–4 gene products, which in turn bind hypoacetylated histones. Histones lacking acetyl groups in specific positions are thought to be critical for repression, but the exact mechanism is still far from clear (see discussions by Pazin and Kadonaga, 1997 [51]; Roth and Allis, 1997 [52]). Competition between transcription initiation and repression governs the frequency of switching between active and silent states [53]. Characteristic of telomeric silencing is that it involves a contiguous sequence of DNA, that it acts on a variety of PolII promoters, and even on PolIII promoters (D. Gottschling, personal communication). Some of these characteristics also apply to ES silencing. Horn and Cross [34] have shown that a heterologous promoter in the downstream part of an ES is largely silenced when the ES is silenced. We have analyzed the ES promoter area and found that the ES promoter can be replaced by a ribosomal DNA promoter without drastically affecting silencing, or the rate of switching [33]. This shows that the switching mechanism is not dependent on the precise sequence of the promoter. These results are compatible with telomeric silencing, but also with other mechanisms for the control of ESs.

The minimal ES promoter of 310 bp [26] replaced by a ribosomal DNA promoter is embedded in 3 kb of sequence that is rather conserved between ESs. To test whether these sequences are essential, we have deleted them in bloodstream form *T. brucei*. Replacement of the sequences between the core promoter and ESAG7 (3' ES sequences) had no effect on transcription, on the ability of the trypanosomes to switch off the 221 ES, nor on the completeness of the repression of the silenced site (unpublished results). It proved more difficult to obtain transformants in which all sequences between the core promoter and the 50 bp repeats (the 5' ES sequences) had been deleted or replaced (unpublished results). Nevertheless, the fact that such clones are obtained at all shows that even the 5' ES sequences are not indispensable for high rates of promoter activity in the ES context. It therefore appears that this high activity requires no unique sequence elements either in the core promoter area (where a ribosomal replacement promoter will do), or 5' or 3' of this core.

We also find, however, that the repression of the silenced promoter is less complete when the ES core promoter is replaced by a ribosomal core promoter [33] or when the 5' ES sequences are deleted or replaced by lambda DNA (unpublished results). There are therefore some sequence-specific elements recognized by the silencing machinery, and this may explain the high conservation of the 5' ES sequences closest to the core promoter.

7 • Is there cross-talk between VSG gene expression sites ?

In the mid 1980's two papers appeared reporting that bloodstream form trypanosomes can exist with two simultaneously active VSG gene ESs (so-called double expressors) [23, 24]. This suggested that ESs are independently activated and inactivated and that cross-talk between ESs does not occur. Absence of cross-talk, although not formally proven, became a generally accepted concept and the basis for mechanistic studies of the control of ESs. It was therefore a surprise that no double expressors were observed in switching experiments using a marked expression site [34, 50]. To test in a more rigorous fashion for double expressors as intermediates in in situ switches (mechanism D in Fig. 2), we generated trypanosomes with two marked ESs. Although the selectable markers made it possible to rapidly select trypanosomes that had switched from one ES to the other, we did not obtain true double expressors (unpublished results). Selection for growth on both drugs led to low level activation of one site and maximal activity of the other, but never to two ESs with the same (high) activity. Our results so far indicate that two ESs cannot be maximally active at the same time. Further support for this idea has come from our observation that switching is often associated with the complete loss of the previously active ES (unpublished results). We have no reason to think that only the two ESs studied are incompatible and our present assumption is that the results with these ESs will hold for all ESs.

If this assumption is correct, how did Cornelissen et al. [23] and Baltz et al. [24] get their double expressors ? With hindsight, we must admit that the results of Cornelissen et al. are not completely conclusive, as there is an alternative explanation for the data (a complex telomere exchange) that could not be tested with the methods available in 1985. Baltz et al. [24] obtained double expressors producing mixed coats and their results look unambiguous. However, their results were obtained with *T. equiperdum* and as this unfortunate parasite is doomed to stay in equines, it may not need multiple ESs anymore [2] and control of ESs may have become more relaxed. Formally, it is also difficult to exclude that the double expressors obtained by Baltz et al. [24] were rapidly switching between two ESs, rather than stably expressing two ESs simultaneously and at maximal rate.

We therefore think that mechanisms for ES control involving cross-talk between ESs cannot be discounted. At present, we do not know at what level this cross-talk occurs. As trypanosomes seem happy with mixed coats [54], counter selection probably does not occur at the level of VSGs. There might be counter selection, however, at the level of ESAG products, mixed products being sub-optimal, or competition for limiting factors required for transcription. These factors could be diffusible, they could represent limited access to a sub-nuclear compartment, or combinations of these. An obvious way to start testing these alternatives, is to create an abbreviated ES in which the sequences between ES promoter and telomere are deleted. We have found that the appropriate targeting construct works in procyclic insect-form trypanosomes (unpublished results) and we are in the process of repeating these experiments with bloodstream trypanosomes. It should be clear from this discussion that none of the mechanisms listed in Fig. 4 can be ruled out, with the exception of DNA rearrangements close to the promoter. The tools are available, however, to settle this important issue in the coming years.

Acknowledgements

The work was supported by grants from the Netherlands Organization for Scientific Research (NWO/SON) to P.B., the Wellcome Trust to R.McC. and M.T., the European Molecular Biology Organization and the European Commission to M.C., and the Gulbenkian PhD Program in Biology and Medicine (Portugal) to I.C.

R E F E R E N C E S

[1] Barry J.D. The relative significance of mechanisms of antigenic variation in African trypanosomes. Parasitol Today; 13; 1997; 212–217.

[2] Borst P, Bitter W, Blundell P, Cross M, McCulloch R, Rudenko G, Taylor MC, Van Leeuwen F. The expression sites for variant surface glycoproteins of *Trypanosoma brucei*. In : Hide G, Mottram JC, Coombs GH, Holmes PH, editors. Trypanosomiasis and Leishmaniasis : Biology and Control. Oxford : British Society for Parasitology/CAB Int. 1997 : 109–131.

[3] Cross GAM. Antigenic variation in trypanosomes : secrets surface slowly. BioEssays; 18; 1996; 283–291.

[4] Donelson JE. Mechanisms of antigenic variation in *Borrelia hermsii* and African trypanosomes. J Biol Chem; 270; 1995; 7783–7786.

[5] Borst P, Rudenko G, Blundell PA, Van Leeuwen F, Cross MA, McCulloch R, Gerrits H, Chaves IMF. Mechanisms of antigenic variation in African trypanosomes. Behring Inst Mitt; 99; 1997; 1–15.

[6] Borst P, Rudenko G, Taylor MC, Blundell PA, Van Leeuwen F, Bitter W, Cross M, McCulloch R. Antigenic variation in trypanosomes. Arch Med Res; 27; 1996; 379–388.

[7] Borst P, Rudenko G. Antigenic variation in African trypanosomes. [Review]. Science; 264; 1994; 1872–1873.

[8] Matthews KR, Gull K. Cycles within cycles : the interplay between differentiation and cell division in *Trypanosoma brucei*. Parasitol Today; 10; 1994; 473–476.

[9] Overath P, Chaudhri M, Steverding D, Ziegelbauer K. Invariant surface proteins in bloodstream forms of *Trypanosoma brucei*. Parasitol Today; 10; 1994; 53–58.

[10] Pays E, Vanhamme L, Berberof M. Genetic controls for the expression of surface antigens in African trypanosomes. Annu Rev Microbiol; 48; 1994; 25–52.

[11] Van der Ploeg LHT, Valerio D, De Lange T, Bernards A, Borst P, Grosveld FG. An analysis of cosmid clones of nuclear DNA from *Trypanosoma brucei* shows that the genes for variant surface glycoproteins are clustered in the genome. Nucl Acids Res; 10; 1982; 5905–5923.

[12] Hoeijmakers JH, Frasch AC, Bernards A, Borst P, Cross GAM. Novel expression-linked copies of the genes for variant surface antigens in trypanosomes. Nature; 284; 1980; 78–80.

[13] Van der Ploeg LH, Schwartz DC, Cantor CR, Borst P. Antigenic variation in Trypanosoma brucei analyzed by electrophoretic separation of chromosome-sized DNA molecules. Cell; 37; 1984; 77–84.

[14] Weiden M, Osheim YN, Beyer AL, Van der Ploeg LHT. Chromosome structure : DNA nucleotide sequence elements of a subset of the minichromosomes of the protozoan *Trypanosoma brucei*. Mol Cell Biol; 11; 1991; 3823–3834.

[15] Pays E, Guyaux M, Aerts D, Van Meirvenne N, Steinert M. Telomeric reciprocal recombination as a possible mechanism for antigenic variation in trypanosomes. Nature; 316; 1985; 562–564.

[16] Rudenko G, McCulloch R, Dirks-Mulder A, Borst P. Telomere exchange can be an important mechanism of Variant Surface Glycoprotein gene switching in *Trypanosoma brucei*. Mol Biochem Parasitol; 80; 1996; 65–75.

[17] Borst P. Discontinuous transcription and antigenic variation in trypanosomes. [Review]. Annu Rev Biochem; 55; 1986; 701–732.

[18] Michels PA, Liu AY, Bernards A *et al.* Activation of the genes for variant surface glycoproteins 117 and 118 in *Trypanosoma brucei.* J Mol Biol ; 166 ; 1983 ; 537–556.

[19] McCulloch R, Rudenko G, Borst P. Gene conversions mediating antigenic variation in *Trypanosoma brucei* can occur in variant surface glycoprotein expression sites lacking 70 base-pair repeat sequences. Mol Cell Biol ; 17 ; 1997 ; 833–843.

[20] Overath P, Stierhof Y-D, Wiese M. Endocytosis and secretion in trypanosomatid parasites -tumultuous traffic in a pocket. Trends Cell Biol ; 7 ; 1997 ; 27–33.

[21] Borst P, Gommers-Ampt JH, Ligtenberg MJL, Rudenko G, Kieft R, Taylor MC, Blundell PA, Van Leeuwen F. Control of antigenic variation in African trypanosomes. Cold Spring Harbor symposia on quantitative biology. DNA Chromosomes ; 58 ; 1993 ; 105–115.

[22] Retzer MD, Kabani A, Button LL, Yu R, Schryvers AB. Production and characterization of chimeric transferrins for the determination of the binding domains for bacterial transferrin receptors. J Biol Chem ; 271 ; 1996 ; 1166–1173.

[22a] Bitter W., Gerrits H., Kieft R., Borst P. The role of transferrin-receptor variation in the host range of *Trypanosoma brucei.* Nature ; 391 ; 1988 ; 499–502.

[23] Cornelissen AW, Johnson PJ, Kooter JM, Van der Ploeg LHT, Borst P. Two simultaneously active VSG gene transcription units in a single Trypanosoma brucei variant. Cell ; 41 ; 1985 ; 825–832.

[24] Baltz T, Giroud C, Baltz D, Roth C, Raibaud A, Eisen H. Stable expression of two variable surface glycoproteins by cloned *Trypanosoma equiperdum.* Nature ; 319 ; 1986 ; 602–604.

[25] Zomerdijk JCBM, Ouellette M, Ten Asbroek ALMA, Kieft R, Bommer AMM, Clayton CE, Borst P. The promoter for a variant surface glycoprotein gene expression site in *Trypanosoma brucei.* EMBO J ; 9 ; 1990 ; 2791–2801.

[26] Zomerdijk JC, Kieft R, Shiels PG, Borst P. Alpha-amanitin-resistant transcription units in trypanosomes : a comparison of promoter sequences for a VSG gene expression site and for the ribosomal RNA genes. Nucl Acids Res ; 19 ; 1991 ; 5153–5158.

[27] Jefferies D, Tebabi P, Pays E. Transient activity assays of the *Trypanosoma brucei* variant surface glycoprotein gene promoter : control of gene expression at the posttranscriptional level. Mol Cell Biol ; 11 ; 1991 ; 338–343.

[28] Rudenko G, Blundell PA, Taylor MC, Kieft R, Borst P. VSG gene expression site control in insect form *Trypanosoma brucei.* EMBO J ; 13 ; 1994 ; 5470–5482.

[29] Biebinger S, Rettenmaier S, Flaspohler J, Hartmann C, Pena-Diaz J, Wirtz LE, Hotz H, Barry JD, Clayton C. The PARP promoter of *Trypanosoma brucei* is developmentally regulated in a chromosomal context. Nucl Acids Res ; 24 ; 1996 ; 1202–1211.

[30] Gottesdiener K, Chung H-M, Brown SD, Lee MG-S, Van der Ploeg LHT. Characterization of VSG gene expression site promoters and promoter-associated DNA rearrangement events. Mol Cell Biol ; 11 ; 1991 ; 2467–2480.

[31] Gottesdiener KM, Goriparthi L, Masucci JP, Van der Ploeg LHT. A proposed mechanism for promoter-associated DNA rearrangement events at a variant surface glycoprotein gene expression site. Mol Cell Biol ; 12 ; 1992 ; 4784–4795.

[32] Zomerdijk JC, Kieft R, Duyndam M, Shiels PG, Borst P. Antigenic variation in *Trypanosoma brucei :* a telomeric expression site for variant-specific surface glycoprotein genes with novel features. Nucl Acids Res ; 19 ; 1991 ; 1359–1368.

[33] Rudenko G, Blundell PA, Dirks-Mulder A, Kieft R, Borst P. A ribosomal DNA promoter replacing the promoter of a telomeric variant surface glycoprotein gene expression site can be efficiently switched on and off in *Trypanosoma brucei.* Cell ; 83 ; 1995 ; 547–553.

[34] Horn D, Cross GAM. A developmentally regulated position effect at a telomeric locus in *Trypanosoma brucei.* Cell ; 83 ; 1995 ; 555–561.

[35] Navarro M, Cross GAM. DNA rearrangements associated with multiple consecutive directed antigenic switches in *Trypanosoma brucei.* Mol Cell Biol ; 16 ; 1996 ; 3615–3625.

[36] Kooter JM, Borst P. Alpha-amanitin-insensitive transcription of variant surface glycoprotein genes provides further evidence for discontinuous transcription in trypanosomes. Nucl Acids Res ; 12 ; 1984 ; 9457–9472.

[37] Rudenko G, Bishop D, Gottesdiener K, Van der Ploeg LHT. Alpha-amanitin resistant transcription of protein coding genes in insect and bloodstream form *Trypanosoma brucei.* EMBO J ; 8 ; 1989 ; 4259–4263.

[38] Rudenko G, Lee MG-S, Van der Ploeg LHT. The PARP and VSG genes of *Trypanosoma brucei* do not resemble RNA polymerase II transcription units in sensitivity to sarkosyl in nuclear run-on assays. Nucl Acids Res ; 20 ; 1992 ; 303–306.

[39] Van der Ploeg LHT, Lee MG-S. Transcription of protein coding genes in trypanosomes by RNA polymerase I. Annu Rev Microbiol (in press).

[40] Shea C, Lee MG-S, Van der Ploeg LHT. VSG gene 118 is transcribed from a cotransposed pol I-like promoter. Cell ; 50 ; 1987 ; 603–612.

[41] Zomerdijk JCBM. Control of gene expression in *Trypano-soma brucei*. Analysis of alpha-amanitin-insensitive trans-cription. Thesis, University of Amsterdam, Rodopi, Amsterdam, 1992 : 1-151.

[42] Pays E, Delauw MF, Laurent M, Steinert M. Possible DNA modification in GC dinucleotides of *Trypanosoma brucei* telomeric sequences : relationship with antigen transcription. Nucl Acids Res ; 12 ; 1984 ; 5235–5247.

[43] Bernards A, Van Harten-Loosbroek N, Borst P. Modification of telomeric DNA in *Trypanosoma brucei* : a role in antige-nic variation ?. Nucl Acids Res ; 12 ; 1984 ; 4153–4170.

[44] Gommers-Ampt JH, Van Leeuwen F, de Beer AL, Vliegen-thart JF, Dizdaroglu M, Kowalak JA, Crain PF, Borst P. D-glu-cosyl-hydroxymethyluracil : a novel modified base present in the DNA of the parasitic protozoan *T. brucei*. Cell ; 75 ; 1993 ; 1129–1136.

[45] Gommers-Ampt JH, Borst P. Hypermodified bases in DNA. FASEB J ; 9 ; 1995 ; 1034–1042.

[46] Van Leeuwen F, Wijsman ER, Kuyl-Yeheskiely E, van der Marel GA, Van Boom JH, Borst P. The telomeric GGGTTA repeats of *Trypanosoma brucei* contain the hypermodified base J in both strands. Nucl Acids Res ; 24 ; 1996 ; 2476–2482.

[47] Grewal SIS, Klar AJS. Chromosomal inheritance of epigene-tic states in fission yeast during mitosis and meiosis. Cell ; 86 ; 1996 ; 95–101.

[48] Kennedy BK, Gotta M, Sinclair DA *et al*. Redistribution of silencing proteins from telomeres to the nucleolus is asso-ciated with extension of life span in *S. cerevisiae*. Cell ; 89 ; 1997 ; 381–391.

[49] Gottschling DE, Aparicio OM, Billington BL, Zakian VA. Posi-tion effect at *S. cerevisiae* telomeres : reversible repres-sion of PolII transcription. Cell ; 63 ; 1990 ; 751–762.

[50] Horn D, Cross GAM. Analysis of *Trypanosoma brucei vsg* expression site switching in vitro. Mol Biochem Parasitol ; 84 ; 1997 ; 189–201.

[51] Pazin MJ, Kadonaga JT. What's up and down with histone deacetylation and transcription ? Cell ; 89 ; 1997 ; 325–328.

[52] Roth SY, Allis CD. Histone acetylation and chromatin assembly : a single escort, multiple dances ?. Cell ; 87 ; 1996 ; 5–8.

[53] Renauld H, Aparicio OM, Zierath PD, Billington BL, Chha-blani SK, Gottschling DE. Silent domains are assembled continuously from the telomere and are defined by promo-ter distance and strength, and by *SIR3* dosage. Genes Dev ; 7 ; 1993 ; 1133–1145.

[54] Munoz-Jordan JL, Davies KP, Cross GAM. Stable expression of mosaic coats of variant surface glycoproteins in *Trypano-soma brucei*. Science ; 272 ; 1996 ; 1795–1797.

[55] Revelard P, Lips S, Pays E. A gene from the VSG expression site of *Trypanosoma brucei* encodes a protein with both leucine-rich repeats and a putative zinc finger. Nucl Acids Res ; 18 ; 1990 ; 7299–7303.

[56] Lips S, Revelard P, Pays E. Identification of a new expres-sion site-associated gene in the complete 30.5 kb sequence from the AnTat 1.3A variant surface protein gene expres-sion site of *Trypanosoma brucei*. Mol Biochem Parasitol ; 62 ; 1993 ; 135–137.

5

Regulation of *vsg* expression site transcription and switching in *Trypanosoma brucei* [1]

George A.M. Cross,
L. Elizabeth Wirtz,
Miguel Navarro

The Rockefeller University, 1230 York Avenue, New York, NY 10021, USA

Abstract

Current understanding of expression-site transcription in *Trypanosoma brucei,* has been refined by recent results of promoter manipulations at *vsg* expression sites (ES) and examination of the behavior of ES promoters in ectopic locations both within the ES and at other loci. In summary, ES promoter sequences inserted into non-transcribed rRNA spacers are generally inactive, or have low activity, in bloodstream and procyclic forms. Some mechanism apparently operates to ensure full activation of a single ES in bloodstream-form trypanosomes and the inactivity of all ES promoters in procyclic forms. As previously shown, a rRNA promoter can replace an ES promoter. In bloodstream forms, the replacement rRNA promoter was down-regulated in a «silent» ES but it was active in procyclic forms [1, 2]. In addition to manipulations of endogenous promoters, we have recently shown that, when an ES promoter is replaced by a T7 promoter, the T7 promoter is unregulated but transcription is attenuated before the *vsg,* and another ES switches on to maintain cell viability. However, T7 transcription is repressed in the context of core ES-promoter sequences in both stages, particularly in procyclic forms. These observations strongly argue that sequences in the vicinity of the ES core promoter play a role in ES control by nucleating critical events in silencing as well as in activation. Deletions of sequences surrounding the ES core promoter, in situ, did not affect its activity or regulation. In bloodstream forms, rRNA or ES promoters inserted adjacent to silent telomeres or to a non-telomeric «basic-copy» *vsg* were > 98% repressed [3, 4]. After transformation to procyclic forms, the sub-telomeric rRNA promoter regained about 10% of its maximal activity but the «basic-copy» rRNA promoter was fully active. Similarly-positioned ES promoters remained silent in procyclic forms. These results suggest that telomere-proximal or *vsg*-proximal sequences might mediate suppression of transcription via position-effects that could be sufficient to suppress the expression of chromosome-internal *vsg* s or telomeric metacyclic *vsgs,* in bloodstream-form trypanosomes. Recent experiments with T7 promoters indicate that sequences within the ES core promoter might be responsible for silencing ES promoters in pro-

1. *Abbreviations* : bp, base pairs; CTR, co-transposed region; ES, expression site; *esag,* ES-associated gene; TPE, telomere position effect; Vsg, variant surface glycoprotein; *vsg,* Vsg gene.

cyclic forms. Precedents for regulatory mechanisms that modulate transcription over large chromatin domains are reviewed and possible models for ES regulation are presented. © 1998 Francqui Foundation. Published by Elsevier Science B.V. All rights reserved.

Keywords : *Trypanosoma brucei;* Antigenic variation; Variant surface glycoprotein; Gene regulation; Transcription; Chromatin structure; T7 polymerase

1 • Introduction

The genome of *Trypanosoma brucei* encodes hundreds of variant surface glycoprotein (Vsg) genes *(vsgs)* or pseudogenes. The actual number is probably quite variable and largely irrelevant. The generally quoted figure of 1000 *vsg s* is an estimate derived from the proportion of clones in a cosmid DNA library that reacted with a probe for the canonical «70-bp» repeats that have been linked to all *vsg s*, except for some that are expressed in metacyclic trypanosomes [5]. It is (or should be) a great source of embarrassment that we (collectively, the laboratories studying this phenomenon) have little idea of the variation in the total number of *vsgs*, or the full range of their diversity, or their organization in the genome, beyond the observation that they are clustered in cosmid clones [5]. The first clear step towards improving this situation, the mapping of chromosome I of *T. brucei* strain 927 by Sara Melville and her colleagues, has produced evidence for an arrangement of *vsgs* that is striking and, if true for other chromosomes, has major implications for how we think about the regulation of antigenic variation. The available data (S. Melville, personal communication), which suggests that *vsgs* are clustered close to the ends of chromosome I, is based on mapping *vsg*-specific probes onto a library of P1 clones that form three «contigs» covering most of chromosome I. These clusters of *vsgs* and separate clusters of *ingi* retrotransposon-like elements [6–8] could account for much of the enormous size variation between sister chromatids, indicated by gel electrophoresis of chromosomal DNA. The sizes of sister chromatid DNAs of chromosome I vary from 1.1 to 1.2 Mbp in strain 927 and from 1.6 to about 4 Mbp in strain 427 (S. Melville, personal communication). This chromosomal arrangement could also account for the «haploid» state of most silent *vsgs* that have been studied.

The expressed *vsg* is always located adjacent to a telomere, only 1–3 kbp upstream of the TTAGGG hexameric telomeric repeats, although at least one additional gene unit can be inserted between the *vsg* and the telomere without apparent phenotype [4]. All telomeres so far identified contain *vsg* «expression sites» (ES). There are two major ES subsets : those that are transcribed in metacyclic forms, in the tsetse salivary gland, and those that are transcribed in the mammalian stage of the life cycle, the so-called bloodstream forms. Bloodstream-form ESs are polycistronic transcription units containing about eight ES-associated genes (*esags*), transcribed from a promoter located 30–50 kbp upstream of the telomere, but metacyclic ESs are transcribed from a promoter immediately upstream of the *vsg* [9, 10] and appear not to contain functional *esags* or the large arrays of 70-bp repeats that are found between the *vsg* and the upstream *esag1* in bloodstream-form ESs [11, 12]. There are approximately 20 of each type of ES. The precise number is probably variable and unimportant, but their different structures probably reduces recombination between them and preserves them as two distinct subclasses. This distinct organization may be particularly important for maintaining the *vsg* diversity expressed by metacyclic forms. Most of our impression of bloodstream-form ES organization is based on the detailed characterization of one ES [13].

2 • Defining the problem

Vsg switching occurs as a result of two fundamental processes : concerted change in the transcriptional status of a pair of ESs, involving silencing of one with activation of another, or recombination events, which allow silent *vsgs* to move to an active ES. Recombination events can either be tidy, whereby «chromosome-internal» «basic-copy» *vsg* cassettes are shuttled into the active site, by a process of duplicative transposition akin to gene conversion, or they can be less specific, as when there is duplicative transposition of large silent telomeric regions into the active ES, or reciprocal recombinations, at random regions of homology, between active and silent telomeres.

A major focus of current investigations is the regulation of ES transcription. The central problem is how to account for the apparent exclusiveness of ES transcription, which appears to be the key to the ordered expression of *vsg* genes. There is a second related question with implications for the first : what is the mechanism responsible for the developmental regulation of ES transcription ? Finally, we must consider what mechanisms silence the majority of *vsgs* that are not in ESs, but whose chromosomal organization remains unclear. Some of these silent *vsgs* may be associated with putative promoters [14] ; others may need to be insulated from readthrough transcription by RNA polymerases initiating at remote promoters.

Before we consider potential mechanisms that could regulate the exclusiveness of ES transcription, we should reconsider the evidence for the tenet that ES transcription is exclusive. There is only one documented example of the simultaneous expression of two *vsgs*, from different bloodstream-form ESs, and the double-expressing cells were quite stable in culture but unstable in animals, reverting to the expression of one of the two doubly expressed Vsgs [15]. This observation implied that two ESs can be transcribed simultaneously but, on reconsideration, this cannot be concluded from the available data. Given that Vsg has a half-life of 30–40 h and *vsg* mRNA has a half-life of 4.5 h [16–19]), cells that express two Vsgs could easily be switching from expression of one to the other less than once per cell division. On the other hand, we cannot ignore the possibility that expression of multiple *vsgs*, from multiple ESs, is a common occurrence. The large *vsg* repertoire, and the relatively few reagents available to explore multiple expression, have limited our ability to pursue this question. A recent report of multiple *vsg* cDNAs, cloned from an apparently antigenically homogeneous population of *T. brucei* [20], needs to be accommodated by any hypothesis that purports to explain Vsg exclusiveness.

In the immunocompetent host, failure to cease transcription of the previous *vsg* would be fatal : double-expressing trypanosomes would not benefit from a switch, but, for several generations, would presumably remain susceptible to antibodies against the original Vsg. Thus, there must be strong selection in vivo against trypanosomes that do not switch decisively. As we will describe later, this situation does not exist in culture, and failure to stably switch is observed in some clones [21].

3 • Precedents for regulating transcription of multiple alleles

There are several situations in which eukaryotic cells repress, or silence, the expression of multiple alleles. The parallel that has been most frequently drawn, for trypanosomes, is mating-type switching in yeast. Another phenomenon that has been well described in yeast, which shares several components with HML/HMR silencing, is the suppression of promoters close to telomeres. This so-called telomere position effect (TPE) is metastable and depends on promoter strength and distance from the telomere [22, 23]. Almost the same set of components is involved in TPE and HML/HMR silencing, except that *SIR* 1 (silent information regulator gene 1) is not required for telomeric silencing. Both HML/HMR silencing and TPE appear to depend upon alterations in chromatin structure, either heterochromatinization or some telomere-specific chromatin structure, but neither is completely understood, although most of the key components and their interactions have probably been defined genetically [24–26]. Unfortunately, we are a long way behind in understanding the genetics of chromatin structure in trypanosomes. Some significant observations have been made. There are differences in chromatin structure between bloodstream-form and procyclic-form trypanosomes [27], in nuclease effects on active and silent ESs [28, 29], and in the rate of elongation of telomeres at active and silent ESs [30]. There is also a novel base modification, β-D-glucosyl-hydroxymethyluracil, which exists in bloodstream forms but not in procyclic forms [31]. Although the existence of this modification was discovered because of differences in restriction endonuclease sensitivity of *vsgs* in active versus silent ESs [32, 33], most of the modification is found in the telomeric repeats [34] and it is not clear if its abundance differs when ESs are silent or transcribed. One thing is clear, however. If the modification is related to ES silencing in bloodstream forms, it cannot be involved in ES silencing in procyclic forms.

In diploid mammalian cells, genomic imprinting and allelic exclusion are widespread phenomena that can be attributed to differences in DNA methylation that are heritable [35–37]. CpG methylation also specifies a chromatin structure that is resistant to site-specific immunoglobulin V(D)J recombination [38]. It has been suggested that the differential methylation in imprinted genes is achieved by a dynamic mechanism that senses gene dosage and adjusts methylation accordingly [39].

The most striking example of allelic control in mammals is X-chromosome inactivation, which silences most or all genes on one of the two X chromosomes in female cells. X-inactivation appears to be mediated in *cis* by a mechanism that is not fully understood. The product of the *Xist* gene is a non-coding RNA that interacts with the X-chromosome from which it is transcribed [40, 41]. The interaction starts at the X-inactivating center, *Xic*, which is within the *Xist* locus, then spreads throughout the chromosome. X-chromosome regulation is considered to be a counting problem. How does the cell count identical elements and inactivate all except one ? The parallel to ES regulation is intriguing. In *Drosophila*, males compensate for having only one X chromosome by up-regulating its transcription. This requires *trans*-acting proteins, encoded by four *msl* (male-specific lethal) genes, that associate along the length of the X chromosome, together with non-coding RNAs that can act in *cis* or in *trans* [42, 43].

Thus, there is an abundance of precedents that may apply to ES regulation but, as in other situations, trypanosomes may have devised an altogether novel mechanism, whose elucidation will continue to challenge us.

4 • Models for positive or negative ES regulation

Although common observation argues against the existence of a single mobile ES-activating element, we cannot discount the possibility that, along with the many gene rearrangements occurring in this system, there could lurk the occasional duplication of a single mobile promoter, or other mobile activating element. However, this hypothesis can probably be discounted. A related hypothesis would be that some form of chromosomal rearrangement, either gross or subtle, occurs during ES activation and inactivation events. Although sporadic chromosomal rearrangements have been reported after ES switches ([44–46]), this issue has not been systematically studied. Characterization of panels of switches, to be discussed in more detail below, show conclusively that ES switching can occur without detectable DNA rearrangements.

As new tools yield better insights into the complexity of nuclear organization in other systems, the long-standing idea that there is a single nuclear transcription site or other physical site-specific effect, at which only one ES transcription complex can be assembled or stabilized, merits renewed investigation. A variation on the single nuclear site model is that ES activation, which likely involves a major reorganization of chromatin structure, requires a critical concentration of a key activator or a series of factors that are present in limiting amounts in the nucleus. The activation of one ES would be a stochastic event, but could be influenced by subtle differences in DNA sequence at the activation/nucleation site, which could cause some ESs to predominate. Because none of the putative participating factors have been identified, this is a somewhat vague concept, but it does make predictions that will be testable in the foreseeable future.

The idea that the default ES state is off and activation requires positive intervention is implicit in the foregoing models. The silent state is not necessarily a passive state, but probably involves specific silencing factors, as in other systems, from which any silent ES can occasionally escape. As already noted, ES silencing and activation appear to be closely coordinated events, suggesting direct crosstalk between ESs. The activated ES could secure its situation by expressing a transcription or translation product that acts in *trans* to tighten the silencing of other ESs. We are currently exploring testable predictions of this hypothesis. If it were true, all manner of situations that interfered with efficient transcription of the currently active ES might cause an ES switch, including the insertion of transcription attenuators or other gratuitous DNA rearrangements, or any cellular event or extracellular intervention that allowed a negative regulator to decay. Variations in ES promoter strength, leading to differences in the efficiency of the presumed specific initiation of ES transcription, would be expected to influence ES dominance and switching rates.

Most available evidence is circumstantial and is compatible with any of these models. Once activated, ES transcription is pretty stable. Certain disruptions of the ES reduce stability or cause a rapid switch (see later and [47]). Metastability of old and new ESs can exist after a switch in vitro [21]. Differential ES stability, or preference for activation of one ES over another, could involve subtle mutations that could affect activation, repression, nuclear localization, or changes in ES products that nucleate chromatin silencing.

Vsg itself is one ES product that, it has been suggested, could select against multiple ES transcription. Although this could select, it is difficult to see how it could regulate. The dimeric Vsg three-dimensional structures are thought to be highly conserved [48]. The question of whether simultaneous expression of two Vsgs is disadvantageous for replication or infection of trypanosomes, or whether constraints intrinsic to Vsg synthesis or coat assembly might enforce the exclusiveness of *vsg* expression, has been the subject of continuing speculation [49–54]. We explored this question experimentally, by inserting a second *vsg* into an active ES, and concluded that parasites expressing two Vsgs have no intrinsic growth disadvantage in vivo or in vitro [55].

5 • DNA sequence requirements for ES promoter function

There is strong but indirect evidence that the *parp* and ES loci are transcribed by RNA Polymerase I (Pol I) ([56]). However, neither the core polymerase subunits nor any accessory transcription factors have been identified, so it is not known whether the three promoters are recognized by the same DNA-binding factors, despite the lack of conservation of their DNA sequences. A 315-bp region containing the core ES promoter can be replaced by a 518-bp fragment containing the rRNA promoter in situ. The remodeled ES remains capable of activation and inactivation in bloodstream forms, but is not fully silenced in procyclic forms [2]. Although the sequences of the core rRNA, bloodstream-form ES, metacyclic-form ES and *parp* promoters are quite distinct [10, 57, 58], hybrid rRNA-*parp* [59] or rRNA-ES promoters [60] can drive reporter-gene expression. In procyclic trypanosomes, a silent chromosomal ES promoter could also be activated by fusing it to a sequence that had no intrinsic promoter activity, but was derived from upstream of the *parp* promoter [61]. These observations suggest an interplay between positive and negative regulatory elements but provide no direct evidence to illuminate the real requirements for regulation of transcription from the ES or *parp* promoters.

Several studies have demonstrated that the minimal DNA sequence required for ES promoter function is short [45, 62–64]. An upstream element, which enhances transcription from the rRNA and *parp* promoters [65, 66], is apparently unnecessary for ES promoter activity. Dissection of the essential sequence elements for ES promoter activity suggests that the same elements are necessary for transcription-initiation in plasmid and chromosomal contexts [60, 64]. Both bloodstream and procyclic forms are able to initiate transcription from an episomal ES promoter, but promoter efficiency, relative to the endogenous locus, is unknown. Early attempts to identify ES promoter-specific double-stranded DNA-binding proteins were unsuccessful [60], although this situation has recently changed [67].

None of these studies were performed on the ES promoter in situ in bloodstream-form trypanosomes. The ES region flanking the core promoter is highly conserved. We decided, therefore, to make deletions of these flanking regions and look for effects on ES transcription regulation in both bloodstream and procyclic forms. No *cis*-acting regulatory sequences that affected ES promoter activity in situ were found in the regions upstream (− 64 to − 729) or downstream (+8 to +962) from the transcription start site, in either active or silent ESs in bloodstream-forms, or in procyclic forms (M. Navarro and G.A.M. Cross, submitted for publication). These deletions also had no effect on ES switching rates.

6 • Gene transfection in bloodstream-form *T. brucei*

The early generations of ES studies, which occupied the 1980s, were highly informative about *vsg* and ES organization but were largely limited to observation rather than experiment, and were performed on several strains of *T. brucei*. The essentially complete sequence of one ES was determined [13], in an effort that was largely responsible for identifying a series of *esags* whose structures tantalize us but whose functions remain largely unknown, with the spectacular exception of the heterodimeric transferrin receptor encoded by *esags* 6 and 7 [68–70]. However, we do not know how widely conserved this prototypical ES structure is.

Arguments about switching rates, the relative merits of laboratory and recently transmitted strains, and the question of whether some ESs are favored over others and, if so, what determines which shall predominate, have persisted, in the absence of rational experiments or common understanding of the issues involved. In the past few years, however, we have developed the ability to genetically manipulate the ES. Insertion of reporter genes into active or silent ESs allows us to capture panels of specific switching events, to measure ES switching frequencies, to explore intrinsic and extrinsic parameters that might affect switching, to more readily map switch-related chromosome rearrangements, and to more easily study cellular and genetic aspects of the developmental regulation of Vsg expression. Hopefully, we will be able to extend these techniques to identify genes that regulate these phenomena.

Despite early resistance to attempting transfection in bloodstream forms in vitro, there really was no alternative for trying to understand antigenic variation. We were therefore pleasantly surprised to discover, when we tackled this problem, that bloodstream forms have several advantages over procyclic forms. The doubling time of bloodstream-form *T. brucei* strain 427 is 6–8 h, compared to 12–16 h for procyclic forms, and bloodstream forms can be easily grown on agar [71–73]. They can grow from single cells with no special nurturing. They have no minimum density requirements and no need for conditioned medium. They have a 10- to 20-fold higher drug sensitivity and sensitive cells die quickly. They retain full animal infectivity and can easily be grown in large quantities. Some selective drugs can be used in vivo [74, 75], allowing large populations to be screened for switches or mutations. They can be easily transformed to procyclic forms, whereas the reverse is not possible without using tsetse. The only disadvantages we have encountered are that electroporation kills a higher proportion of target cells, therefore the overall transfection efficiency is lower, and stable episomal vectors are not available. These last two problems combine, currently, to rule out the possibility of genetic complementation by transfection in bloodstream forms, although this can be achieved in procyclic forms [76].

7 • ES mapping during multiple independent and consecutive switches

As a starting point for a new generation of genetic studies, we decided to revisit the question of whether chromosome rearrangements could be consistently detected during ES switching. We used two approaches to insert selectable markers into silent ESs. We could place a reporter cassette at any position in a silent ES if we included a promoter and a downstream selectable marker, to enable the recombinant cells to be recovered [3]. We had some concern that the necessary inclusion of a promoter in this cassette could influence the parameters, like switching rate, that we sought to study. We found no evidence of this. The other approach was to use very low drug concentrations to insert a promoterless drug-resistance gene downstream of the endogenous ES promoter, relying on the low level of transcription initiation at a «silent» ES promoter [1, 75]. Again, this approach could be criticized for selecting cells with incompletely silenced promoters, but this criticism could be dispelled by inserting the cassette into an active ES, then turning the ES off and simply measuring the reporter transcript without selection. We found no significant difference in the «off» activity regardless of whether the initial insertion was made into a silent or an active ES (M. Navarro and G.A.M. Cross, unpublished observations).

Accurate measurements of ES activation rates could be made with positive selectable markers (encoding drug-resistance genes) inserted into ESs. The initial measurements [21, 75] held no surprises : «neutral» ES insertions showed activation frequencies in the range of 10^{-6}, as previously noted for «off» rates in the same clones [77]. As will be discussed below, other ES manipulations could dramatically increase the switching rate.

In one study, restriction mapping within and beyond the ES failed to detect any DNA rearrangements in multiple independent identical switches [21]. In another study [75], we mapped independent consecutive on-off-on switches between two specific ESs. Direct analysis of ES promoters, showed that their numbers (average 27 ± 3) varied. The first activation of the 121 ES was always associated with deletion of the upstream tandem promoter in this ES, but no further rearrangements were detected in consecutive off/on switches of this ES. It is interesting to note that an identical deletion of a duplicated promoter in the same ES had previously been characterized in great detail during inactivation of this ES [45, 46]. However, in another set of experiments, we detected no rearrangement in the same duplicated promoter region following inactivation of this ES in nine independent clones [21]. These and related observations suggest that recombination might occur at a significant frequency between the highly conserved sequences around ES promoters and we suggest that, at least in some cases, ES switching may occur after a period of chromosomal interactivity that may or may not leave tangible evidence in the form of detectable sequence changes.

The overall conclusion from these new studies is that chromosomal rearrangements are not essential for ES switching, which confirms established prejudice based on more limited data.

8 • Telomere stability at active and silent ESs

Changes in telomere length have been reported to be associated with ES switching [78]. We measured the telomere restriction fragment length, at several silent and activated ES, in sets of clones that had or had not undergone ES switching [21]. The data showed that silent telomeres were relatively stable but an actively transcribed ES telomere was unstable, as was also previously shown for a rRNA promoter in a mini-chromosome [79], and the length becomes heterogeneous within the cell population during clonal growth. Cloning, therefore, involves selection of cells with different telomere lengths rather than inducing shortening, as previously suggested [30, 80].

In some organisms, telomeres appear to interact with each other and with the nuclear envelope [81]. One model for ES switching would have the ESs interact physically during the switch process, leading to end exchange, which could be appealing if telomeric chromatin structure were responsible for silencing and this state could be transferred by end exchange. This does not appear to be the case, however, as we saw no increases in telomere length, in any of the switched clones, beyond what would be expected during normal growth [30, 80]. Other observations suggest that there is no relation between telomere length and ES switching, except in one case where a telomere became extremely short and could neither grow nor be activated (D. Horn and G.A.M. Cross, unpublished observations).

9 • Is there a role for telomere-induced silencing in antigenic variation ?

We found strong suppression of ES, *parp* and rRNA promoters placed in the immediate vicinity of a silent telomeric *vsg* in bloodstream-form trypanosomes [3, 4]. Repression was reduced about 10-fold when the rRNA promoter cassette was moved 14 kbp further upstream, but it was not abolished at this distance, as it would have been in yeast. It seems entirely possible that this «telomeric» silencing would be sufficient to minimize transcription from metacyclic promoters in bloodstream forms, but repression nucleated by changes in telomeric chromatin structure would be unlikely to be responsible for silencing of far-upstream ES promoters.

How are non-telomeric *vsgs* maintained in a silent state ? It seems likely that most *vsgs* are organized in large clusters [5], sometimes associated with *ingi* retrotransposon-like elements [6–8]. Their location and organization could simply leave them promoterless and insulated from readthrough by the trypanosome Pol II, which seems to transcribe polycistronically over long distances. On the other hand, these *vsgs* may lie in regions of chromatin that are actively silenced, perhaps in the immensely variable subtelomeric regions of the chromosome (S. Melville, personal communication). rRNA or ES promoters inserted adjacent to a non-telomeric «basic copy» *vsg118* had < 5% or undetectable activity, respectively, in bloodstream forms [4]. This also suggests that a *vsg*-associated or a promoter-associated sequence may be important for silencing. Sub-telomeric repeats, 29-bp motifs, or telomeric TTAGGG repeats, are not found at this locus [82], but conserved octamer and hexadecamer sequences are found 3' of all *vsgs* [83].

In the same study, after transformation to procyclic forms, the activity of a telomere-proximal rRNA promoter increased to about 10% of its maximum level, but the ES promoter remained inactive. At the «basic-copy» *vsg118*, the ES promoter regained about 15% activity but the rRNA promoter was completely de-repressed. Previous studies, in procyclic forms, had shown no evidence of telomere-dependent silencing of the *parp* promoter on small linear artificial chromosomes [84] or on an endogenous mini-chromosomal rRNA promoter lying about 7 kb upstream of telomeric repeats [79]. However, although these cells were resistant to high levels of G418, the steady-state level of *neo* mRNA was significantly lower than when the same cassette was integrated into a 2-Mbp chromosome, so some telomere-associated suppression may have occurred on the artificial chromosomes.

At present, we cannot reconcile our observations of ectopic ES promoters with those reported elsewhere [85], which showed that an ES promoter inserted into a rRNA untranscribed spacer could be active in both bloodstream-form and procyclic-form trypanosomes. The ES promoter sequences used in the two studies are subtly different, which may account for the differing results. Also, it is not entirely clear how active rRNA promoters are in ectopic locations, in general. Recent experiments (M. Navarro and L.E. Wirtz, unpublished observations) suggest that rRNA promoters are significantly repressed in bloodstream forms and are up-regulated in procyclic forms.

Our current conclusions are that ES promoters and rRNA promoters inserted into bloodstream-form ESs are restrained by position effects related to their proximity to telomeres, *vsgs*, or other features of the ES, or by virtue of some counting mechanism relying on Pol I core promoter elements themselves. The manifestation of repression could be due to restraints on transcription initiation and/or elongation. In procyclic forms, inserted rRNA promoters appeared to be fully de-repressed, except at a telomere, but ES promoters remained silent in any context, which we attribute to the absence of developmentally regulated ES promoter-specific factors or to promoter-specific active silencing, rather than a position effect.

10 ● ES alterations that affect switching rates

Disruption of the co-transposed region (CTR), immediately upstream of the expressed *vsg*, can cause a dramatic increase in the rate at which the ES is switched off and a new ES is switched on [47]. Deletion of most of the CTR in two ESs caused a greater than 100-fold increase in the rate of ES switching. Other insertions into an active ES also increased the switch frequency. A more dramatic effect was observed when the entire CTR and the 5' coding region of the expressed *vsg221* were deleted. In this case a new ES was activated within a few cell divisions. The low transfection efficiency, and the continuous growth in the presence of drug selection, ensured that the selection of a sub-population from a contaminant in the starting cell line would be highly improbable. All of the observed switches occurred without additional detectable DNA rearrangements in the switched ES. Deletion of the 70-bp repeats or a *vsg* pseudogene upstream of the CTR did not affect ES stability. Several speculative interpretations of these observations are possible, the most intriguing of which is that the CTR plays some role in modulating chromatin conformation at an ES. An alternative and perhaps more likely explanation is that the disruption caused a rather non-specific effect on transcription through the ES, which allowed (and required) another ES to be activated.

The other situation in which we have observed an essentially immediate ES switch is upon replacement of the active ES promoter with the T7 promoter, or insertion of a T7 promoter upstream of the active ES promoter. Both of these manipulations, for reasons that we can speculate about, appear to inactivate the ES, although the T7 promoter itself is fully active in this context (M. Navarro and L.E. Wirtz, manuscript in preparation). Once again, it was striking that the cells did not die but switched. All of these observations lead irresistibly to the conclusion that disabling an ES, by various interventions, can permit the cells to switch to an alternative ES. The switches can only be detected when the drug-resistance gene, associated with the targeting cassette, is transcribed to the necessary level at its insertion site. With the associated T7 promoter, which is fully functional, this is no problem. One possible explanation of these observations would be that some product of ES transcription, either RNA or protein, either stabilizes, in *cis*, the active ES or stabilizes, in *trans*, the repression of inactive sites. Another explanation is that deletion of these elements from the active ES could cause it to vacate a subnuclear transcription site and allow another ES to occupy it.

11 • Stability of the switched state

In yeast, silencing of HML or HMR loci can be split into three distinct phases, establishment, maintenance and inheritance [25], and this provides a good paradigm for the ES. Establishment is the genetic switch; separate, additional or overlapping components may be necessary to maintain the silent state; inheritance of the silenced state in the replicated chromosome may involve considerations additional to those involved in establishment and maintenance [25]. We have evidence that not all progeny clones may have the same stability for some time after a switch. After drug selection, which ensured that the switched populations were initially pure, some clones became heterogeneous after further growth in the absence of drug [21]. Examination of individual cells, with antibodies to Vsgs, showed the presence of cells expressing both parental and progeny Vsg, and cells that had reverted to expressing only the parental Vsg. Such a situation would not be seen after switches in immunocompetent animals because unstable switches and revertants would be strongly selected against.

12 • Using the T7 promoter as a probe
for epigenetic control at the *vsg* ES

The recent recognition of chromatin remodeling as a major modulator of transcription, in higher eukaryotes, has emphatically refocussed the problem of transcription regulation at the level of template accessibility [86–90]. The interaction of the single-subunit bacteriophage T7 polymerase with its promoter has been used in other systems as a reporter for *cis* elements mediating chromatin accessibility [91, 92] (Fig. 1).

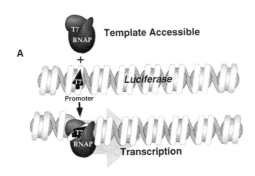

FIGURE 1

T7 transcription as a reporter for *cis* elements mediating silencing of chromatin domains. (A) T7 promoters integrated into trypanosome chromatin can direct efficient reporter gene expression when the phage polymerase is expressed endogenously (L.E. Wirtz and G.A.M. Cross, manuscript in preparation). (B) Regulatory strategies relying on silencing or heterochromatinization that impact the accessibility of the polymerase to its promoter and template are reflected at the level of T7-mediated reporter activity, providing an experimental approach for the definition of *cis* elements influencing chromatin structure.

We have used chromosomally integrated T7 promoters, with linked luciferase reporters, to investigate sequence requirements of epigenetic control mechanisms at ESs. T7 transcription provides a means of overcoming the difficulty inherent in distinguishing silenced from mutationally inactivated promoters, by separating the obvious role of ES core promoter elements in transcription initiation from any role they might have in silencing. Two targeting strategies were used to replace an active ES promoter by a T7 promoter. In the first, the entire ES promoter was replaced with the concise 20-bp T7 promoter. In the second, the T7 promoter was flanked upstream by an ES core promoter, intact except for a start site mutation to block elongation by the endogenous polymerase. The integrated T7 promoter was down-regulated (strongly so in procyclic forms) only in the context of the ES core promoter elements, revealing a role for the core promoter in ES repression.

The overlap of the ES core promoter region with elements involved in silencing is suggestive of competitive or antagonistic interaction between activation and silencing mechanisms, consistent with chromatin structure analyses showing conservation of DNase hypersensitive sites between silent and active ES promoters (see below).

13 • Support for a «repressed and ready-to-go» model for ES transcription

There are previous findings suggesting at least a low level of transcription initiation occurs at more than one, and maybe many, ES promoters in bloodstream forms and, at a much lower level, from many ES promoters in procyclic forms [1]. The ratio of transcripts originating from the active versus silent ESs was about 33 : 2 in bloodstream forms. Secondly, there is the implication, from other results, that extensive transcription of multiple ESs can occur in certain situations. In particular, multiple *vsg* transcripts were detected in a line of *T. rhodesiense* that was expressing the predominant *vsg* from a metacyclic ES [20]. However, this line may not represent a typical situation : it could represent a mutation leading to specific de-repression of telomeric *vsgs* driven by proximal promoters rather than far-upstream ES promoters.

Insertion of selectable markers into silent ESs has allowed us to detect ES promoter activity in other than the active ES (M. Navarro and G.A.M. Cross, Molecular Parasitology Meeting, Woods Hole, 1995). In some experiments, we tried to activate a *neo*-tagged silent 121 ES in cells where the 221 ES was active. We obtained G418-resistant clones that did not switch, but continued to express *vsg* 221. Thus, in these clones, two ES promoters were active while only one ES was fully transcribed, suggesting that productive transcription (defined as transcription that generates viable amounts of Vsg) requires more than initiation at the ES promoter.

The idea that facilitating or lifting restraints on elongation might be the regulating step in ES transcription has also been considered previously [1, 2]. Perhaps the strongest support for the existence of such a mechanism comes from studies of *parp* (procyclin) transcription. *parp* transcription, like ES transcription, is thought to be a consequence of Pol I, but expression of *parp* and *vsg* are restricted to the opposite life-cycle stage. However, in bloodstream forms, the *parp* locus is transcribed to a significant extent, but elongation appears to be attenuated within 1 kbp of the promoter [93, 94].

Early studies showed that chromatin adjacent to the transcribed *vsg* was hypersensitive to endonuclease [28]. Other studies, however, showed no evidence for different nucleosome structures between active and silent ESs [29]. In contrast, we find that nucleosome structure is conserved around active and silent ES promoters, but is disordered downstream. We also looked for chromatin alterations around the ES promoter that could be associated with *cis*-acting regulatory sequences. A marker gene, inserted 1 kbp downstream of

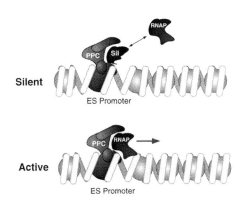

FIGURE 2

Occupancy of the core promoter region by DNA-binding protein complexes at silent or active ESs : a speculative model of a transcriptional complex in bloodstream-form *T. brucei*. The promoter protein complex (PPC) bound to DNA may contain silencing factors (Sil) responsible for repression in silent ESs. Upon activation, PPC would recruit the RNA polymerase holoenzyme (RNAP) and, possibly, other activating factors.

an ES promoter, was used to map the position of nuclease hypersensitive sites, using an indirect end-labeling technique. Treatment with either DNase I or Micrococcal nuclease indicated the presence of a prominent hypersensitive site within the core ES promoter. This hypersensitive site was present in both active and silent ES promoters, suggesting that a protein complex is bound to the core promoter, irrespective of the transcriptional state. In addition, less intense nuclease-hypersensitive sites were detected upstream and downstream of the core promoter, in both active and silent ESs (M. Navarro and G.A.M. Cross, submitted for publication).

From these observations, and the conservation of nuclease hypersensitive sites at silent and active ES promoters, we suggest that all ES core promoters are occupied by a specific DNA-binding protein complex (Fig. 2).

The same proteins could be bound to both silent and active ES promoters, with the outcome of their presence (activation or repression) depending upon other proteins or nuclear interactions. Alternatively, different proteins could bind to identical or adjacent sites within a silent or active promoter. Low-level transcription from a «silent» ES promoter, as described above, could be a consequence of leaky silencing, leading to intermittent exchange of silencing and activating proteins in the promoter-bound complex. We are currently exploring these alternatives.

14 • Conclusions

We have considered several models for ES regulation, drawing parallels to other potentially relevant systems, but with an appreciation that these do not represent mutually exclusive mechanisms. Multiple mechanisms might work in concert. As suggested elsewhere [95], the activity of ES promoters might still be controlled by sequence changes far upstream of the regions that have been mapped. However, our recent analyses of multiple independent switches show that ES inactivation can occur without detectable rearrangements as far upstream as 200 kbp from the *vsg*, but we almost always see telomere length changes, for which a regulatory role has been suggested [78] in switched clones, but not restricted to the telomeres involved in the switch. Taken together, our experiments suggest, tentatively, that ES switching may occur after a period of subtle and infrequent chromosomal interactivity that may or may not leave tangible evidence in the form of detectable sequence changes.

There remains a strong probability that productive ES transcription is determined by a change in chromatin topology : maybe there is a unique subnuclear compartment in which the necessary components for ES transcription can assemble. Based on the possible involvement of Pol I in ES transcription, the nucleolus has been suggested as a candidate site [14]. However, many dispersed rRNA genes [96] are presumably transcribed, so it seems likely that the nucleolus can accommodate several transcription units on multiple chromosomes. Thus, the nucleolar location idea is not persuasive, although another unique subnuclear location may provide the basis for exclusiveness. Digestion with certain restriction endonucleases and single-strand-specific nucleases S1 and *Bal* 31 clearly distinguished active and silent ESs, even when transcription was interrupted [29]. The existence of single-stranded regions within the active ES was interpreted to indicate that the active ES was under torsional stress due to the telomere being constrained by attachment to a nuclear matrix structure. The nature of this attachment and whether it can account for the exclusiveness of ES transcription remains unknown.

The study of antigenic variation has moved from observation to experimentation. Recent experiments suggest several levels of regulation of *vsg* expression but have not defined the mechanisms that allow productive transcription from one among many ES promoters in bloodstream-form *T. brucei*. Many observations now suggest that ES switching is not accompanied by consistent or obligatory rearrangements of ES sequences and that more subtle chromosomal interactions are required to hand off transcription from one ES to another. Our ability to insert selectable markers into silent ESs allows us to measure *vsg* switching rates at the genomic level, and identify contextual factors that influence the sequence of *vsg* expression.

A great deal of further work will be necessary to elucidate the mechanisms of *vsg* regulation and chromatin silencing in *T. brucei*. Even in better studied systems, especially in yeast where genetic experiments are relatively simple, the mechanisms of silencing are not fully understood, although most of the key components have probably been identified. Whether we will be able to develop real genetic approaches to identifying key components of genetic regulation in trypanosomes remains to be discovered. Although there are hints that genetic selections could be developed, the obstacles remain daunting. Success might come sooner through knowing the complete inventory of the *T. brucei* genome, which would allow us to make more connections with other better characterized systems, via genomic analysis.

Aknowledgements

Our work is supported by grant number AI21729 from the National Institutes of Health.

REFERENCES

[1] Rudenko G., Blundell P.A., Taylor M.C., Kieft R., Borst P. VSG gene expression site control in insect form *Trypanosoma brucei*. EMBO J; 13; 1994; 5470-5482.

[2] Rudenko G., Blundell P.A., Dirks-Mulder A., Kieft R., Borst P. A ribosomal DNA promoter replacing the promoter of a telomeric VSG gene expression site can be efficiently switched on and off in *T. brucei*. Cell; 83; 1995; 547-553.

[3] Horn D., Cross G.A.M. A developmentally regulated position effect at a telomeric locus in *Trypanosoma brucei*. Cell; 83; 1995; 555-561.

[4] Horn D, Cross GAM. Position-dependent and promoter-specific regulation of gene expression in *Trypanosoma brucei*. EMBO J. in press.

[5] van der Ploeg L.H.T., Valerio D., De Lange T., Bernards A., Borst P., Grosveld F.G. An analysis of cosmid clones of nuclear DNA from *Trypanosoma brucei* shows that the genes for variant surface glycoproteins are clustered in the genome. Nucleic Acids Res; 10; 1982; 5905-5923.

[6] Murphy N.B., Pays A., Tebabi P., Coquelet H., Gyaux M., Steinert M., Pays E. *Trypanosoma brucei* repeated element with unusual structural and transcriptional properties. J Mol Biol; 195; 1987; 855-871.

[7] Pays E., Murphy N.B. DNA-binding fingers encoded by a trypanosome retroposon. J Mol Biol; 197; 1987; 147-148.

[8] Smiley B.L., Aline R.F.J., Myler P.J., Stuart K. A retroposon in the 5' flank of a *Trypanosoma brucei* VSG gene lacks insertional terminal repeats. Mol Biochem Parasitol; 42; 1990; 143-152.

[9] Alarcon C.M., Son H.J., Hall T., Donelson J.E. A monocistronic transcript for a trypanosome variant surface glycoprotein. Mol Cell Biol; 14; 1994; 5579-5591.

[10] Nagoshi Y.L., Alarcon C.M., Donelson J.E. The putative promoter for a metacyclic VSG gene in African trypanosomes. Mol Biochem Parasitol; 72; 1995; 33-45.

[11] Barnes D.A., Mottram J.C., Agabian N. Bloodstream and metacyclic variant surface glycoprotein gene expression sites of *Trypanosoma brucei gambiense*. Mol Biochem Parasitol; 41; 1990; 101-114.

[12] Graham S.V., Matthews K.R., Shiels P.G., Barry J.D. Distinct developmental stage-specific activation mechanisms of trypanosome VSG genes. Parasitology; 101; 1990; 361-367.

[13] Lips S., Revelard P., Pays E. Identification of a new expression site-associated gene in the complete 30.5 kb sequence from the AnTat 1.3A variant surface protein gene expression site of *Trypanosoma brucei*. Mol Biochem Parasitol; 62; 1993; 135-138.

[14] Shea C., Lee M.G.-S., van der Ploeg L.H.T. VSG gene 118 is transcribed from a cotransposed Pol-I-like promoter. Cell; 50; 1987; 603-612.

[15] Baltz T., Giroud C., Baltz D., Roth C., Raibaud A., Eisen H. Stable expression of two variable surface glycoproteins by cloned *Trypanosoma equiperdum*. Nature; 319; 1986; 602-604.

[16] Bulow R., Nonnengasser C., Overath P. Release of the variant surface glycoprotein during differentiation of bloodstream to procyclic forms of *Trypanosoma brucei*. Mol Biochem Parasitol; 32; 1989; 85-92.

[17] Seyfang A., Mecke D., Duszenko M. Degradation, recycling, and shedding of *Trypanosoma brucei* variant surface glycoprotein. J Protozool; 37; 1990; 546-552.

[18] Duszenko M, Seyfang A. Endocytosis and intracellular transport of variant surface glycoproteins in trypanosomes. In : Tartakoff AM, editor. Advances in Cell and Molecular Biology of Membranes : Membrane Traffic in Protozoa, 2B. JAI Press, Greenwich, CT, 1993 : 227–258.

[19] Ehlers B., Czichos J., Overath P. RNA turnover in *Trypanosoma brucei.* Mol Cell Biol; 7; 1987; 1242-1249.

[20] El-Sayed N.M.A., Alarcon C.M., Beck J.C., Sheffield V.C., Donelson J.E. cDNA expressed sequence tags of *Trypanosoma brucei rhodesiense* provide new insights into the biology of the parasite. Mol Biochem Parasitol; 73; 1995; 75-90.

[21] Horn D., Cross G.A.M. Analysis of *Trypanosoma brucei vsg* expression site switching in vitro. Mol Biochem Parasitol; 84; 1997; 189-201.

[22] Gottschling D.E., Aparicio O.M., Billington B.L., Zakian V.A. Position effect at *S. cerevisiae* telomeres : reversible repression of pol II transcription. Cell; 63; 1990; 751-762.

[23] Renauld H., Aparicio O.M., Zierath P.D., Billington B.L., Chhablani S.K., Gottschling D.E. Silent domains are assembled continuously from the telomere and are defined by promoter distance and strength, and by SIR3 dosage. Genes Dev; 7; 1993; 1133-1145.

[24] Loo S., Rine J. Silencers and domains of generalized repression. Science; 264; 1994; 1768-1771.

[25] Loo S., Rine J. Silencing and heritable domains of gene expression. Annu Rev Cell Biol; 11; 1995; 519-548.

[26] Zakian V.A. Structure, function and replication of *Saccharomomyces cerevisiae* telomeres. Annu Rev Genet; 30; 1996; 141-172.

[27] Hecker H., Betschart B., Burri M., Schlimme W. Functional morphology of trypanosome chromatin. Parasitol Today; 11; 1995; 79-83.

[28] Pays E., Lheureux M., Steinert M. The expression linked copy of surface antigen gene in *Trypanosoma brucei* is probably the one transcribed. Nature; 292; 1981; 265-267.

[29] Greaves D.R., Borst P. *Trypanosoma brucei* variant-specific glycoprotein gene chromatin is sensitive to single-strand-specific endonuclease digestion. J Mol Biol; 197; 1987; 471-483.

[30] Bernards A., Michels P.A.M., Lincke C.R., Borst P. Growth of chromosome ends in multiplying trypanosomes. Nature; 303; 1983; 592-597.

[31] Gommers-Ampt J.H., van Leeuwen F., De Beer A.L.J., Vliegenthart J.F.G., Dizdaroglu M., Kowalak J.A., Crain P.F.,

Borst P. beta-D-Glucosyl-hydroxymethyluracil : a novel modified base present in the DNA of the parasitic protozoan *T. brucei.* Cell; 75; 1993; 1129-1136.

[32] Bernards A., van Harten-Loosbroek N., Borst P. Modification of telomeric DNA in *Trypanosoma brucei;* a role in antigenic variation. Nucleic Acids Res; 12; 1984; 4153-4170.

[33] Pays E., Delauw M.F., Laurent M., Steinert M. Possible DNA modification in GC dinucleotides of *Trypanosoma brucei* telomeric sequences; relationship with antigen gene transcription. Nucleic Acids Res; 12; 1984; 5235-5247.

[34] van Leeuwen F., Wijsman E.R., Kuyl-Yeheskiely E., van der Marel G.A., van Boom J.H., Borst P. The telomeric GGGTAA repeats of *Trypanosoma brucei* contain the hypermodified base J in both strands. Nucleic Acids Res; 24; 1996; 2476-2482.

[35] Laird P.W., Jaenisch R. The role of DNA methylation in cancer genetic and epigenetics. Annu Rev Genet; 30; 1996; 441-464.

[36] Nakao M., Sasaki H. Genomic imprinting : significance in development and diseases and the molecular mechanisms. J Biochem; 120; 1996; 467-473.

[37] Neumann B., Barlow D.P. Multiple roles for DNA methylation in gametic imprinting. Curr Opin Genet Dev; 6; 1996; 159-163.

[38] Hsieh C.L., Lieber M.R. CpG methylated mini-chromosomes become inaccessible for V(D)J recombination after undergoing replication. EMBO J; 11; 1992; 315-325.

[39] Shemer R., Birger Y., Dean W.L., Reik W., Riggs A.D., Razin A. Dynamic methylation adjustment and counting as part of imprinting mechanisms. Proc Natl Acad Sci USA; 93; 1996; 6371-6376.

[40] Penny G.D., Kay G.F., Sheardown S.A., Rastan S., Brockdorff N. Requirement for Xist in X chromosome inactivation. Nature; 379; 1996; 131-137.

[41] Clemson C.M., McNeil J.A., Willard H.F., Lawrence J.B. Xist RNA paints the inactive X chromosome at interphase : evidence for a novel RNA involved in nuclear chromosome structure. J Cell Biol; 132; 1996; 259-275.

[42] Meller V.H., Wu K.H., Roman G., Kuroda M.I., Davis R.L. Rox1 RNA paints the X chromosome of male *Drosophila* and is regulated by the dosage compensation system. Cell; 88; 1997; 445-457.

[43] Amrein H., Axel R. Genes expressed in neurons of adult male *Drosophila.* Cell; 88; 1997; 459-469.

[44] Cornelissen A.W., Kooter P.J., Johnson J.M., van der Ploeg L.H.T., Borst P. Two simultaneously active VSG gene

transcription units in a single *Trypanosoma brucei* variant. Cell; 41; 1985; 825-832.

[45] Gottesdiener K., Chung H.-M., Brown S.D., Lee M.G.-S., van der Ploeg L.H.T. Characterization of VSG gene expression site promoters and promoter-associated DNA rearrangement events. Mol Cell Biol; 11; 1991; 2467-2480.

[46] Gottesdiener K.M., Goriparthi L., Masucci J.P., van der Ploeg L.H.T. A proposed mechanism for promoter-associated DNA rearrangement events at a variant surface glycoprotein gene expression site. Mol Cell Biol; 12; 1992; 4784-4795.

[47] Davies K.P., Carruthers V.B., Cross G.A.M. Manipulation of the *vsg* co-transposed region increases expression-site switching in *Trypanosoma brucei*. Mol Biochem Parasitol; 86; 1997; 163-177.

[48] Blum M.L., Down J.A., Gurnett A.M., Carrington M., Turner M.J., Wiley D.C. A structural motif in the variant surface glycoproteins of *Trypanosoma brucei*. Nature; 362; 1993; 603-609.

[49] Agur Z., Abiri D., van der Ploeg L.H.T. Ordered appearance of antigenic variants of African trypanosomes explained in a mathematical model based on a stochastic switch process and immune-selection against putative switch intermediates. Proc Natl Acad Sci USA; 86; 1989; 9626-9630.

[50] Agur Z. Mathematical models for African trypanosomiasis. Parasitol Today; 8; 1992; 128-129.

[51] Agur Z. Double expressor switch intermediates. Parasitol Today; 11; 1995; 24.

[52] Timmers H.T.M., De Lange T., Kooter J.M., Borst P. Coincident multiple activations of the same surface antigen gene in *Trypanosoma brucei*. J Mol Biol; 184; 1987; 81-90.

[53] Barry D., Turner C.M.J. Mathematical models for African trypanosomiasis. Parasitol Today; 8; 1992; 128-129.

[54] Borst P., Rudenko G. Antigenic variation in African trypanosomes. Science; 264; 1994; 1872-1873.

[55] Munoz-Jordan J.L., Davies K.P., Cross G.A.M. Stable expression of mosaic coats of variant surface glycoproteins in *Trypanosoma brucei*. Science; 272; 1996; 1795-1797.

[56] Chung H.M., Lee M.G.-S., van der Ploeg L.H.T. RNA polymerase I-mediated protein-coding gene expression in *Trypanosoma brucei*. Parasitol Today; 8; 1992; 414-418.

[57] Zomerdijk J.C.B.M., Kieft R., Shiels P.G., Borst P. Alpha-amanitin-resistant transcription units in trypanosomes: A comparison of promoter sequences for a VSG gene expression site and for the ribosomal RNA genes. Nucleic Acids Res; 19; 1991; 5153-5158.

[58] Graham S.V., Barry J.D. Transcriptional regulation of metacyclic variant surface glycoprotein gene expression during the life cycle of *Trypanosoma brucei*. Mol Cell Biol; 15; 1995; 5945-5956.

[59] Janz L., Clayton C. The PARP and rRNA promoters of *Trypanosoma brucei* are composed of dissimilar sequence elements that are functionally interchangeable. Mol Cell Biol; 14; 1994; 5804-5811.

[60] Vanhamme L., Pays A., Tebabi P., Alexandre S., Pays E. Specific binding of proteins to the noncoding strand of a crucial element of the variant surface glycoprotein, procyclin, and ribosomal promoters of *Trypanosoma brucei*. Mol Cell Biol; 15; 1995; 5598-5606.

[61] Qi C.C., Urmenyi T., Gottesdiener K.M. Analysis of a hybrid PARP/VSG ES promoter in procyclic trypanosomes. Mol Biochem Parasitol; 77; 1996; 147-159.

[62] Zomerdijk J.C.B.M., Ouellete M., ten Asbroek A.L.M.A., Kieft R., Bommer A.M.M., Clayton C.E., Borst P. The promoter for a variant surface glycoprotein gene expression site in *Trypanosoma brucei*. EMBO J; 9; 1990; 2791-2801.

[63] Jefferies D., Tebabi P., Pays E. Transient activity assays of the *Trypanosoma brucei* variant surface glycoprotein gene promoter: control of gene expression at the post-transcriptional level. Mol Cell Biol; 11; 1991; 338-343.

[64] Pham V.P., Qi C.C., Gottesdiener K.M. A detailed mutational analysis of the VSG gene expression site promoter. Mol Biochem Parasitol; 75; 1996; 241-254.

[65] Sherman D.R., Janz L., Hug M., Clayton C. Anatomy of the *parp* gene promoter of *Trypanosoma brucei*. EMBO J; 10; 1991; 3379-3386.

[66] Brown S.D., Huang J., van der Ploeg L.H.T. The promoter for the procyclic acidic repetitive protein (PARP) genes of *Trypanosoma brucei* shares features with RNA polymerase I promoters. Mol Cell Biol; 12; 1992; 2644-2652.

[67] Pham VP, Rothman PB, Gottesdiener KM. Binding of trans-acting factors to the double-stranded VSG expression site promoter of *Trypanosoma brucei*. Mol Biochem Parasitol 1997; 89: 11–23.

[68] Steverding D., Stierhof Y.D., Chaudhri M., Ligtenberg M., Schell D., Beck-Sickinger A.G., Overath P. ESAG 6 and 7 products of *Trypanosoma brucei* form a transferrin binding protein complex. Eur J Cell Biol; 64; 1994; 78-87.

[69] Ligtenberg M.J.L., Bitter W., Kieft R., Steverding D., Janssen H., Calafat J., Borst P. Reconstitution of a surface transferrin binding complex in insect form *Trypanosoma brucei*. EMBO J; 13; 1994; 2565-2573.

[70] Salmon D., Geuskens M., Hanocq F., Hanocq-Quertier J., Nolan D., Ruben L., Pays E. A novel heterodimeric transferrin receptor encoded by a pair of VSG expression site-associated genes in *T. brucei.* Cell; 78; 1994; 75-86.

[71] Carruthers V.B., Cross G.A.M. High-efficiency clonal growth of bloodstream- and insect-form *Trypanosoma brucei* on agarose plates. Proc Natl Acad Sci USA; 89; 1992; 8818-8821.

[72] Carruthers V.B., van der Ploeg L.H.T., Cross G.A.M. DNA-mediated transformation of bloodstream-form *Trypanosoma brucei.* Nucleic Acids Res; 21; 1993; 2537-2538.

[73] Vassella E., Boshart M. High molecular mass agarose matrix supports growth of bloodstream forms of pleomorphic *Trypanosoma brucei* strains in axenic culture. Mol Biochem Parasitol; 82; 1996; 91-105.

[74] Murphy N.B., Muthiani A.M., Peregrine A.S. Use of an in vivo system to determine the G418 resistance phenotype of bloodstream-form *Trypanosoma brucei brucei* transfectants. Antimicrob Agents Chemother; 37; 1993; 1167-1170.

[75] Navarro M., Cross G.A.M. DNA rearrangements associated with multiple consecutive directed antigenic switches in *Trypanosoma brucei.* Mol Cell Biol; 16; 1996; 3615-3625.

[76] Sommer J.M., Hua S.B., Li F.S., Gottesdiener K.M., Wang C.C. Cloning by functional complementation in *Trypanosoma brucei.* Mol Biochem Parasitol; 76; 1996; 83-89.

[77] Lamont G.S., Tucker R.S., Cross G.A.M. Analysis of antigen switching rates in *Trypanosoma brucei.* Parasitology; 92; 1986; 355-367.

[78] Myler P.J., Aline R.F.J., Scholler J.K., Stuart K.D. Changes in telomere length associated with antigenic variation in *Trypanosoma brucei.* Mol Biochem Parasitol; 29; 1988; 243-250.

[79] Zomerdijk J.C.B.M., Kieft R., Borst P. A ribosomal RNA gene promoter at the telomere of a mini-chromosome in *Trypanosoma brucei.* Nucleic Acids Res; 20; 1992; 2725-2734.

[80] Pays E., Laurent M., Delinte K., vanMeirvenne N., Steinert M. Differential size variations between transcriptionally active and inactive telomeres of *Trypanosoma brucei.* Nucleic Acids Res; 11; 1983; 8137-8147.

[81] Gilson E., Laroche T., Gasser S.M. Telomeres and the functional architecture of the nucleus. Trends Cell Biol; 3; 1993; 128-134.

[82] Liu A.Y.C., van der Ploeg L.H.T., Rijsewijk F.A.M., Borst P. The transposition unit of VSG gene 118 of *Trypanosoma brucei :* presence of repeated elements at its border and absence of promoter associated sequences. J Mol Biol; 167; 1983; 57-75.

[83] Majumder H.K., Boothroyd J.C., Weber H. Homologous 3'-terminal regions of mRNAs for surface antigens of different antigenic variants of *Trypanosoma brucei.* Nucleic Acids Res; 9; 1981; 4745-4753.

[84] Patnaik P.K., Axelrod N., van der Ploeg L.H.T., Cross G.A.M. Artificial linear mini-chromosomes for *Trypanosoma brucei.* Nucleic Acids Res; 24; 1996; 668-675.

[85] Biebinger S., Rettenmaier S., Flaspohler J., Hartmann C., Penadiaz J., Wirtz L.E., Hotz H.R., Barry J.D., Clayton C. The PARP promoter of *Trypanosoma brucei* is developmentally regulated in a chromosomal context. Nucleic Acids Res; 24; 1996; 1202-1211.

[86] Felsenfeld, G. Chromatin unfolds. Cell 1996; 86 : 13–19.

[87] Struhl K. Chromatin structure and RNA polymerase II connection : implications for transcription. Cell; 84; 1996; 179-182.

[88] Roth S.Y., Allis C.D. Histone acetylation and chromatin assembly : a single escort, multiple dances. Cell; 87; 1996; 5-8.

[89] Ptashne M., Gann A. Transcriptional activation by recruitment. Nature; 386; 1997; 569-577.

[90] Werner M.H., Burley S.K. Architectural transcription factors : proteins that remodel DNA. Cell; 88; 1997; 733-736.

[91] Jenuwein T., Forrester W.C., Qiu R.G., Grosschedl R. The immunoglobulin μ enhancer core establishes local factor access in nuclear chromatin independent of transcriptional stimulation. Genes Dev; 7; 1993; 2016-2032.

[92] Jenuwein T., Forrester W.C., Fernandezherrero L.A., Laible G., Dull M., Grosschedl R. Extension of chromatin accessibility by nuclear matrix attachment regions. Nature; 385; 1997; 269-272.

[93] Pays E., Coquelet H., Tebabi P., Pays A., Jefferies D., Steinert M., Koenig E., Williams R.O., Roditi I. *Trypanosoma brucei :* Constitutive activity of the VSG and procyclin gene promoters. EMBO J; 9; 1990; 3145-3151.

[94] Vanhamme L., Berberof M., Le Ray D., Pays E. Stimuli of differentiation regulate RNA elongation in the transcription units for the major stage-specific antigens of *Trypanosoma brucei.* Nucleic Acids Res; 23; 1995; 1862-1869.

[95] Zomerdijk J.C.B.M., Kieft R., Duyndam M., Shiels P.G., Borst P. Antigenic variation in *Trypanosoma brucei :* a telomeric expression site for variant-specific surface glycoprotein genes with novel features. Nucleic Acids Res; 19; 1991; 1359-1368.

[96] van der Ploeg L., Smith C.L., Polvere R.I., Gottesdiener K.M. Improved separation of chromosome-sized DNA from *Trypanosoma brucei,* stock 427-60. Nucleic Acids Res; 17; 1989; 3217-3227.

6

VSG gene control and infectivity strategy of metacyclic stage *Trypanosoma brucei* [1]

J. David Barry,
Sheila V. Graham,
Michael Fotheringham,
Vincent S. Graham,
Kerri Kobryn,
Ben Wymer

Wellcome Unit of Molecular Parasitology, University of Glasgow, The Anderson College, 56 Dumbarton Rd, Glasgow G11 6NU, UK

Abstract

As the metacyclic trypanosome stage develops in the tsetse fly salivary glands, it initiates expression of variant surface glycoproteins (VSGs) and does so by each cell activating, at random, one from a small subset of metacyclic VSG (M-VSG) genes. Whereas differential activation of individual VSG genes in the bloodstream occurs as a function of time, to evade waves of antibody, it is believed that the aim in the metacyclic stage is simultaneously to generate population diversity. M-VSG genes are activated in their telomeric loci and belong to monocistronic transcription units, unlike all other known trypanosome protein-coding genes, which appear to be transcribed polycistronically. The promoters of these metacyclic expression sites (M-ESs) have the unique property, in this organism, of being switched on and off in a life-cycle stage specific pattern. We have found that the 1.22 M-ES promoter is regulated according to life cycle stage, differential control being exerted through different elements of the promoter and under the influence of its genomic locus. We have characterized in detail the telomeres containing the 1.22 and 1.61 M-ESs. Upstream of the M-ES is a possibly haploid, non-transcribed region with some degenerate sequences homologous with expression site associated genes (ESAGs) that occur in bloodstream VSG expression sites. Further upstream (respectively, 22 and 13 kb upstream of the 1.22 and 1.61 VSG genes) are α-amanitin sensitive transcription units that may be polycistrons and are transcribed in all examined life cycle stages. They contain a number of genes. The differences between metacyclic and bloodstream ESs may have important consequences for life cycle regulation, genetic stability, phenotype complexity and adaptability of the metacyclic stage as it infects different host species. © 1998 Francqui Foundation. Published by Elsevier Science B.V. All rights reserved.

Keywords : *Trypanosoma brucei*; Metacyclic stage; VSG gene

1. *Abbreviations* : B-ES, bloodstream expression site; ELC, expression linked copy; ES, expression site; ESAG, expression site associated gene; M-ES, metacyclic expression site; M-VSG, metacyclic variant surface glycoprotein; PCR, polymerase chain reaction; RT-PCR, reverse transcription PCR; VSG, variant surface glycoprotein.

1 ● Introduction

The metacyclic stage of *Trypanosoma brucei* in the tsetse fly has a critical task, the establishment of infection in the mammal. It is preadapted for life in the mammal, having many of the structures and functions of bloodstream trypanosomes and does not proliferate in the fly, merely existing there for up to several days, awaiting transmission to its new host. Functionally, this form is equivalent to the short stumpy bloodstream stage, which has the task of transmission from mammal to fly. Of these two, the metacyclic form appears to have the greater degree of preadaptation, possibly because the mammal presents a more antagonistic environment for which the metacyclic stage must be prepared. One major difference between these two transmissions is in the processes for changing from expression of one type of protective coat to another. Most stages in the tsetse fly are coated with the invariant procyclin glycoproteins [1], and mammal-infective stages are coated instead with the variant surface glycoprotein (VSG) [2]. Whereas the stumpy form carries the VSG coat into the fly and replacement with the procyclin coat ensues, seemingly in response to environmental change [1], change from procyclin to VSG coat occurs as an intrinsic part of the differentiation step from epimastigote to metacyclic stage in the fly's salivary glands [3]. The initiation of VSG coat synthesis at this point includes a complex set of events, involving aspects of VSG gene activation strategy, control of gene expression and even genome organization, that differ markedly from what is currently thought to be the norm in *T. brucei.* Here we explore these aspects and attempt to relate them to the tasks facing the metacyclic population.

2 ● A strategy for VSG activation in the metacyclic population

In mammalian hosts, the VSG surface coat acts to shield invariant surface antigens from host immunity and to thwart non-specific immune mechanisms [4]. However, the VSG itself is a potent immunogen, and the infection survives only through the ability of the parasite to undergo antigenic variation, the periodic switching to expression of a different VSG and consequent evasion of the oncoming wave of specific antibodies [5, 6]. Each trypanosome has an enormous repertoire of VSGs, in *T. brucei* encoded in at least 1000 distinct structural genes, which in any trypanosome are expressed singly. The success of antigenic variation in prolonging chronic infection is associated with a hierarchical expression of VSGs, resulting in the repertoire becoming used progressively with time, and with a constant trickle of VSG switching. A number of gene activation mechanisms are involved in antigenic variation, as discussed below. The general switch rate is about 10^{-2} switch generation^{-1} per trypanosome, a value that becomes diminished during prolonged syringe passaging in laboratory animals [7, 8]. Time, therefore, is a key element in the strategy of antigenic variation.

Time does not apply in the strategy for VSG activation in the metacyclic stage. Instead, the goal is to develop a population heterogeneous in VSGs which is thought to increase the probability of infecting hosts which already have antibodies as a result of previous infections [9]. Heterogeneity is achieved by the use of a specific subset of VSGs known as the metacyclic (M-) VSG repertoire, which contains up to 27 different VSGs [10, 11]. As with bloodstream trypanosomes, each metacyclic cell expresses just one VSG. The M-VSG repertoire is notable for its relative constancy, the same set becoming activated each time a cloned trypanosome line is transmitted through flies and each VSG being expressed on the same proportion of cells within the metacyclic population, regardless of the last VSG expressed by the bloodstream trypanosomes that originally infected the fly [12]. Occasional changes in the M-VSG repertoire, however, prevent its exploitation in vaccine development [13].

Comparison of the VSG activation strategies used in the metacyclic and bloodstream populations shows that basic features apply to both, but that the differences could be attributed to the time factor. Both systems use a large repertoire of genes, from which one is expressed in any cell. It is in the differential activation of VSGs that differences are apparent. In the bloodstream, this is a sophisticated process that, besides occurring with time, selects genes in a hierarchical fashion, extending the time over which the repertoire becomes used [14, 15]. It also switches divergently, each VSG type having the capability of spawning several types [16]. In the metacyclic stage these effects do not occur. Instead, differential activation involves merely the immediate generation of a heterogeneous population.

A very complex set of processes is responsible for VSG activation and switching, and an important route to gaining understanding is to establish basic dynamics and patterns of expression within trypanosome populations. For the metacyclic stage, this has been undertaken in several ways. One very informative way has been study of the epimastigote-metacyclic differentiation on the wall of the salivary glands, using scanning electron microscopy of trypanosomes to which are bound labelled antibodies specific to individual M-VSGs. This approach has revealed a number of basic features of M-VSG activation [3]. The VSG coat appears while pre-metacyclic cells are still attached to the wall, and the random (Poisson) frequency of labelled trypanosomes spatially on the gland wall shows that the decision to initiate VSG synthesis coincides with selection of a specific VSG from the metacyclic repertoire. This also tells us that selective VSG activation is a random process and that M-VSG activation occurs polyclonally within the population, which means that activation events can be identified only by clonal study. Finally, it also graphically displays that the genes encoding the MVSG repertoire are qualitatively distinct from other VSG genes, becoming activated repeatedly and independently within the differentiating population.

It is clear that the VSG activation systems operating in the fly and in the bloodstream are distinct. Sometimes the VSG being expressed by bloodstream trypanosomes used to infect the fly is preferentially reactivated following transmission from the fly into mice but it does not appear in the metacyclic population [17]. Furthermore, when the trypanosomes initially infecting the fly express an M-VSG, presenting an opportunity for increased representation of that VSG in the metacyclic population, no effect is apparent [18]. Hence, not only are the systems distinct, but they also are controlled according to their life cycle stage. The entire M-VSG repertoire can probably be activated during chronic bloodstream infections initiated by injection of bloodstream trypanosomes not expressing M-VSGs, showing that M-VSG genes can be activated by both systems [10, 19].

3 • Distinct gene activation and expression systems

The major differences between the metacyclic and bloodstream VSG systems extend to their genetic organization and control. Much is known about the bloodstream system, but study of the metacyclic system has been constrained by technical limitations : scant availability of metacyclic cells and the inherent high VSG switching rate of tsetse fly transmissible lines. In the near future, the availability of single-cell reporter systems and polymerase chain reaction (PCR) methods will relieve some of these limitations. To date, the approach used has depended on the fact that fly-transmitted trypanosomes continue to express M-VSGs for several days in mammals, despite having differentiated to bloodstream stages [17, 20]. Therefore, injection of metacyclic cells will yield just enough trypanosomes for molecular study. This phase of infection has been used to clone cDNAs for several M-VSGs [21]. In a separate approach, bloodstream trypanosomes expressing M-VSGs have been cloned and used as a source of cDNAs [22].

The organization, activation and expression of bloodstream VSG genes are reviewed extensively elsewhere [5, 6, 8, 23]. With some exceptions that are encoded by mosaic genes, each VSG is encoded by a separate, intact gene. Upstream of most is a set of several repeated sequence units each about 70 bp long. Most of this gene repertoire, estimated indirectly to number about 1000, are thought to be organized in arrays within chromosomes and never to be transcribed in those loci. Instead, they are activated by being duplicated into telomeric bloodstream expression sites (B-ESs), which are long, polycistronic transcription units containing several kilobases of 70 bp repeats and a set of non-VSG genes known as expression site associated genes (ESAGs). Each ESAG belongs to a large, diverse family including members within B-ESs and at other genomic loci. The duplication event copies usually the entire coding sequence and the sequence running upstream to the 70 bp repeat region. The duplicates, known as expression linked copies (ELCs), are temporary, being eliminated when another gene is copied into that B-ES. This appears to be a straightforward way of solving the formidable problem of expressing the gene repertoire individually. However, there is added complexity, in that there is a set of VSG genes, located at the telomeres of the estimated 100 mini-chromosomes in the nucleus, which appear to be activated essentially by the same duplication mechanism. On top of that, there are up to 20 distinct B-ESs in each trypanosome, requiring an extra mechanism, not yet fully elucidated, to ensure that only one is transcribed at any time [24]. Toggling of the transcriptional state between an active B-ES, containing one VSG gene, and a silent B-ES containing another VSG gene results in a switch in the expressed VSG without any gene movement. A number of other mechanisms associated with switching between B-ESs have been described [8]. The common feature of gene activation is that, one way or another, a gene comes under the control of an active promoter.

For M-VSG genes, activation in the tsetse fly occurs in situ, at least as observed within days of introduction of metacyclic cells into mice. Study of infections initiated with uncloned populations had suggested in situ activation [25], but more direct evidence has been obtained from infections arising from single metacyclic cells [26]. The previous evidence that the systems for activation of specific VSG genes differ between the bloodstream and metacyclic stages gains support upon examination of routes of M-VSG gene activation by bloodstream, rather than metacyclic, trypanosomes. For several M-VSG genes, an ELC is generated in the bloodstream, presumably in a B-ES [26–28]. The M-VSG genes cloned from cDNA obtained from mice following fly transmission have no 70 bp repeat units upstream [21], whereas those cloned from bloodstream trypanosomes that had activated M-VSG genes during mammal infection, without involvement of the metacyclic stage, have just one or two repeat units [27]. When the latter type of M-VSG gene forms an ELC, the upstream limit of the copy maps to the short 70 bp region [27]. Such duplications are frequent, suggesting that independent activation in bloodstream stages may be easier if some 70 bp units are present. For those M-VSG genes with no upstream 70 bp units, activation in the bloodstream is infrequent but does involve duplication of the gene [28]. In one case, an M-VSG gene (MVAT4) has been found to be activated in situ in bloodstream trypanosomes [29] but, as discussed below, this required very intensive selection that may have resulted in use of a cryptic promoter sequence.

The in situ activation of M-VSG genes in the tsetse fly means that these genes occupy metacyclic expression sites (M-ES). We have studied the structure of two, by nuclear run-on analysis using trypanosomes derived in mice from metacyclic cells. An unusual result was obtained, revealing that both are only about 4.5 kb long and contain only one gene, the M-VSG gene itself [30]. In fact, both are monocistrons. Study of the intensively selected bloodstream line in which the MVAT4 VSG gene had become activated in situ also revealed that it is expressed from a monocistron [29], but the relationship of that monocistron to the M-ES as activated in the tsetse fly is unknown. The only other monocistrons observed as yet in *T. brucei* are those transcribed by RNA polymerase III and containing genes for small RNA species [31]. So far, other protein-coding genes have been observed to belong to polycistrons. The M-ESs are transcribed by an α-amanitin resistant polymerase, in common with the B-ESs and the procyclin polycistrons [26]. The exact significance of the use of possibly RNA polymerase I for these surface coat encoding transcription units is unclear, although it may be significant that all are transcribed at a high level in the appropriate life cycle stage, but at a lower level or not at all in other life cycle stages.

One other feature of M-ESs became apparent from the nascent RNA analyses. Unlike other promoters in this organism, the life cycle stage-specific regulation of the M-ES promoters operates through a transcriptional switch [26]. This contrasts with the B-ES and procyclin promoters, which do not become completely inactive at any of the studied life cycle stages, instead being up and down regulated as required [32]. Absence of transcriptional silencing does not present much of a problem, as trypanosomes employ, fairly extensively, post-transcriptional regulatory mechanisms with the consequence that the transcriptional state of a gene does not necessarily relate directly to presence or level of its protein product [33]. However, the M-VSG genes appear so far to be unique, being subject to transcriptional control.

The physical linkage of ESAGs and bloodstream VSG genes may allow their expression to be coordinate, and some ESAGs encode proteins required, like the VSGs, in the bloodstream stage [34]. The monocistronic character of M-ESs uncouples such coordination of transcription, with an important effect on the phenotype of the metacyclic cell, as we discuss below.

4 • Stage-specific promoters

One possible explanation for the stage-specific transcriptional switch of M-ESs is that their promoters are qualitatively different from other trypanosome promoters. The differential life cycle stage activity of the promoter for the ILTat 1.22 M-ES has been investigated by linking it to a reporter gene and reintroducing it into trypanosomes of different life cycle stages. When reintroduced on an episomal plasmid into metacyclic-derived cells in transient transfection assays, as expected it displayed activity [30]. In transient transfections of bloodstream cells, however, a higher activity was demonstrated, in contrast with the observed lack of activity in its own locus, as seen in transcriptional run-on assays. To examine this further, a similar reporter cassette was integrated into the 1.22 telomere and into the non-transcribed region of the ribosomal RNA gene locus, which lies within a chromosome. In bloodstream trypanosomes, the 1.22 promoter proved to be 50 times more active in the ribosomal RNA locus than in its telomeric locus (S.V. Graham, B. Wymer and J.D. Barry, submitted). This suggests that there is repression of the 1.22 promoter mediated specifically by telomeric location in the bloodstream stage. For the procyclic stage, different data were obtained. The 1.22 promoter is normally inactive in this stage, and this lack of activity was observed also in the transient transfection assays and after integration of the reporter cassette into either the ribosomal RNA or the 1.22 telomeric locus [30] (S.V. Graham, B. Wymer and J.D. Barry, submitted). In the case of the procyclic stage, therefore, it is likely that the structure (sequence) of the promoter prevents its use for initiation of transcription.

Dissection of the 1.22 promoter reveals complexity (S.V. Graham, B. Wymer and J.D. Barry, submitted). Its 5' half can provide full activity in bloodstream form transient transfection experiments while the 3' half has no activity but serves to allow accurate transcription initiation. In metacyclic-derived trypanosomes, however, neither portion alone has significant activity and the whole promoter region is required for full activity. In procyclic cells none of these three promoter fragments is active. With this in mind, and since promoter activity in bloodstream form transient transfection is an artifact of removal of the promoter sequence from control in a chromosomal context, it seems likely that the 5' activity is the component of the promoter which is subject to this form of down-regulation in bloodstream trypanosomes. For three other genes, encoding the MVAT4, MVAT5 and AnTat 11.17 M-VSGs, DNA fragments located approximately 3 kb upstream of the genes display promoter activity in procyclic form transient transfections [29, 35, 36]. In addition, there is some evidence that a putative promoter for the MVAT5 M-VSG gene can be activated in bloodstream trypanosomes (expressing another VSG on their surface) [35], but the intensive selection involved in isolating this trypanosome may have resulted in an alteration in normal regulation. There is no evidence that any of these three putative metacyclic promoters is actually functional at the metacyclic stage and sequence analysis has shown that they have homology with the 1.22 M-VSG gene promoter 5' portion, but not the 3' portion. Further analysis may reveal whether these putative promoters require other sequences for accurate regulation in the metacyclic stage.

Similar reporter gene studies have shown that a B-ES promoter is regulated differently from the 1.22 promoter, displaying activity in all three of the populations (metacyclic-derived, bloodstream and procyclic) that we have tested [30]. In general, transfection studies reflect what occurs in vivo, namely that the two types of VSG gene promoter behave very differently from each other, although both are subject to position effects within their own loci [37, 38]. In the case of the M-ES promoter, its proximity to the tract of short sequence repeat units at the end of the chromosomal duplex makes it a prime candidate for regulation by a classical telomere position effect, as we discuss below.

5 • Structure and expression of telomeric regions containing M-VSG genes

The structure of the chromosomal region upstream of M-ESs is of interest for several reasons. As is common, it may contribute directly to regulation of the promoter. There is also the matter of the absence of ESAGs from M-ESs, raising the question whether some may reside upstream, in a separate transcription unit. The chromosomal environment should also be important in the recombinational interaction of the M-ES with the rest of the genome. Early indications were that the M-ES is flanked upstream by what appeared to be haploid sequence [26, 39], and it was speculated that this may act to prevent recombination between the two types of ES, thereby separately maintaining their control systems [9]. To define the upstream region

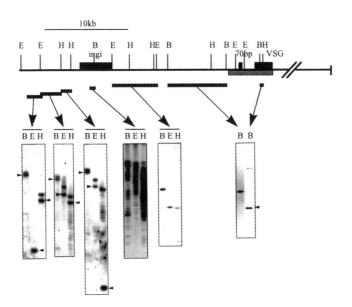

FIGURE 1

Southern probing of the 1.22 telomeric region. Genomic DNA from ILTat 1.22 bloodstream trypanosomes was digested with : *Bam* HI (B); *Eco* RI (E); or *Hin*dIII (H) and separated by agarose gel electrophoresis, then Southern blotted. The filter was probed with radiolabelled fragments derived from the 1.22 telomere as shown and filters were washed to high stringency (0.1 × SSC, 65 °C) and subsequent autoradiographs are shown. In lanes containing extra fragments not predicted from the map of the cloned 1.22 region, the predicted fragment is shown with an arrowhead. In the map, restriction enzyme sites are : *Bam* HI (B); *Eco* RI (E); and *Hin*dIII (H). The black boxes represent : the Ingi retroposon (ingi), the single 70 bp unit (70 bp) and the 1.22 VSG gene (VSG). The grey box depicts the monocistronic transcription unit and the vertical bar the end of the chromosome.

and to begin to address these questions, we have now characterized extensively upstream of the 1.22 and 1.61 genes.

To define the physical limit of the apparently haploid, non-transcribed region, three approaches can be used. One is to identify where diploidy occurs upstream, as conventional genes are diploid in the trypanosome [40, 41]. A second approach is to generate a transcription map and a third is to undertake comprehensive sequencing, searching for genes. We have applied all three approaches to both the 1.22 and 1.61 telomeres, making use of three overlapping lambda clone inserts which we have isolated for each telomere. These span 28 kb upstream of the 1.22 VSG gene, and 36 kb for the 1.61 gene.

In Fig. 1, a series of fragments from the 1.22 telomere have been probed onto a Southern blot of genomic DNA from bloodstream form trypanosomes. It can be seen that, with two exceptions, only single fragments are detected over 17 kb upstream of the VSG gene. The exceptions are with the VSG gene probe, which also detects the ELC of the 1.22 gene that was being expressed in the trypanosome clone from which the DNA was extracted, and the probe covering the region from 12 to 17 kb upstream, which contains a *Hin*dIII site and therefore detects two bands in that digest (lane «H»). Beyond 17 kb upstream is one copy of the retrotransposon ingi, and that probe detects the many copies in the genome [42, 43]. Further upstream, however, from − 22 to − 28 kb, all probes detect two fragments for most digests. This pattern is not incompatible with diploidy running upstream from − 22 kb. However, probing of other *T.*

brucei stocks reveals not such a straightforward story, there being also evidence of involvement of non-homologous chromosomes. This study has not included measurement of DNA content, so ploidy cannot be concluded. To resolve this issue, we are now mapping these fragments to characterized chromosome bands separated by pulsed field gel electrophoresis (with S.E. Melville, University of Cambridge). An essentially similar story has been obtained for the 1.61 telomere, for which 14 kb upstream of the VSG gene have been probed. At high stringency mostly single bands are detected, with the notable exception of the fragment containing 70 bp repeat units, which shares sequence extensively throughout the genome. At lower stringency, multiple banding becomes apparent with some fragments.

To determine a transcription map, several techniques have been applied. Nuclear run-on assaying reveals that both telomeric regions do contain transcriptionally active regions, well upstream from the VSG gene.

For the 1.22 chromosome (Fig. 2), the ingi element detects nascent RNA from bloodstream trypanosomes, but this could arise from many ingi-containing loci, and not necessarily this one. There is no transcription between the *Hin*dIII and *Apa* I sites immediately upstream of the ingi, and then all fragments covering from − 22 to − 28 kb (limit of cloned region) upstream of the VSG gene are transcribed. This transcription is α-amanitin sensitive. Similar data are obtained with the procyclic stage and metacyclic-derived cells expressing the 1.22 M-ES. For the 1.61 chromosome, bloodstream

FIGURE 2

Transcriptional run-on analysis of the upstream region of the 1.22 telomere. Nascent RNA, radiolabelled in nuclei from bloodstream form trypanosomes (ILTat 1.2), was applied as a probe [30] to a Southern blot of the four fragments from the upstream limit of the cloned region of the 1.22 telomere. Control hybridizations were to trypanosome ribosomal DNA and tubulin cloned sequences. The top two photographs show ethidium bromide stained gels separating the ribosomal DNA (R) and tubulin (T) fragments and the four test fragments, two of which were digested into two fragments. Below is the autoradiograph resulting from probing with the radiolabelled RNA. At the bottom is the same experiment except that the hybridization was performed in the presence of 1 mg ml⁻¹ α-amanitin. The filters were washed at high stringency. In the map, the relevant restriction enzyme sites are shown: *Bam* HI (B); *Eco* RI (E); *Hin*dIII (H); *Nco* I (N); and *Apa* I (A). The excised plasmid band is indicated in the gel photograph. Grey boxes depict transcribed regions and the VSG gene and 70 bp repeat region are indicated.

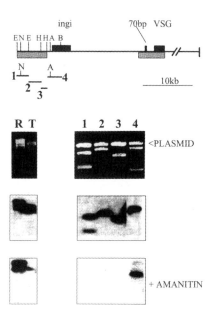

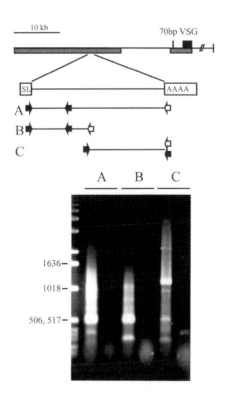

FIGURE 3

RT-PCR detection of a mature transcript from the 1.61 telomere. The A, B and C line drawings depict three separate RT-PCR strategies in which the open arrow shows the position and orientation of the reverse transcriptase primer relative to the mature transcript depicted below the map and the filled arrows show the subsequent PCR primers. The photograph is of an ethidium bromide stained electrophoretic gel in which are separated the RT-PCR products. For each of A, B and C the left hand lane has the reaction products and the right hand lane is a control lacking reverse transcriptase. The major band from each reaction represents the specific product and together they demonstrate a discrete mature, trans-spliced and polyadenylated transcript of the size predicted from Northern analysis. In the map of the telomere, the grey boxes depict transcribed regions and the VSG gene and 70 bp repeat region are indicated. Molecular size standards are in the leftmost gel lane and relevant lengths are shown to the left of the photograph. SL represents the universal mRNA spliced leader and AAAA the poly[A] tail.

stage transcription is detected on all fragments from about – 13 kb to the cloned limit at – 36 kb, and a similar extent is observed in procyclic cells. Again, this is α-amanitin sensitive. The downstream ends of these transcribed stretches coincide approximately with the transition from (possibly) haploid to (possibly) diploid sequence.

Northern analysis of total RNA reveals several bands arising from these transcribed regions, but not from downstream. For the 1.61 chromosome, four bands are reproducibly detected, whose lengths in order from the telomere-proximal end are 1.85, > 4, > 2 and > 4 kb. We have examined the first of these by reverse transcription PCR (RT-PCR) (Fig. 3).

Using combinations of oligo[dT], an oligonucleotide complementary to the universal mRNA spliced leader and primers designed from sequence within the region under study, reverse transcriptase-dependent PCR products were obtained that, together, reveal a trans-spliced, polyadenylated RNA molecule about 1.85 kb long, transcribed in the same orientation as the VSG gene. These data are suggestive of closely-linked genes occupying a polycistron, a typical organization within the trypanosome genome.

FIGURE 4

Functional maps of the 1.22 and 1.61 tel-omeres. Data are compiled from restriction enzyme mapping of lambda clone DNA and trypanosome genomic DNA; nuclear run-on, Northern and RT-PCR analyses; and DNA sequencing. The lambda clone inserts are shown. All sequences of interest, including the VSG genes and any of homology with known sequences, are depicted by black boxes, with brackets to show incomplete genes. Orientations of sequences (relative to homologues) are shown by arrowheads : direction of transcription is under study. Transcribed regions are shown by grey boxes. The scale at the bottom represents kilobases upstream of the start of the VSG coding sequence.

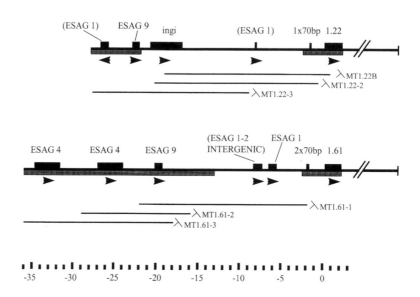

We have sequenced, in both orientations, most of the 28 kb upstream of the 1.22 gene and all 36 kb upstream of the 1.61 gene (Fig. 4).

A number of regions homologous with known trypanosome sequences have been detected, and none of significant homology with any other sequences. In the non-transcribed region between the M-ES and the α-amanitin sensitive transcribed region upstream, the 1.22 chromosome contains brief runs of sequence homologous to members of the ESAG 1 family [44, 45], but no open reading frame is present. The 1.61 chromosome contains what appears to be an intact ESAG 1 homologue in the silent region and, just upstream, homology with the B-ES sequence spanning from the end of ESAG 2 through some of the intergenic region and the start of ESAG 1 [46], but again there is no open reading frame present. In the transcribed regions upstream, several homologues of ESAGs have been identified. With the exception of the ESAG 1 homologue at − 26 kb in the 1.22 chromosome, all these have intact open reading frames, and those on the 1.61 chromosome tally with the RNA species detected. These will be described in detail elsewhere.

All these data point towards a similar organization in the two chromosomes studied, summarized in Fig. 4. In the metacyclic stage, the M-ESs are transcribed as discrete units and are flanked upstream by a silent region that may be haploid and contains some scattered sequences homologous with ESAG 1 and 2. Further upstream, in possibly diploid regions, are α-amanitin sensitive transcription units, that are likely to be part of polycistrons and, unlike the M-ESs, are transcribed in bloodstream, procyclic and metacyclic-derived trypanosomes (the last stage not yet tested for 1.61). These units contain members of some of the ESAG gene families.

6 • Gene expression and infectivity strategies in the life cycle

Our findings reveal extensive differences between M-ESs and B-ESs in both gene organization and transcription. Some of these differences are likely to have major consequences for the cell phenotype which we believe may result in the individual metacyclic cell being more adaptable than the bloodstream stages. As an infective stage that is faced with the task of infecting any of a number of possible mammalian species, the metacyclic population would benefit from adaptability.

Our demonstration of various footprints, that is, mainly degenerate sequences, of ESAGs in the non-transcribed region upstream of the M-ESs suggests that M-ESs arose from B-ESs. This seems plausible if we accept that trypanosomes initially had a protective surface coat which then became adapted for antigenic variation, with the significant advantage to the parasite of prolonged growth in the face of antibody responses. Expression of a mixed set of VSGs by the metacyclic stage can then be viewed as a more recent adaptation, arising from a need for this population to break through existing humoral immunity in new hosts already immune to many VSGs [9]. If so, then the B-ES would have evolved to the M-ES, with important changes including moving to monocistronic transcription, life-cycle stage transcriptional switching and uncoupling of strict coexpression of a single set of ESAGs.

Are these differences of functional significance ? Possibly. One consequence of the monocistronic organization is that the promoter is very close to the end of the chromosome and clearly a candidate for telomere silencing. The ends of linear chromosomes in eukaryotes require binding of a number of silencing proteins for physical stability [47]. One other effect of binding, at least in yeast, is that closely adjacent promoters become silenced reversibly and clonally. It would be highly unusual if trypanosomes did not have such a fundamental stability mechanism, and they do have telomere-binding proteins [48, 49]. It has been proposed that a promoter silencing effect could be associated with regulation of trypanosome B-ES promoters [37, 38], but that effect would have to be exerted over a much longer distance than measured in yeast, where silencing extends merely 3–16 kb from the telomeric tract of DNA repeats, the length range depending in part on the presence of sub-telomeric sequences [50]. Artificial overexpression of the yeast SIR3 protein, which has a critical role in silencing, extends the effect merely up to 20 kb from the tract [50, 51]. It seems clear that M-ES promoters, located about 5 kb from the telomere tract, are candidates for telomere silencing [30], while the B-ES promoters, at approximately ten times that distance, require at least a modified effect. One intriguing possibility with M-ES promoters is that a telomere position effect may have been recruited to help achieve accurate regulation, simply because there is a general lack of promoter switch mechanisms in the trypanosome. In this hypothesis, the monocistronic structure of the M-ES and the brevity of the 70 bp region would ensure that the promoter is appropriately close to the telomere tract.

One major difference between the two types of ES is the number of 70 bp repeat units. We believe this is of functional significance. In mammals, the 1.22 gene is duplicated frequently into B-ESs, in every case the upstream limit of duplication mapping to the single 70 bp unit flanking this gene [27]. Despite this ability to move, the 1.22 (also known as 7.1) gene is very stable, having remained steadfastly within the M-VSG repertoire for many years in the field [13], suggesting it is not an efficient recipient in gene conversion. The indications are, therefore, that the number of repeat units can dictate, in an inverse relationship, the ability of a locus to act as a donor in gene conversion. Possession of the minimum number of repeat units by the M-ES would then ensure that the two types of ES, and their regulation mechanisms, remain distinct.

Uncoupling of the physical linkage between ESAGs and the expressed VSG gene releases the metacyclic cell from the strictly monoallelic ESAG expression that occurs as a consequence of the transcription of only single B-ESs in bloodstream trypanosomes. As at least some ESAG products are essential in the bloodstream, there is a reasonable likelihood that metacyclic cells require their expression as a prerequisite for infectivity. It is therefore not surprising that ESAG stable transcripts are readily detected in trypanosomes early in fly-transmitted infection, when M-ESs are being transcribed [52]. In fact, their level is greater than in bloodstream trypanosomes expressing B-ESs. It has been proposed by Borst and colleagues [53] that the range of allelic forms of ESAG products expressible by bloodstream trypanosomes may exist to cope with the parasite's host range, each isoform being optimum within a particular host species. Elevated ESAG expression in the metacyclic cell may be a consequence of simultaneous expression of several isoforms of each ESAG, increasing its chances of infecting the unknown host species it enters. It will be interesting to determine the contribution of ESAGs in B-ESs and elsewhere in the genome to the abundant transcripts detected following tsetse fly transmission; at least some are α-amanitin resistant, indicating provenance from B-ESs [52].

Acknowledgements

We are grateful to the Wellcome Trust and the Medical Research Council for research and personal funding and the M and D foundation for funding KK. Thanks to R. McCulloch for critical reading of the manuscript. JDB is a Wellcome Trust Senior Lecturer.

R E F E R E N C E S

[1] Roditi I., Schwarz H., Pearson T.W., Beecroft R.P., Liu M.K., Richardson J.P., Buhring H.J., Pleiss J., Bulow R., Williams R.O., Overath P. Procyclin gene expression and loss of the variant surface glycoprotein during differentiation of *Trypanosoma brucei*. J Cell Biol; 108; 1989; 737-746.

[2] Vickerman K. On the surface coat and flagellar adhesion in trypanosomes. J Cell Sci; 5; 1969; 163-194.

[3] Tetley L., Turner C.M.R., Barry J.D., Crowe J.S., Vickerman K. Onset of expression of the variant surface glycoproteins of *Trypanosoma brucei* in the tsetse fly studied using immunoelectron microscopy. J Cell Sci; 87; 1987; 363-372.

[4] Barry JD. The biology of antigenic variation in African trypanosomes. In : Hide G, Mottram JC, Coombs GH, Holmes PH, editors. Trypanosomiasis and Leishmaniasis : Biology and Control. Oxford : CAB International, 1997 : 89–107.

[5] Borst P., Rudenko G., Taylor M.C., Blundell P.A., van Leeuwen F., Bitter W., Cross M., McCulloch R. Antigenic variation in trypanosomes. Arch Med Res; 27; 1996; 379-388.

[6] Cross G.A.M. Antigenic variation in trypanosomes-secrets surface slowly. Bioessays; 18; 1996; 283-291.

[7] Turner C.M.R., Barry J.D. High frequency of antigenic variation in *Trypanosoma brucei rhodesiense* infections. Parasitology; 99; 1989; 67-75.

[8] Barry J.D. The relative significance of mechanisms of antigenic variation in African trypanosomes. Parasitol Today; 13; 1997; 212-218.

[9] Barry J.D., Graham S.V., Matthews K.R., Shiels P.G., Shonekan O.A. Stage specific mechanisms for activation and expression of variant surface glycoprotein genes in *Trypanosoma brucei*. Biochem Soc Trans; 18; 1990; 708-710.

[10] Esser K.M., Schoenbechler M.J., Gingrich J.B. *Trypanosoma rhodesiense* blood forms express all antigen specificities relevant to protection against metacyclic (insect form) challenge. J Immunol; 129; 1982; 1715-1718.

[11] Turner C.M.R., Barry J.D., Maudlin I., Vickerman K. An estimate of the size of the metacyclic variable antigen repertoire of *Trypanosoma brucei rhodesiense*. Parasitology; 97; 1988; 269-276.

[12] Hajduk S.L., Cameron C.R., Barry J.D., Vickerman K. Antigenic variation in cyclically transmitted *Trypanosoma brucei*. Variable antigen type composition of metacyclic trypanosome populations from the salivary glands of *Glossina morsitans*. Parasitology; 83; 1981; 595-607.

[13] Barry J.D., Crowe J.S., Vickerman K. Instability of the *Trypanosoma brucei rhodesiense* metacyclic variable antigen repertoire. Nature; 306; 1983; 699-701.

[14] Capbem A., Giroud C., Baltz T., Mattern P. *Trypanosoma equiperdum :* Etude des variations antigeniques au cours de la trypanosomose experimentale du lapin. Exp Parasitol; 42; 1977; 6-13.

[15] Barry J.D. Antigenic variation during *Trypanosoma vivax* infections of different host species. Parasitology; 92; 1986; 51-65.

[16] Miller E.N., Turner M.J. Analysis of antigenic types appearing in first relapse populations of clones of *Trypanosoma brucei*. Parasitology; 82; 1981; 63-80.

[17] Hajduk S.L., Vickerman K. Antigenic variation in cyclically transmitted *Trypanosoma brucei*-variable antigen type composition of the first parasitemia in mice bitten by trypanosome-infected *Glossina morsitans*. Parasitology; 83; 1981; 609-621.

[18] Turner C.M.R., Barry J.D., Vickerman K. Independent expression of the metacyclic and bloodstream variable antigen repertoires of *Trypanosoma brucei rhodesiense*. Parasitology; 92; 1986; 67-73.

[19] Barry J.D., Hajduk S.L., Vickerman K., Le Ray D. Detection of multiple variable antigen types in metacyclic populations of *Trypanosoma brucei*. Trans R Soc Trop Med Hyg; 73; 1979; 205-208.

[20] Barry J.D., Emery D.L. Parasite development and host responses during the establishment of *Trypanosoma brucei* infection transmitted by tsetse fly. Parasitology; 88; 1984; 67-84.

[21] Lenardo M.J., Rice-Ficht A.C., Kelly G., Esser K.M., Donelson J.E. Characterization of the genes specifying two metacyclic variable antigen types in *Trypanosoma brucei rhodesiense*. Proc Natl Acad Sci USA; 81; 1984; 6642-6646.

[22] Cornelissen A.W.C.A., Bakkeren G.A.M., Barry J.D., Michels P.A.M., Borst P. Characteristics of trypanosome variant antigen genes active in the tsetse fly. Nucleic Acids Res; 13; 1985; 4661-4676.

[23] Pays E., Vanhamme L., Berberof M. Genetic controls for the expression of surface antigens in African trypanosomes. Annu Rev Microbiol; 48; 1994; 25-52.

[24] Horn D., Cross G.A.M. Analysis of *Trypanosoma brucei* VSG expression site switching in vitro. Mol Biochem Parasitol; 84; 1997; 189-201.

[25] Lenardo M.J., Esser K.M., Moon A.M., Vanderploeg L.H.T., Donelson J.E. Metacyclic variant surface glycoprotein genes of *Trypanosoma brucei* subsp *rhodesiense* are activated in situ, and their expression is transcriptionally regulated. Mol Cell Biol; 6; 1986; 1991-1997.

[26] Graham S.V., Matthews K.R., Shiels P.G., Barry J.D. Distinct, developmental stage-specific activation mechanisms of trypanosome VSG genes. Parasitology; 101; 1990; 361-367.

[27] Matthews K.R., Shiels P.G., Graham S.V., Cowan C., Barry J.D. Duplicative activation mechanisms of two trypanosome telomeric VSG genes with structurally simple 5' flanks. Nucleic Acids Res; 18; 1990; 7219-7227.

[28] Lu Y., Alarcon C.M., Hall T., Reddy L.V., Donelson J.E. A strand bias occurs in point mutations associated with variant surface glycoprotein gene conversion in *Trypanosoma rhodesiense*. Mol Cell Biol; 14; 1994; 3971-3980.

[29] Alarcon C.M., Son H.J., Hall T., Donelson J.E. A monocistronic transcript for a trypanosome variant surface glycoprotein. Mol Cell Biol; 14; 1994; 5579-5591.

[30] Graham S.V., Barry J.D. Transcriptional regulation of metacyclic variant surface glycoprotein gene expression during the life cycle of *Trypanosoma brucei*. Mol Cell Biol; 15; 1995; 59455956.

[31] Nakaar V., Tschudi C., Ullu E. An unusual liaison-small nuclear and cytoplasmic RNA genes team up with transfer RNA genes in trypanosomatid protozoa. Parasitol Today; 11; 1995; 225228.

[32] Roditi I. The VSG-procyclin switch. Parasitol Today; 12; 1996; 47-49.

[33] Clayton C., Hotz H.R. Post-transcriptional control of PARP gene expression. Mol Biochem Parasitol; 77; 1996; 1-6.

[34] Steverding D., Stierhof Y.D., Fuchs H., Tauber R., Overath P. Transferrin-binding protein complex is the receptor for transferrin uptake in *Trypanosoma brucei*. J Cell Biol; 131; 1995; 1173-1182.

[35] Nagoshi Y.L., Alarcon C.M., Donelson J.E. The putative promoter for a metacyclic VSG gene in African trypanosomes. Mol Biochem Parasitol; 72; 1995; 33-45.

[36] Vanhamme L., Pays A., Tebabi P., Alexandre S., Pays E. Specific binding of proteins to the non-coding strand of a crucial element of the variant surface glycoprotein, procyclin, and ribosomal promoters of *Trypanosoma brucei*. Mol Cell Biol; 15; 1995; 5598-5606.

[37] Horn D., Cross G.A.M. A developmentally-regulated position effect at a telomeric locus in *Trypanosoma brucei*. Cell; 83; 1995; 555-561.

[38] Rudenko G., Blundell P.A., Dirksmulder A., Kieft R., Borst P. A ribosomal DNA promoter replacing the promoter of a telomeric VSG gene expression site can be efficiently switched on and off in *Trypanosoma brucei*. Cell; 83; 1995; 547-553.

[39] Matthews K.R., Shiels P.G., Graham S.V., Cowan C., Barry J.D. Duplicative activation mechanisms of two trypanosome telomeric VSG genes with structurally simple 5' flanks. Nucleic Acids Res; 18; 1990; 7219-7227.

[40] Borst P., Van der Ploeg M., Van Hoek J.F.M., Tas J., James J. On the DNA content and ploidy of trypanosomes. Mol Biochem Parasitol; 6; 1982; 13-23.

[41] Tait A., Turner C.M.R., Le Page R.W.F., Wells J.M. Genetic evidence that metacyclic forms of *Trypanosoma brucei* are diploid. Mol Biochem Parasitol; 37; 1989; 247-255.

[42] Kimmel B.E., Olemoiyoi O., Young J.R. Ingi, a 5.2 kb dispersed sequence element from *Trypanosoma brucei* that carries half of a smaller mobile element at either end and has homology with mammalian LINEs. Mol Cell Biol; 7; 1987; 1465-1475.

[43] Murphy N.B., Pays A., Tebabi P., Coquelet H., Guyaux M., Steinert M., Pays E. *Trypanosoma brucei* repeated element

with unusual structural and transcriptional properties. J Mol Biol; 195; 1987; 855-871.

[44] Cully D.F., Ip H.S., Cross G.A.M. Coordinate transcription of variant surface glycoprotein genes and an expression site associated gene family in *Trypanosoma brucei*. Cell; 42; 1985; 173-182.

[45] Morgan R.W., El-Sayed N.M.A., Kepa J.K., Pedram M., Donelson J.E. Differential expression of the expression site associated gene I family in African trypanosomes. J Biol Chem; 271; 1996; 9771-9777.

[46] Graham S.V., Matthews K.R., Barry J.D. *Trypanosoma brucei*. Unusual expression-site-associated gene homologies in a metacyclic VSG gene expression site. Exp Parasitol; 76; 1993; 96-99.

[47] Zakian V.A. Structure, function, and replication of *Saccharomyces cerevisiae* telomeres. Annu Rev Genet; 30; 1996; 141-172.

[48] Eid J.E., Sollner-Webb B. St-l, a 39-kilodalton protein in *Trypanosoma brucei*, exhibits a dual affinity for the duplex form of the 29-base-pair sub-telomeric repeat and its C-rich strand. Mol Cell Biol; 15; 1995; 389-397.

[49] Field H., Field M.C. *Leptomonas seymouri, Trypanosoma brucei* — a method for isolating trypanosomatid nuclear factors which bind *Trypanosoma brucei* single stranded G-rich telomere sequence. Exp Parasitol; 83; 1996; 155-158.

[50] Renauld H., Aparicio O.M., Zierath P.D., Billington B.L., Chhablani S.K., Gottschling D.E. Silent domains are assembled continuously from the telomere and are defined by promoter distance and strength, and by SIR3 dosage. Genes Dev; 7; 1993; 1133-1145.

[51] Strahl-Bolsinger S., Hecht A., Luo K.H., Grunstein M. SIR2 and SIR4 interactions differ in core and extended telomeric heterochromatin in yeast. Genes Dev; 11; 1997; 83-93.

[52] Graham S.V., Barry J.D. Expression site-associated genes transcribed independently of variant surface glycoprotein genes in *Trypanosoma brucei*. Mol Biochem Parasitol; 47; 1991; 31-41.

[53] Borst P, Bitter W, Blundell PA, Cross M, McCulloch R, Rudenko G, Taylor MC, van Leeuwen F. The expression sites for variant surface glycoproteins of *Trypanosoma brucei*. In : Hide G, Mottram JC, Coombs GH, Holmes PH, editors. Trypanosomiasis and Leishmaniasis : Biology and Control. Oxford : CAB International, 1997 : l09–131.

7

Controls of the expression of the Vsg in *Trypanosoma brucei* [1]

Luc Vanhamme,
Etienne Pays

Laboratory of Molecular Parasitology, Department of Molecular Biology, Free University of Brussels, 67 rue des chevaux, 1640 Rhode St. Genèse, Belgium

Abstract

We present an overview of the regulation of *vsg* expression, focusing on initiation and elongation of transcription as well as processing and stabilization of the transcripts. We propose a model where common factors are involved in the reverse controls of the genes for the two main stage-specific antigens, the Vsg and procyclin: a cross-talk between the two transcription units would allow a fast rerouting of limiting factors at differentiation, thereby allowing the expression of only one type of antigen at a time. A similar mechanism would ensure that only one *vsg* ES is fully expressed at a time in bloodstream forms. © 1998 Francqui Foundation. Published by Elsevier Science B.V. All rights reserved.

Keywords: *vsg* expression; *Trypanosoma brucei*; Procyclin; Antigens

1 • Introduction

During their life-cycle African trypanosomes are continuously covered with a uniform surface coat consisting entirely of one major species of protein, procyclin during the procyclic stage and the variant surface glycoprotein, or Vsg, during both the metacyclic stage in the fly salivary glands and the bloodstream stage in the mammal. The expression of procyclin and Vsg is mutually exclusive, except for short periods at the transition between successive stages. Whereas the role of procyclin is unclear, it has been known for two decades that the Vsg is the principal means by which trypanosomes escape the immune reaction of their host. Through regular changing of the Vsg the parasite exhausts the immune system which is continuously condemned to react to new surface determinants. The genetic basis of this antigenic variation involves the switching of the gene cod-

1. Abbreviations: ES, expression site; esag, expression site-associated gene; Vsg (vsg), variant surface glycoprotein (gene).

ing for the Vsg (see the paper by Pays and Nolan in this issue). Thus, the expression of the Vsg is subjected to a double level of control : it is regulated throughout the life-cycle and, once the decision to turn on Vsg expression is taken, populations expressing different Vsgs succeed each other during the infection. While different aspects of the controls involved in antigenic variation are discussed in depth in other papers of this issue, this review will focus on the mechanisms underlying the stage-specificity and abundance of the Vsg.

2 • The Vsg : a differentiation marker

The regulation of Vsg expression has been extensively studied, not only because this protein is the basis of antigenic variation, but also because it represents an ideal differentiation marker, due to its strict stage-specificity combined with a very high level of expression.

2.1 The *vsg* promoter, the *vsg* polymerase

In the bloodstream form, the synthesis of the *vsg* mRNA must be very efficient, since transcription of this single gene accounts for as much as 10% of the total polyadenylated mRNA of the cell. Probably related to this special requirement, the RNA polymerase at work on the *vsg* exhibits unusual properties. For example, it resembles the ribosomal polymerase (pol I) by its resistance to the drug α-amanitin [1, 2] and to the detergent sarkosyl [3] and by the high rate of primary transcription as measured in run-on transcription assays [4]. On the other hand, its requirement for divalent cations (Mg^{2+} and Mn^{2+}) is consistent with a type II RNA polymerase [5, 6], and, moreover, nascent *vsg* transcripts are not localized in the nucleolus, the usual place for transcripts by pol I (see the paper by P. Borst in this issue). Therefore, the *vsg* polymerase shares properties with both RNA polymerases I and II. The possibility of a mix between polymerase I and II subunits seems to be unlikely, since in other eukaryotes the catalytic domain and the region determining α-amanitin sensitivity of RNA polymerase II are contained in the same subunit of the enzyme [7].

The transcription unit of the *vsg* is a 45–60-kb sequence located in a telomeric expression site (ES) (see other papers in this issue). The start site was mapped using UV irradiation which greatly enhances the level of detectable nascent transcripts in the region of the promoter [8–10]. Deletional analysis showed that the last 70-bp preceding the transcription start site are sufficient to ensure maximal activity as monitored by transient expression assays of a reporter gene [11, 12]. In two parallel studies this 70-bp region was analyzed by mutagenesis [13, 14]. Both groups agreed on the importance of

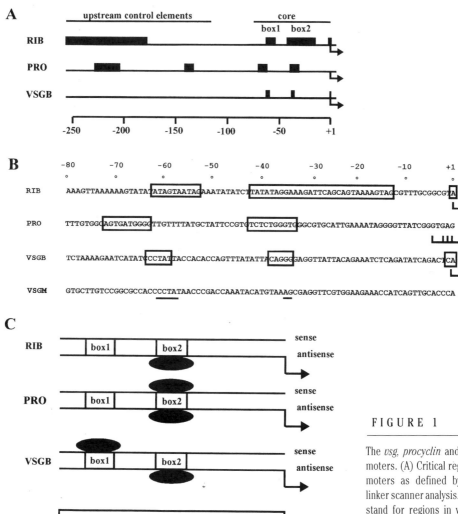

two short stretches around positions − 60 and − 37 (that we termed box 1 and box 2). Insertional and deletional analysis also showed that a correct spacing between boxes 1 and 2 was critical for promoter activity. These characteristics are reminiscent of ribosomal core promoters and, indeed, a linker scanner analysis of the trypanosome ribosomal promoter pointed to two important sequences at positions similar to boxes 1 and 2, in addition to an upstream control element not present in the *vsg* promoter [11]. Interestingly, the procyclin promoter appeared to be similar to both the ribosomal and *vsg* promoters [15, 16] (see Fig. 1 for a summary).

FIGURE 1

The *vsg, procyclin* and ribosomal promoters. (A) Critical regions of the promoters as defined by mutational or linker scanner analysis. The black boxes stand for regions in which the mutations drastically decrease the promoter activity [11, 13, 15, 16]. Arrows indicate the transcription start sites at position +1. (B) Sequences of the *vsg*, ribosomal and *procyclin* core promoters. Boxed sequences represent the regions in which mutations drastically decrease the promoter activity [11, 13, 15, 16]. Underlined sequences are regions homologous to boxes 1 and 2 in a metacyclic *vsg* promoter [13]. (C) Summary of what is known about common factors binding to the *vsg*, ribosomal and *procyclin* promoters. The black ellipse represents a single-stranded DNA binding factor (see text for details).

Thus, the *vsg* promoter looks like the core of the ribosomal and *procyclin* promoters, although there is no extensive sequence homology. Could it be that parts of these promoters are functionally equivalent ? The fact that chimeric promoters in which the second half of the *vsg* promoter is replaced by the equivalent region of the ribosomal core promoter are perfectly functional [13], seems to support this view. In addition, similar chimeras between the *procyclin* and the ribosomal promoter were also found to be functional [17], and in situ the *vsg* promoter can be replaced by a ribosomal promoter without affecting the transcriptional control of the ES [18].

If parts of these promoters are exchangeable, do they also share common transcription factors ? We addressed this question by performing bandshift assay and UV crosslinking studies [13]. The results suggested that the same protein of ~40 kDa binds to the noncoding strand of the second half of the *vsg* promoter and the *procyclin* and ribosomal core promoters. Interestingly, the same protein also appeared to bind to the sense strand of box 1 of the *vsg* promoter (M. Berberof, L. Vanhamme, P. Tebabi and E. Pays, unpublished data), as well as to the sense strand of box 2 of the *procyclin* promoter [13], albeit with a lower affinity (these data are summarized in Fig. 1C). An extensive mutational analysis revealed that the minimal sequence required for binding in boxes 1 and 2 of the *vsg* promoter was 5'-TCCCTAT-3' and 5'-CCCCTGT-3', respectively, and that the 1st, 6th and 7th bases can be mutated leading to a consensus of 5'-XCCCTXX-3' (Berberof et al., unpublished). Sequences roughly fitting this consensus can be found in the second half of the *procyclin* (CCCCTAT) and ribosomal (GGCCTAT) core promoters.

Several metacyclic *vsg* promoters have been characterized recently [13, 19, 20]. These promoters are located between 2 and 3-kb upstream of the *vsg*, and drive α-amanitin resistant transcription. The limited data available at present suggest that they also contain boxes 1 and/or 2 [13].

Taken together, these data suggest that the transcription promoters for the major stage-specific antigens share at least some common factors. In support of this conclusion, a reduction of ongoing transcription in the *vsg* ES has been observed in transgenic trypanosomes where huge numbers of *procyclin* promoters have been integrated [21]. The factors shared between the *vsg* and *procyclin* promoters may be borrowed from the rDNA promoters to ensure high processivity and meet the requirement for a high expression. However, the *vsg* promoter differs from the two others by the absence of upstream control elements. The *vsg* promoter could contain only the minimal elements necessary for the recruitment of the transcription machinery while a different mechanism may be involved in regulating the accessibility of chromatin and, consequently, in deciding to turn expression on or off. This hypothesis is consistent with the observation that the activity of the *vsg* promoter depends on the site where it is experimentally integrated in the genome [22–24]. In particular, it can be activated if placed adjacent to a *procyclin* promoter [25, 26]. This effect is independent of the orientation, and the sequences responsible for this effect have been located in the upstream region of the *procyclin* promoter. Thus, the upstream control elements of the *procyclin* and ribosomal promoters could behave as enhancers for heterologous promoters by allowing a better access to DNA in chromatin.

2.2   Initiation and elongation of transcription

In most reported cases, eukaryotes regulate the expression of genes at the level of transcription initiation. Thus, the report that in transient expression assays of episomal constructs the *procyclin* and *vsg* promoters were able to drive transcription of a reporter gene in both procyclic and bloodstream forms [12] came as a surprise. This finding suggests that the two major developmental forms of the parasite contain all the machinery necessary for transcription of both stage specific antigens. Furthermore, run-on transcription assays indicated that these two promoters are also active during both stages in situ [4]. The level of nascent transcripts from the *vsg* promoter region was found to be roughly the same during both stages, while the level of transcription in the region of the *procyclin* promoter in the bloodstream form was ~10–20% of that in the procyclic form [4]. How then, is it possible that transcripts of the *vsg* and *procyclin* genes are undetectable at the procyclic and bloodstream stages, respectively ? A solution to this question was provided by results from run-on assays, conducted in nuclei from pleomorphic bloodstream forms before and after the induction of differentiation into procyclic forms [27] (L. Vanhamme and E. Pays, unpublished results). As differentiation was induced, the amount of nascent transcripts from the *vsg* ES decreased, and this decrease was amplified as the distance from the promoter increases. The *procyclin* transcription units behaved in the contrary fashion : when differentiation was triggered, the amount of transcripts was increased and the increase was amplified with the distance from the promoter. The same results were obtained with a *procyclin* transcription unit tagged with reporter sequences. The best explanation of this data is a reverse control of transcription elongation in the two transcription units (Fig. 2).

As soon as differentiation from bloodstream to procyclic forms is triggered, a brake is imposed on RNA elongation in the *vsg*

FIGURE 2

Initiation and elongation of transcription in the *procyclin* transcription unit and the *vsg* ESs. A B C D E stand for five different *vsg* ESs. The *procyclin* transcription unit drawn is from the *parp A* locus. V: *vsg* gene; α: *procyclin* α gene; β: *procyclin* β; gene; G: *gresag* 2.1 gene; P: *procyclin*-associated gene. The arrows and black ellipses represent transcription start sites and RNA polymerase, respectively. Bold lines represent the DNA, with terminal dots for the telomeric repeats in the case of the *vsg* ESs. Waved lines represent the extent of transcription (nascent RNA). See text for details.

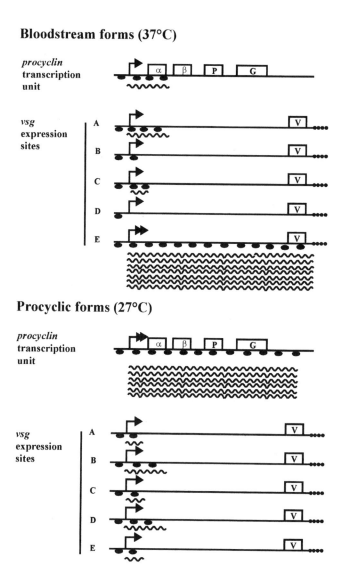

Bloodstream forms (37°C)

Procyclic forms (27°C)

ES while at the same time RNA elongation is stimulated in the *procyclin* transcription units.

These results raise yet another question : are all the *vsg* ESs subjected to this regulation of transcription elongation ? To address this question RT-PCR was performed on transcripts from the beginning of the *vsg* ES using primers specific for regions that are conserved between the known ESs [28] (L. Vanhamme and E. Pays, unpublished results). These reactions amplified a heterogeneous population of products in procyclic forms, suggesting that during this stage transcription is initiated on all the ESs. In bloodstream forms, the major part of the population of PCR products was amplified from the active ES while 5% of the products were amplified from other ESs, indicating that while the vast majority of transcription occurs in the active ES, initiation also occurs in other sites.

The combination of these data is best accounted for by the model presented in Fig. 2. Both in *procyclin* transcription units and in all *vsg* bloodstream ESs, part or all of the initiation transcription (recruitement of the transcription machinery at the promoter and promoter clearance) happens constitutively during all parasitic stages. Transcription elongation, however, is controlled in a stage-specific way, i.e. it occurs only in the transcription unit of the stage-specific antigen. Furthermore, in the bloodstream form, elongation fully proceeds in only one ES at a time and is abortive in all the other ESs. This phenomenon is likely due to a difference of chromatin structure between the active and inactive ESs. This model is supported by the recent observation that drug-resistance can be conferred to trypanosomes following the targeting of drug-resistance genes close to the promoter of silent ESs [29].

2.3 Post-transcriptional controls

In trypanosomes most genes are organized in polycistronic transcription units, although genes depending on the same promoter can be differentially regulated [30]. This is indeed the case in the *vsg* ES where there are drastic differences in the levels of expression of the *esag*s and the *vsg*. This implies that in trypanosomes, postranscriptional controls play an important role in the regulation of gene expression in general, and in the *vsg* ES in particular.

In transient activity assays, the 3' untranslated region (3'-UTR) of the *vsg* mRNA was found to influence the expression of a reporter gene in a stage-specific way (upregulation in bloodstream forms and downregulation in procyclic forms) [31]. These results were confirmed using stable transformants where a Cat reporter gene flanked or not with the *vsg* 3'-UTR was integrated in the *tubulin* locus. In these transformants, the 3'-UTR was shown to influence the steady state levels of Cat mRNA, but by different mechanisms in the two developmental forms. In bloodstream forms the presence of the 3'-UTR stabilized the mRNA, but this was not observed in procyclic forms. Since the 3'-UTR was without influence on the rate of transcription, RNA maturation (namely transsplicing and polyadenylation) was left as the only level where the UTR can exert its negative action in this last case [31]. Alteration of RNA processing could be a general mechanism to interfere with the expression of stage-specific genes (and in particular *esag*s), since the rare *esag* 6 and 7 mRNAs that are detected in procyclic forms show aberrant processing [32, 33] (Fig.3).

In other eukaryotes, stabilization (or destabilization) of mRNAs often involves interaction with proteins, and specifically, with short lived proteins in the case of strongly regulated messengers. The following result suggests that this is also true in trypanosomes, in particular for *vsg* and *esag* mRNAs. When bloodstream forms are treated with inhibitors of protein synthesis, Northern blot analysis showed a rapid decrease in the amount of steady state mRNAs encoding the Vsg and some Esags, and a combined treatment with actinomycin D and pulse-chase analysis allowed the demonstration that this effect was due to destabilization of the mRNAs [34] (L. Vanhamme, S. Postiaux and E. Pays, unpublished data).

That the 3'-UTR of the *vsg* mRNA plays a role in a parasitic stage where it is not normally present poses a paradox. This paradox was resolved by an experiment where transgenic bloodstream

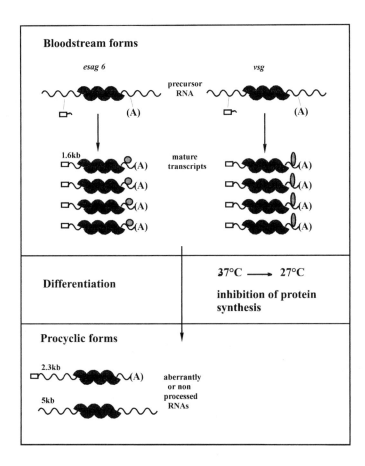

FIGURE 3

The posttranscriptional control of *vsg* and *esag* 6 expression. The waved lines represent transcripts, with the thicker section designating the open reading frame. The open rectangle represents the miniexon and the grey circles and ellipses represent labile stabilizing protein factors. See text for details.

trypanosomes expressing the *cat* gene followed or not by the 3'-UTR of the *vsg* mRNA were induced to differentiate into procyclic forms. As soon as differentiation was triggered, a strong inhibition of reporter gene expression was observed in the transformants containing the 3'-UTR [31]. This result suggested that the 3'-UTR is involved in the rapid disappearance of the *vsg* mRNA during the differentiation from the bloodstream to the procyclic form.

Finally, we tried to delineate the regions of the 3'-UTR which are responsible for its action. This 3'-UTR is very short (70 nt) and comprises two obvious features, a polypyrimidine tract of 20 nt and two stretches (8- and 16-mer) which are conserved in all the *vsg* mRNAs sequenced to date. Deletional analyses suggested that both the polypyrimidine tract and the conserved elements are involved in the regulatory action of the 3'-UTR. More unexpectedly, the end of the *vsg* open reading frame was found to be a necessary element of the polypyrimidine tract [31].

The above data fit the model presented in Fig. 3.

In bloodstream forms the 3'-UTR of the *vsg* mRNA is involved in the stabilization of the RNA, which occurs at least partly through an interaction with labile factors. The same or different factors also stabilize some *esag* mRNAs (L. Vanhamme, S. Postiaux and E. Pays, unpublished data). As soon as differentiation to procyclic forms is triggered, the combination of cold shock and inhibition of protein synthesis [35] promotes the rapid loss of these stabilizing factors and, therefore, induces a relative destabilization of the mRNAs. In addition, the 3'-UTR interferes with efficient maturation of the *vsg* mRNA. Such an effect also happens in other bloodstream-specific mRNAs such as those of certain *esag*s [32, 33].

2.4   Translation and protein modification

As opposed to the case of procyclin, there is no evidence that the translation of the *vsg* mRNA is regulated. Rather the following data suggest that there is no major stage-specific control of translation. A Vsg gene devoid of its 3'-UTR was placed under the control of a *procyclin* promoter and expressed in procyclic forms. Efficient synthesis and surface presentation of this Vsg were detected in these cells, indicating that the Vsg can be correctly processed in procyclic forms. However, the presence of some incomplete molecules may reflect possible levels of interference [36].

3 • Conclusion

The genetic mechanisms involved in antigenic variation of African trypanosomes have been the subject of intense research during the last 15 years. They are now relatively well documented, but several processes, such as the in situ (in)activation of ESs, are still not understood. One fact that is totally clear is the reduced hope for a vaccine based on the Vsg molecule. However, a trypanosome unable to perform antigenic variation would likely be disabled in front of the immune system. One way to prevent antigenic variation would be to interfere with the expression machinery. This machinery has yet to be characterized, and none of the factors involved in its control have been identified to date.

The concomitant study of the controls involved in *procyclin* and *vsg* expression allowed us to propose the following hypothesis. Common factors could be involved in the mutually exclusive expression of these two antigens through differential use on alternate genomic sites at different moments of the parasitic cycle. Indeed, at least part of the *vsg* and *procyclin* promoters are functionally interchangeable, and these promoters appear to bind common factors. However, transcription fully proceeds on each of them at only one stage of the parasitic cycle. Therefore, a common set of transcription factors could be exchanged between them at each transition between different stages of the parasitic cycle. This view is further supported by the reversed profile of elongation observed on the *procyclin* and *vsg* transcription units during differentiation from the bloodstream to the procyclic form. A similar mutually exclusive use of factors may also occur in bloodstream forms between the different *vsg* ESs, to ensure rapid expression of alternative transcription units upon switching of ESs.

The same kind of phenomenon could also be envisaged for RNA binding factors. Indeed, the *vsg* and *procyclin* mRNA levels are inversely regulated during differentiation from the bloodstream to the procyclic form, or in the presence of inhibitors of protein synthesis. Moreover, the respective 3'-UTRs of these mRNAs have opposite actions on the expression of a reporter gene at different stages of the parasitic cycle.

In summary, a cross-talk between the *procyclin* and *vsg* transcription units but also between the different *vsg* ESs would ensure that only one of them is fully transcribed at any moment. Abortive engagement of RNA polymerase on promoters of most, if not all, transcription units that are not expressed would allow fast rerouting of the transcription machinery from the active unit to another, as soon as environmental changes require it.

Acknowledgements

The work in our laboratory was financed by the Belgian FRSM and FRC-IM, a research contract with the Communaute Française de Belgique (ARC), the Interuniversity Poles of Attraction Programme — Belgian State, Prime Minister's Office-Federal Office for Scientific, Technical and Cultural Affairs, and by the Agreement for Collaborative Research between ILRAD (Nairobi) and Belgian Research Centres. E.P. thanks the Francqui Foundation (Brussels) for helpful support. L.V. is Research Associate of the Belgian National Fund for Scientific Research.

REFERENCES

[1] Kooter J.M., Borst P. α-Amanitin-insensitive transcription of variant surface glycoprotein genes provides further evidence for discontinuous transcription in trypanosomes. Nucl Acids Res; 12; 1984; 9457-9472.

[2] Rudenko G., Bishop D., Gottesdiener K., Van der Ploeg L.H.T. Alpha-amanitin resistant transcription of protein coding genes in insect and bloodstream form *Trypanosoma brucei*. EMBO J; 8; 1989; 4259-4263.

[3] Rudenko G., Lee M.S.G., Van der Ploeg L.H.T. The PARP and VSG genes of *Trypanosoma brucei* do not resemble RNA polymerase II transcription units in sensitivity to the addition of sarkosyl in nuclear run-on assays. Nucl Acids Res; 20; 1991; 303-306.

[4] Pays E., Coquelet H., Tebabi P., Pays A., Jefferies D., Steinert M., Koenig E., Williams R.O., Roditi I. *Trypanosoma brucei*: constitutive activity of the VSG and *procyclin* promoters. EMBO J; 9; 1990; 3145-3151.

[5] Grondal E.J.M., Evers R., Kosubek K., Cornelissen A.W.C.A. Characterization of the RNA polymerases of *Trypanosoma brucei*: trypanosomal mRNAs are composed of transcripts derived from both RNA polymerase II and III. EMBO J; 8; 1989; 3383-3389.

[6] Pays E., Vanhamme L., Berberof M. Genetic controls for the expression of surface antigens in african trypanosomes. Annu Rev Microbiol; 48; 1994; 25-52.

[7] Archambault J., Friesen J.D. Genetics of the RNA polymerases I, II, and III. Microbiol Rev; 57; 1993; 703-724.

[8] Pays E., Tebabi P., Pays A., Coquelet H., Revelard P., Salmon D., Steinert M. The genes and transcripts of an antigen expression site from *Trypanosoma brucei*. Cell; 57; 1989; 835-845.

[9] Gottesdiener K., Chung H.M., Brown S.D., Lee M.G.S., Van der Ploeg L.H.T. Characterization of VSG gene expression site promoters and promoter-associated DNA rearrangement events. Mol Cell Biol; 11; 1991; 2467-2480.

[10] Zomerdijk J.C.B.M., Ouellette M., ten Asbroek A.L.M.A., Kieft R., Bommer A.M.M., Clayton C., Borst P. The promoter for a variant surface glycoprotein gene expression site in *Trypanosoma brucei*. EMBO J; 9; 1990; 2791-2801.

[11] Zomerdijk J.C.B.M., Kieft R., Shiels P.G., Borst P. Alpha-amanitin-resistant transcription units in trypanosomes: a comparison of promoter sequences for a VSG gene expression site and for the ribosomal RNA genes. Nucl Acids Res; 19; 1991; 5153-5158.

[12] Jefferies D., Tebabi P., Pays E. Transient activity assays of the *Trypanosoma brucei* VSG gene promoter: control of gene expression at the post-transcriptional level. Mol Cell Biol; 13; 1991; 338-343.

[13] Vanhamme L., Pays A., Tebabi P., Alexandre S., Pays E. Specific binding of proteins to the noncoding strand of a crucial element of the variant surface glycoprotein, procyclin, and ribosomal promoters of *Trypanosoma brucei*. Mol Cell Biol; 15; 1995; 5598-5606.

[14] Pham V.P., Qi C.C., Gottesdiener K.M. A detailed mutational analysis of the VSG gene expression site promoter. Mol Biochem Parasitol; 75; 1996; 241-254.

[15] Sherman D.R., Janz L., Hug M., Clayton C. Anatomy of the PARP promoter of *Trypanosoma brucei*. EMBO J; 10; 1991; 3379-3386.

[16] Brown S.D., Huang J., Van der Ploeg L.H.T. The promoter for the procyclic acidic repetitive protein (PARP) genes of *Trypanosoma brucei* shares features with RNA polymerase I promoters. Mol Cell Biol; 12; 1992; 2644-2652.

[17] Janz L., Clayton C. The PARP and rRNA promoters of *Trypanosoma brucei* are composed of dissimilar sequence elements that are functionally interchangeable. Mol Cell Biol; 14; 1994; 5804-5811.

[18] Rudenko G., Blundell P.A., Dirks–Mulder A., Kieft R., Borst P. A ribosomal DNA promoter replacing the promoter of a telomeric VSG expression site can be efficiently switched on and off in *Trypanosoma brucei.* Cell; 83; 1995; 547-553.

[19] Nagoshio Y.L., Alarcon C., Donelson J.E. The putative promoter for a metacyclic VSG gene in african trypanosomes. Mol Biochem Parasitol; 72; 1995; 33-45.

[20] Graham S.V., Barry J.D. Transcriptional regulation of metacyclic variant surface glycoprotein gene expression during the life cycle of *Trypanosoma brucei.* Mol Cell Biol; 15; 1995; 5945-5956.

[21] Lee M.G.S. A foreign transcription unit in the inactivated VSG gene expression site of the procyclic form of *Trypanosoma brucei* and formation of large episomes in stably transformed trypanosomes. Mol Biochem Parasitol; 69; 1995; 223-238.

[22] Jefferies D., Tebabi P., Le Ray D., Pays E. The *ble* resistance gene as a new selectable marker for *Trypanosoma brucei :* fly transmission of stable procyclic transformants to produce antibiotic resistant bloodstream forms. Nucl Acids Res; 21; 1993; 191-195.

[23] Zomerdijk J.C.B.M., Kieft R., Borst P. Insertion of the promoter for a variant surface glycoprotein gene expression site in a RNA polymerase II transcription unit of procyclic *Trypanosoma brucei.* Mol Biochem Parasitol; 57; 1993; 295-304.

[24] Biebinger S., Rettenmaier S., Flaspohler J., Hartmann C., Pena-Diaz J., Wirtz L.E., Hotz H.R., Barry J.D., Clayton C. The PARP promoter of *Trypanosoma brucei* is developmentally regulated in a chromosomal context. Nucl Acids Res; 24; 1996; 1202-1211.

[25] Urmenyi T.P., Van der Ploeg L.H.T. PARP promoter-mediated activation of a VSG expression site promoter in insect form *Trypanosoma brucei.* Nucl Acids Res; 23; 1995; 1010-1018.

[26] Qi C.C., Urmenyi T., Gottesdiener K.M. Analysis of a hybrid PARP/VSG ES promoter in procyclic trypanosomes. Mol Biochem Parasitol; 77; 1996; 147-159.

[27] Vanhamme L., Berberof M., Le Ray D., Pays E. Stimuli of differentiation regulate RNA elongation in the transcription units for the major stage-specific antigens of *Trypanosoma brucei.* Nucl Acids Res; 23; 1995; 1862-1869.

[28] Rudenko G., Blundell P.A., Taylor M.C., Kieft R., Borst P. VSG gene expression site control in insect form *Trypanosoma brucei.* EMBO J; 13; 1994; 5470-5482.

[29] Navarro M., Cross G.A.M. DNA rearrangements associated with multiple consecutive directed antigenic switches in *Trypanosoma brucei.* Mol Cell Biol; 16; 1996; 3615-3625.

[30] Vanhamme L., Pays E. Control of gene expression in trypanosomes. Microbiol Rev; 59; 1995; 223-240.

[31] Berberof M., Vanhamme L., Tebabi P., Pays A., Jefferies D., Welburn S., Pays E. The 3'-terminal region of the mRNAs for the VSG and procyclin can confer stage specificity to gene expression in *Trypanosoma brucei.* EMBO J; 14; 1995; 2925-2934.

[32] Coquelet H., Tebabi P., Pays A., Steinert M., Pays E. *Trypanosoma brucei :* enrichment by UV of intergenic transcripts from the variable surface glycoprotein gene expression site. Mol Cell Biol; 9; 1989; 4022-4025.

[33] Pays E., Coquelet H., Pays A., Tebabi P., Steinert M. *Trypanosoma brucei :* posttranscriptional control of the variable surface glycoprotein gene expression site. Mol Cell Biol; 9; 1989; 4018-4021.

[34] Elhers B., Czichos J., Overath P. RNA turnover in *Trypanosoma brucei.* Mol Cell Biol; 7; 1987; 1242-1249.

[35] Bass K.E., Wang C.C. Transient inhibition of protein synthesis accompanies differentiation of *Trypanosoma brucei* from bloodstream to procyclic forms. Mol Biochem Parasitol; 56; 1992; 129-140.

[36] Paturiaux-Hanocq F, Zitzmann N, Hanocq-Quertier J, Vanhamme L, Rolin S, Geuskens M, Ferguson MAJ, Pays E. Expression of a variant surface glycoprotein of *Trypanosoma gambiense* in procyclic forms of *Trypanosoma brucei* shows that the cell type dictates the nature of the glycosylphosphatidylinositol membrane anchor attached to the glycoprotein. Biochem J 1997; 324 : 885–95

8

Bruce thinks that the infection passes immediately through the proboscis of the fly, which is something like a vaccinating needle and this
presents no difficulty if the blood be rich in trypanosome. Bruce him-
self found — and later on we will see other examples of the same —
that in South Africa the big game… have only a very small proportion
of tsetse parasites in the blood. Under these circumstances I may
assume that, to make the infection possible, the trypanosomes
increase in the *Glossina* or undergo some process of development,
similar to the malaria parasite in the mosquito.

Robert Koch, 1904

Unravelling the procyclin coat of Trypanosoma brucei

Isabel Roditi [a],
André Furger [a],
Stefan Ruepp [a],
Nadia Schürch [a],
Peter Bütikofer [b]

[a] *Institut für Allgemeine Mikrobiologie
Universität Bern Switzerland.*

[b] *Institut für Biochemie und Molekular-
biologie Universität Bern Suitzerland.*

1 • Introduction

For nearly 15 years after the discovery of trypanosomes
by David Bruce in 1894, it was believed that the transmission of
the parasite by tsetse flies was entirely mechanical. Although
Robert Koch thought it might be otherwise [1], and had in fact
succeeded in isolating and culturing parasites from the fly midgut [2], these were not deemed to be of any significance as they
were not infective for animals and therefore did not fulfil Koch's
own postulates. Not until 1909, with the detection of new infectious forms in the salivary glands of a single fly, was it conceded
that there might be some form of developmental cycle in the
insect vector [2], although it was still regarded as a minor route
of transmission. Nevertheless, this discovery provided sufficient
impetus for Bruce and his colleagues to embark on a systematic
study of different forms of the parasite in the tsetse fly and within
an astonishingly short time they were able to present the following conclusions [3] :

1. That *Trypanosoma [brucei] gambiense* multiplies in the gut of about one in every 20 *Glossina palpalis* which have fed on an infected animal.

2. That the flies become infective, on an average, 34 days after their first feed.

3. That a fly may remain infective for 75 days.

Procyclic and epimastigote forms of *Trypanosoma brucei* — the proliferating forms in the tsetse fly cited in Ref. [2], are covered by a glycoprotein coat composed of procyclins (otherwise known as procyclic acidic repetitive proteins). Just as these stages of the life cycle escaped attention for many years, the identification of their coat lagged almost two decades behind that of the variant surface glycoprotein (VSG) coat of bloodstream forms [4–8]. This was due to the fact that procyclins could not be detected by several procedures used for the identification of proteins, which had the effect of rendering them all but invisible to the unsuspecting biochemist [9].

Bloodstream form trypanosomes sequentially express a large repertoire of different VSGs, a process known as antigenic variation [10]. In addition to protecting invariant membrane structures from recognition by the immune system, the VSG coat also prevents destruction of the parasites by complement-mediated lysis. Procyclins are first expressed when bloodstream forms differentiate into procyclic forms in the tsetse fly midgut and progressively replace the VSG coat within the space of a few hours [11–13]. It is vital that this change of coat is tightly regulated since either the loss of VSG or premature expression of procyclins (which are invariant and potentially highly immunogenic) would be lethal in the mammalian host. As will be discussed below, the regulation of procyclin expression is extremely complex as it occurs at several different levels in both stages of the life cycle and is, in many respects, a mirror image of VSG regulation. Several different aspects of VSG expression are covered by recent reviews [14–19] and we therefore focus exclusively on the regulation and function of procyclins.

2 • Procyclin expression sites

Procyclin genes are organised in tandem arrays of two or three copies on two pairs of chromosomes (Fig. 1; [7, 20]). The first published sequences differed in both their coding regions and 3' untranslated regions, but as they were derived from three unrelated isolates of *T. brucei*, it was not clear whether this reflected strain differences or whether each trypanosome expressed several types of procyclin. Recently, a close inspection of all the sequences deposited in the Par-

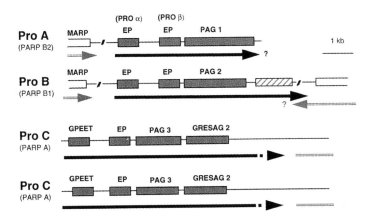

FIGURE 1

Procyclin expression sites in their genomic contexts. In *T. brucei* strain 427
each expression site begins with a pair
of procyclin genes. These encode proteins with internal dipeptide (EP) or
pentapeptide (GPEET) repeats. PAG,
procyclin-associated gene [33, 42]. PAG
1 and PAG 2 diverge within the coding region [33]; there is probably an additional
gene 3' of PAG 2 (hatched box; Roditi, I.,
unpublished). GRESAG 2, gene related
to ESAG 2 [47]. The transcription units
upstream of Pro A and B both end with a
microtubule-associated repetitive protein (MARP) gene [49]. Black arrows, α-
amanitin-resistant transcription. Grey
arrows, α-amanitin-sensitive transcription. The Pro B transcription unit may
partially overlap with an α-amanitin-sensitive transcription unit in the opposite
orientation (Bodenmueller, K., Pays, E.,
Roditi, I., unpublished). α-Amanitin-sensitive transcripts hybridise with a region
downstream of Pro C but are not necessarily derived from it [42]. The nomen-
clature in boldface type is according to
Koenig et al. [20], and that in brackets
according to Mowatt and Clayton [7]. The
original analyses were performed with
different strains of trypanosomes and it
was not until the identification of locus-
specific PAGs [33] that the two systems
could be matched unequivocally.

asite Genome Database (28 at the last count) revealed that they fall into four classes [21]. Three of these encode proteins with extensive glutamic acid-proline dipeptide repeats (EP in the single letter amino acid code), but can be distinguished by specific residues in their N-terminal domains and the presence or absence of glycosylation sites. The fourth class encodes a protein with an internal pentapeptide repeat (GPEET) and no glycosylation sites. In *T. brucei* strain 427 each class is present in two copies per diploid genome [21]. The same genes are present in *T. brucei* strain 227, together with an additional copy, encoding a glycosylated form of EP, which most probably arose through unequal crossover [20]. It therefore seems likely that most strains will contain at least one copy of each class of procyclin gene.

Each of the four procyclin loci is an active expression site (Fig. 1). In contrast to bloodstream forms, in which only one of several potential expression sites is active at a time, transcription can occur simultaneously from two or more procyclin expression sites at once [7, 22]. That this is true for individual cells, and not merely a population phenomenon, has now been confirmed by the selective deletion and tagging of all four sites in *T. brucei* 427 [21]. Interest-ingly, these experiments also revealed that the majority of EP procyc-lin transcripts were derived from one particular expression site. It is not yet known, however, if this is also the case for other strains of *T. brucei*, nor is it known whether trypanosomes have the capacity to up- or down-regulate expression from a particular expression site.

The procyclin expression sites, in common with the blood-stream and metacyclic VSG expression sites and ribosomal gene clus-ter, are transcribed by an α-amanitin-resistant RNA polymerase [20, 23–25]. All of the promoters have two key elements at a similar dis-tance upstream of the transcription start site [26, 27]. To some extent the domains are interchangeable: hybrid promoters containing ribosomal sequences (ribosome-procyclin and ribosome-VSG) are fully functional [28, 29], but VSG-procyclin promoter hybrids are 12–20-fold less active than the wild type VSG promoter [29]. The RNA polymerase responsible for procyclin and VSG transcription has not been identified unambiguously. While the activity of hybrid promoters and the resistance to α-amanitin and Sarcosyl [30] all point to RNA polymerase I (Pol I), the effects of different cations and the metal chelator 1,10-phenanthroline are more in keeping with Pol II [31]. It is possible, however, that the polymerase is a modified form of Pol I. A factor of 40 kDa, which binds to the non-coding strand of all three promoters, has been identified by a combination of gel mobility shifts and UV cross-linking [29]. While this again points to a common polymerase, which might be Pol I or a modified form of it, it should be borne in mind that the different RNA polymerases of higher eukaryotes share transcription factors that were initially thought to be specific [32], and that distinguishing between polymerases may be less clearcut than was previously thought.

3 • RNA processing

In common with the majority of protein coding genes in trypanosomes, the procyclins form part of polycistronic transcription units (Fig. 1; [33]). The messenger RNAs are transcribed as precursors which are then processed into (mainly) monocistronic mRNAs by the addition of a 39 nucleotide mini-exon (or splice leader) at the 5' end and a poly(A) tail at the 3' end of the mature transcript. The sequences required for efficient *trans*-splicing, a polypyrimidine stretch followed by the dinucleotide AG, were first determined for procyclin mRNAs [34]. Very similar sequences direct *cis*-splicing in other eukaryotes and it has recently been demonstrated that 3' splice sites from some human and yeast genes can be used for *trans*-splicing by *T. brucei* [35]. Somewhat unexpectedly perhaps, it is unpredictable whether 3' splice sites from different kinetoplastids will also function across the species barrier. The splice acceptor site for GARP (the procyclin analogue of *T. congolense)* does not function in *T. brucei* and conversely, the procyclin splice acceptor site is not used by *T. congolense* [36], although it directs trans-splicing at the correct position in *Leishmania major* (Probst M, Furger A, Roditi I, unpublished data).

Pyrimidine-rich regions also serve as signals for cleavage and polyadenylation [37–40]. In transcription units where genes are tightly clustered — with intergenic regions of < 150 bp — a single element can specify cleavage and polyadenylation ~60–90 bases upstream of the start of the polypyrimidine tract as well as *trans*-splicing of the RNA at the AG dinucleotide. When genes are further apart,

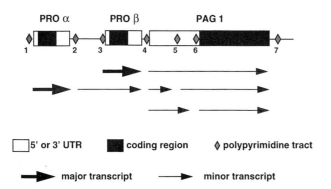

PRO α   PRO β   PAG 1

☐ 5' or 3' UTR   ■ coding region   ◊ polypyrimidine tract

➤ major transcript   → minor transcript

FIGURE 2

Messenger RNAs derived from the Pro A locus [39]. A polycistronic precursor is processed into mature mRNAs, each beginning with a mini-exon and ending with a poly(A) tail. Polyadenylation of the procyclin- α mRNA and *trans*-splicing of the major procyclin- β mRNA are specified by two separate polypyrimidine tracts (2 and 3, respectively), although a small proportion of mRNAs derived from the procyclin- β gene are alternatively spliced at position 2. Several other polypyrimidine tracts (4–7) serve as signals for both mini-exon addition and polyadenylation, resulting in five alternatively processed PAG 1 mRNAs.

however, the two processes become uncoupled, possibly owing to constraints on the distance between the polypyrimidine tract and the 3' processing site. In the case of the procyclin α and β genes, which are ~600 bp apart, there are two distinct polypyrimidine tracts which specify 3' processing of the α-gene transcript and *trans*-splicing of the β-gene transcript, respectively (Fig. 2; [38–40]).

Although the two functions have been separated in vivo, both these elements are bifunctional to some extent [39–41]. The role of the procyclin 3' untranslated region (UTR) in polyadenylation is still not entirely resolved. In initial experiments with essentially monocistronic constructs, a deletion of all but the last 7 bp of the 3' UTR (ΔUTR) had no effect on the choice of polyadenylation site [38]. In contrast, when bicistronic constructs were used, there appeared to be competition between the two polypyrimidine tracts, giving rise to approximately equimolar amounts of the correctly processed mRNA and a longer transcript [41]. This was only observed with the ΔUTR deletion and not with constructs containing an intact 3' UTR, suggesting that sequences within this region may suppress 3' processing from the distal element.

4 • Procyclin-associated genes

Procyclin-associated genes (PAGs) are found downstream of the procyclin genes in each expression site and are coordinately transcribed by the same α-amanitin-resistant RNA polymerase (Fig. 1). Three PAGs have been identified to date [33, 42]. All three have unusually long 5' UTRs which are 98% identical for the first 550 bases. The polypeptide encoded by PAG 1 is related to ESAG (expression site-associated gene) 6 and 7 proteins, which together constitute the transferrin binding protein of bloodstream forms [43–45]. An unusual feature of PAG 1 transcripts is that there are several alternatively spliced and polyadenylated forms that are potentially polycistronic, bicistronic or monocistronic mRNAs [39]. PAG 2 is most closely related to PAG 1, and may also give rise to several alternatively spliced transcripts [46]. By analogy with ESAGs 6 and 7, it is possible that the PAG 1 and 2 polypeptides also form a dimer that functions as a receptor, but for a different ligand since procyclic forms do not bind transferrin [43, 44]. PAG 3 presents more of an enigma, both in terms of expression and possible function. The 606 base pair open reading frame (ORF) potentially encodes a glycoprotein with a trans-membrane domain [42], but it shows no homology to known sequences. A single transcript of 1.3 kb is detected on Northern blots; alternatively spliced transcripts must also be present at low levels since they can be detected by PCR (Vassella E and Roditi I, unpublished data), but none of these transcripts corresponds to a conventional monocistronic mRNA. The transcript from GRESAG 2 (gene related to ESAG 2), which occurs immediately downstream of PAG 3 [47] is also unusual because it contains a split ORF. At present we can only speculate that translation of these mRNAs, if it occurs, might conceivably involve mechanisms such as internal initiation, frameshifting or alternative codon usage, none of which has previously been described for trypanosomatids.

5 • Boundaries of the procyclin expression sites

The procyclin expression sites are α-amanitin-resistant islands of transcription that are flanked by classical Pol II transcription units (Fig. 1). The transcription units upstream of Pro A and B [20] (equivalent to PARP B2 and B1; [7]) are in the same orientation as the procyclin expression sites; each contains a microtubule-associated repetitive protein (MARP) gene [20, 48]. α-Amanitin-sensitive transcription proceeds approximately 1 kb beyond MARP [49], which is probably the last gene in the transcription unit. This is followed by a non-transcribed region of almost 2 kb, after which transcription begins from the procyclin promoter [49]. The Pro A and B expression sites diverge within the coding regions of PAG 1 and 2 [33]. In Pro A, α-amanitin-resistant transcription continues beyond the 3' end of PAG 1 [33], but the end of the transcription unit has not been mapped precisely. Transcription of the Pro B expression site extends ~5 kb beyond PAG 2 and may accommodate an additional gene (Roditi I, unpublished data). Further downstream there is at least one gene, in the opposite orientation, that is transcribed by Pol II (Bodenmueller K, Pays E and Roditi I, unpublished data). Only one procyclin expression site (Pro C/PARP A) has been sequenced in its entirety [42]. This expression site contains four genes — two procyclin genes, PAG 3 and GRESAG 2. It has been established by nuclear run-on analysis that α-amanitin-resistant transcription terminates 7.5–9.5 kb downstream of the promoter. A region further downstream also hybridises with nascent transcripts, but these are α-amanitin-sensitive. Transcription of these sequences appears to occur at similar levels in both procyclic and bloodstream forms, but stable RNAs are only detectable in the latter. It is not certain, however, to what extent these are derived from the 3' flanking region as there are several cross-hybridising sequences in the genome. The transition from α-amanitin-resistant to -sensitive transcription is consistent with the presence of a terminator in this region and, indeed, there are at least three separate elements downstream of the procyclin expression site capable of reducing expression of a reporter gene in transient transfection assays [42]. When integrated into the tubulin locus, a fragment spanning these elements attenuates transcription from the procyclin promoter in an orientation-dependent manner, but does not abolish it completely.

6 • Stage-specific regulation of transcription

The induction of procyclin expression as bloodstream forms differentiate into procyclic forms is partly achieved at the level of transcription. Transcription initiation from endogenous procyclin promoters is approximately one order of magnitude greater in procyclic forms than in bloodstream forms [49] and the same holds true for a tagged promoter integrated into a procyclin locus [50]. The activity of the promoter can also be stage-regulated in a different genomic context. When it is integrated into the tubulin locus, it is capable of driving α-amanitin resistant transcription in procyclic forms [50] provided sequences 5' of the core promoter are present (Berberof M, Pays E, personal communication). In bloodstream forms, however, the promoter does not function and instead there is read through from the upstream tubulin promoter by Pol II [50]. These results are open to more than one interpretation. It has been suggested that there might be a requirement for a terminator of Pol II transcription, such as is presumably present between the MARP and procyclin genes, in order to prevent interference between the two polymerases. Alternatively, there may be a requirement for sequences which either cause changes in the chromatin structure or contain binding sites for specific factors which then recruit the correct polymerase. This might also explain why an inverted procyclin promoter is able to stimulate transcription from a VSG promoter, integrated into the Pol II locus, that is otherwise poorly active in procyclic forms [51].

Elongation of transcription from the procyclin expression sites is also developmentally regulated [50]. Under optimal conditions for differentiation — a drop in temperature from 37 to 27 °C, the addition of citrate and *cis*-aconitate, and the appropriate medium — transcription of the procyclin genes is stimulated 9-fold after 3 h, while that of GRESAG 2 is stimulated 40-fold. This phenomenon appears to be independent of the sequence since similar ratios were obtained with tagged expression sites containing hygromycin and CAT genes immediately downstream of the promoter (6-fold increase in transcription after 3 h) and plasmid sequences further downstream (30-fold increase). At the same time transcription of the barren region in the VSG expression site and 18S ribosomal RNAs was reduced, although less spectacularly (4–6-fold).

7 • Post-transcriptional regulation

Given the polycistronic organisation of the procyclin expression sites and the relatively small degree of transcriptional control, it is not surprising that there is an additional requirement for post-transcriptional regulation. The procyclins and PAGs, for example, although derived from the same primary transcript, differ more than 100-fold in their relative amounts of steady state mRNA [33]. There are potentially several different contributory factors including RNA stability and the efficiency with which the transcripts are processed and exported to the cytoplasm.

The 3' UTRs of procyclin mRNAs are composed of distinct domains which influence expression in both bloodstream forms and procyclic forms [41, 52–56]. One 3' UTR, which has been analysed in detail, contains three distinct elements that map to separate stem-loops in the predicted secondary structure (LI–III; [41]). While such theoretical structures should always be treated with caution, the fol-

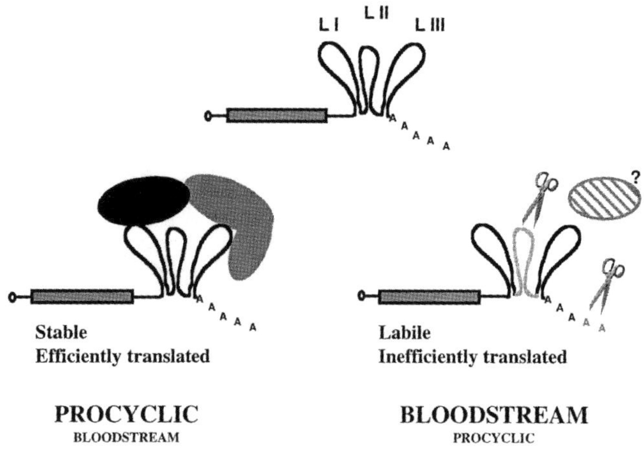

FIGURE 3

Schematic representation of a procyclin mRNA in different conformations. The 3' UTR is predicted to form three stem-loops (LI-III) [41, 55], with the conserved 16mer at the top of LIII. In the stable conformation (the major species in procyclic forms) one or more factors binding to positive elements in the outer stem-loops would stabilise the mRNA and ensure efficient translation. In the absence of these factors the mRNA would be rapidly degraded by endo- or exonucleases. There might also be additional RNA-binding proteins (hatched oval) which act as translational repressors. The procyclin coding region itself (grey box) is not intrinsically unstable [55], but it might contribute to the degradation of mRNAs in bloodstream forms by recruiting nucleases to the 3' UTR.

lowing model is consistent with the data (Fig. 3). There are two positive elements, a 16mer which forms the top of the stem-loop in LIII and an element in LI which is destroyed by deletion of the first 40 base pairs of the 3' UTR [41, 53, 55]. Both the sequence and the secondary structure of the 16mer are conserved in different types of procyclin 3' UTR as well as the GARP 3' UTR [53, 57, 58]. The central stem-loop (LII) contains at least one negative element [41, 54, 55] that spans a region with two stretches of six to seven uridine residues (previously designed the H-element; [54]). Although the sequence of this element is not perfectly conserved, motifs containing single-stranded «U bulges» are found in all procyclin and GARP 3' UTRs [55].

Both the positive and negative elements have an effect on steady state RNA levels, RNA turnover and translation and all of them function in procyclic and bloodstream forms, although to different extents. Deletion of either positive element reduced steady state mRNA (~2-fold) and protein levels (a minimum of 8-fold) in both stages of the life cycle. In procyclic forms, deletion of the LII domain caused a 3-fold increase in steady state mRNA levels with a parallel rise in the amount of protein [41]. Double deletions of LII and the 16mer also gave high levels of expression. The fact that the 16mer deletion had no effect once the negative element had been removed suggests that it might function as an anti-repressor, rather than as a positive element in its own right. In bloodstream forms, the effect of deleting the LII domain is more complex as there appears to be an additional layer of translational or post-translational control which also depends on the coding region [55]. When CAT was used as the reporter gene, enzyme activity was clearly detectable in all cases, and there was a graded response depending on the mutation. Deletion of the entire LII domain caused a 6-fold increase in the relative amount of mRNA and a 30-fold increase in CAT activity compared to the wild type; other mutations gave intermediate amounts of mRNA and protein [55].

A somewhat different picture emerged when GARP was used as the reporter gene. In this case the protein was detected only in stable transformants which had major deletions in LII, and the amount of GARP expressed by cell lines with different mutations was low and remarkably constant [55]. Since the GARP polypeptide is not detectable in bloodstream forms of *T. congolense* (although the mRNA is, Barry JD and Jefferies D, personal communication) it is possible that there are further controls operating at the level of translation or post-translational processing. This also appears to hold true for procyclin itself. When the procyclin coding region was linked to a truncated 3' UTR, the mRNA accumulated to surprisingly high levels in bloodstream forms ($\geq$ 25% of that in procyclic forms), but no protein could be detected, again suggesting that expression might be regulated at the level of translation or further downstream [55].

We have tested the effect of 3' UTR mutations on RNA turnover in procyclic forms [41] (for recent data on RNA turnover in bloodstream forms see [56]). Endogenous procyclin mRNAs have a $t_{1/2}$ of ~60 min in cells treated with actinomycin D. Very similar values ($t_{1/2}$ ~ 50 min) were obtained for chimaeric transcripts consisting of the GARP coding region and the wild type procyclin 3' UTR. Deletion of either positive element in LI or LIII (Fig. 2) reduced the $t_{1/2}$ of the chimaeric transcripts to ≤ 15 min, whereas removal of the entire LII domain stabilised the RNA, increasing the $t_{1/2}$ to ~100 min. All these results can be summarised in a model (Fig. 3) in which the procyclin RNA exists in two conformations, a stable, efficiently translated form (which predominates in procyclic forms) and a labile, poorly translated form (which predominates in bloodstream forms). In neither case, however, is the alternative form completely absent. In the stable conformation, factors binding to the two outer positive elements would protect the RNA from degradation by nucleases. In the absence of these factors, however, the RNA could be accessible to endonucleases, which might cleave within LII, and/or deadenylases. It is not clear whether the decrease in stability alone would be sufficient to account for the reduction in expression. It is possible that additional proteins are involved in repressing translation, since deletion of the 16mer reduces the recruitment of the mRNA into polysomes (Fig. 4).

8 • Effects of protein synthesis inhibitors

The treatment of bloodstream forms with a variety of protein synthesis inhibitors induces the accumulation of procyclin mRNA in both monomorphic and pleomorphic trypanosomes [59, 60]. This effect is not due to increased transcription [60]. The mRNA is polyadenylated and it is exported from the nucleus to the cytoplasm where

FIGURE 4

Deletion of the conserved 16mer causes a greater reduction in polysome-associated mRNA than in total mRNA. Procyclic form trypanosomes were stably transformed with constructs containing GARP linked to the procyclin wild type (wt) 3' UTR or a 3' UTR lacking the 16mer (Δ16mer; [41]). Northern blots of total RNA and polysomal RNA (isolated according to [11] and [60], respectively) were hybridised with probes for GARP and tubulin. The relative amount of polysome-associated mRNA mirrors the amount of protein as the GARP-Δ16mer cell line expresses the protein at only 4% of the level obtained with GARP-wt [41].

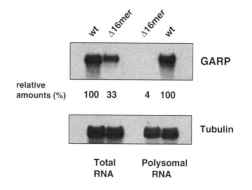

it is capable of associating with polysomes. These results point to the presence of labile factors that are negative regulators of procyclin expression in bloodstream forms. These might act by interfering with processing of the primary transcript in the nucleus or alternatively they might degrade mature mRNAs in the cytoplasm. Hybrid transcripts consisting of the GARP coding region flanked by the procyclin UTRs also accumulate when cells are treated with cycloheximide. The target of these factors within the mRNA is unknown, but it does not appear to be the 3' UTR [55].

9 ● Structure of procyclins

The different forms of EP procyclin contain up to 29 copies of a dipeptide repeat, while the GPEET form contains six pentapeptide repeats followed by only three EP repeats. Data obtained by both nuclear magnetic resonance and molecular modelling suggest that tandem EP repeats form extended structures [11, 61]. Proteins with multiple EP repeats have also been identified in other organisms. These include the Ton B protein of *E. coli* [61], the mammalian ryanodine receptor [62] and an X-linked PEST-containing transporter [63]. Polypeptides containing EP repeats are also encoded by several cDNA clones isolated from rat brain and skeletal libraries [64]. The GPEET motif, in contrast, is much rarer and only two regions of rather weak similarity have been identified in other proteins. These occur in the von Hippel–Lindau disease tumour suppressor [65] and in peritrophin-95, a gut-associated protein of the fly *Lucilia cuprina* (GenBank™ accession number U23828).

EP and GPEET are coexpressed on the surface of procyclic forms [21]. Both forms of procyclin are attached to the plasma membrane by a GPI anchor that shares the same core structure as the VSG anchor, but is considerably larger, and is responsible for the anomalous migration of procyclin on SDS-polyacrylamide gels [66–68]. A membrane-associated trans-sialidase on the surface of living procyclic forms is capable of transferring sialic acid to the GPI anchor from an external substrate [69, 70]. It is not clear why procyclins and VSGs employ different GPI anchors, but since the procyclin polypeptides are predicted to be much less bulky than the VSGs, a highly substituted GPI structure might provide the parasite with a form of armour plating that protects the membrane against digestive enzymes or trypanocidal factors in the fly midgut.

The signal peptides of the three different classes of EP are identical, and that of GPEET differs at only one position out of 27 [21]. Despite this high degree of conservation, purified forms of EP and

FIGURE 5

Effect of increasing time in culture on the relative amounts of EP and GPEET procyclin. *T. brucei* STIB 247 was obtained from R. Brun (Swiss Tropical Institute, Basel) shortly after cyclical transmission and transformation of bloodstream forms to procyclic forms. Cells were labelled with [^{3}H]myristate [67]. The lanes contain equal amounts of radioactivity. Procyclic forms were sampled after (a) 1 month in culture, (b) 3 months, (c) > 6 months.

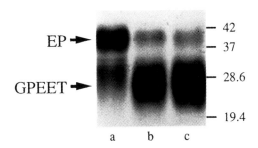

GPEET have different N-terminal amino acids. The first residue of mature EP is Ala$_{28}$ [8] (see [21] for numbering), whereas that of GPEET has been determined as Val$_{35}$ [68] or Gly$_{40}$ [67]. It is not clear whether these differences reflect the situation in vivo or are due to different extents of proteolysis during the purification procedures. The hydrophobic C-terminal peptides of the various forms of procyclin are slightly less conserved than the signal peptides, but in all cases cleavage and GPI anchor addition are predicted to occur at the last glycine residue in the precursor [66, 67, 71].

Additional post-translational modifications of procyclins include N-linked glycosylation of EP and phosphorylation of GPEET. The N-linked oligosaccharide is a homogenous structure Man$_5$GlcNAc$_2$ [68]. In cells which have been manipulated so that they exclusively express either glycosylated or unglycosylated EP [21], the two forms migrate as broad bands that can be distinguished by their electrophoretic mobilities (M_r ~ 40–45 kDa and ~ 34–41 kDa, respectively; Ruepp S, unpublished). There is only a single type of GPEET polypeptide, but the mature glycoprotein also exists in two forms. The bulk migrates as a diffuse band of 22–32 kDa (Fig. 5) and is phosphorylated [67]. In contrast, un(der)phosphorylated GPEET migrates as a doublet of 20/21 kDa and partitions differently in solvents.

10 • Variation in coat composition

The procyclin coat has previously been regarded as homogeneous because the protein(s) purified by three independent procedures either yielded a single N-terminal sequence [8] or amino acid compositions that were consistent with it [66, 71]. In retrospect, this was due, at least in part, to the use of techniques such as concanavalin A-affinity chromatography which selectively enriched for glycosylated forms of EP. It has recently been shown, however, that GPEET, and not EP, is the major procyclin expressed by established procyclic forms of *T. brucei* 427 [67, 68]. It was also reported that this strain predominantly expressed EP shortly after differentiation from bloodstream forms to procyclic forms, but showed increased GPEET expression as the cells were passaged [68]. We have also obtained similar results with STIB 247 procyclic forms over a period of two months (Fig. 5). This is not invariably the case, however, because we have identified other strains which express high levels of EP [67], and continue to do so irrespective of the length of time that they have been maintained in culture (Bütikofer P, Ruepp S, Boschung M, Roditi I, unpublished observation). A further complication is that there appears to be intrastrain differences, since established procyclic forms of *T. brucei* 427 from two laboratories express different levels of EP [67, 68].

In addition to changes in the ratio of EP to GPEET, there is also the potential for variation in the type of EP that the cells express. No unglycosylated EP was detected in *T. brucei* 427 [68]. In all strains that we have examined, the size of EP (40–45 kDa) is consistent with the expression of the glycosylated form alone [67] and does not change when the cells are maintained in culture (Fig. 5). It is possible that other strains express the non-glycosylated form; alternatively there might be differences between the types of EP expressed by procyclic and epimastigote forms. Finally, although there are no data as yet, it should also be taken into consideration that the relative amounts of phosphorylated and unphosphorylated GPEET may not be constant.

11 • Function of procyclins

Although it is now 10 years since the identification of the first procyclin genes [6, 7], the function of the coat remains largely a matter of conjecture. Putative functions include protection against digestion by hydrolases in the tsetse fly midgut and a role in tropism by directing the parasite to the correct compartment for further growth and differentiation [9]. It has also been suggested that procyclins might be the targets of two activities identified in tsetse flies : one is a trypanocidal factor which kills procyclic forms, while the other stimulates further differentiation and migration of the parasites to the mouthparts [72]. The observation that these activities can be modulated by feeding either sugars or lectins to infected flies [72, 73] has led to the proposal that the trypanocidal factors might themselves be lectins which bind to N-linked carbohydrates on procyclins. It has recently been shown that concanavalin A, which is a plant lectin, kills procyclic forms in vitro [74]. This may be mediated by binding to mannose residues on glycosylated EP, but the situation in vivo is likely to be different (see below).

Knocking out genes by homologous recombination has been feasible for several years [75], but it only became a precision tool once the signals for RNA processing and post-transcriptional regulation were defined. In particular, when attempting to link specific genes to subtle changes in phenotype, it is essential that the expression of the adjacent genes is not perturbed. We have recently succeeded in deleting all six EP genes and one out of two GPEET genes from *T. brucei* 427 procyclic forms [21]. It was not possible to delete the last endogenous copy of GPEET without first integrating another copy elsewhere in the genome [21], nor could it be compensated for by overexpression of EP (Kurath U, Ruepp S, unpublished data), suggesting that the two forms of procyclin are functionally distinct. The EP-negative trypanosomes showed no differences to the parental strain in terms of population doubling time, susceptibility to complement-mediated lysis or sensitivity to proteases in vitro. In contrast, their ability to establish heavy infections in the tsetse midgut was reduced more than 5-fold, but this phenotype could be reversed by the reintroduction of a single, highly expressed EP gene [21]. These results indicate that EP, even though it is a minor component of the coat of this particular strain (~15–20%; [67]), plays an important role in the survival of trypanosomes in the fly. The fact that cells expressing either the glycosylated or unglycosylated form of EP were equally efficient at establishing infections makes it unlikely that trypanocidal factors act by binding to N-linked sugars on the former. It is possible, however, that GPEET is the target for this activity. Although GPEET contains no N-linked glycosylation sites, there might be O-linked glycosylation of some threonine residues in the pentapeptide repeat. It is also conceivable that the interaction involves sugar residues on the tsetse molecules rather than on the procyclins themselves.

12 • GARP—the procyclin analogue of *T. congolense*

T. congolense is closely related to *T. brucei* and it is also transmitted by tsetse flies. GARP (glutamic acid/alanine-rich protein) is considered to be the procyclin analogue of *T. congolense* although the polypeptide sequences are totally unrelated. In common with procyclins it is stage-specifically expressed on the surface of procyclic and epimastigote forms [57, 76]. It also shares the properties of being a highly acidic glycoprotein which, like its procyclin counterparts, is largely resistant to proteases. GARP can be expressed in *T. brucei*, where it is correctly routed to the plasma membrane and integrated into the surface coat [77]. There are differences in post-translational modification, however, since GARP expressed in *T. brucei* is smaller and not recognised by monoclonal antibodies which recognise carbohydrate epitopes on the native protein from *T. congolense* [77].

Only one GARP gene, from a strain of the *T. congolense* Savannah subgroup, has been sequenced [57]. Internal peptide sequences which were obtained from a strain from the Kilifi subgroup differed at a total of four positions out of 54 [76]. Savannah and Kilifi isolates of *T. congolense* are so divergent that it is debatable whether they can be considered a single species [78], so it is still an open question whether a given strain expresses one or more types of GARP and if there are functional differences. Interestingly, monoclonal antibodies directed against GARP carbohydrates also react with the surface of *T. simiae* procyclic forms [76], but the gene is not detectable by hybridisation [79].

There are clear differences in the organisation and transcription of GARP and procyclin genes. The GARP genes are organised in long arrays that may contain >10 tandemly repeated copies (Roditi I, unpublished; Barry JD, Rangarajan D, personal communication). In contrast to the procyclin genes, they are transcribed by an α-amanitin-sensitive RNA polymerase [36]. The GARP promoter does not function in *T. brucei,* nor does the procyclin promoter drive transcription in *T. congolense.* The RNA processing signals for GARP and procyclins are also not interchangeable [36] which makes it all the more surprising that both the sequence and the predicted secondary structure of the 16mer as well as the «U bulges» are conserved in the 3' untranslated region of the mRNA [55, 57, 58]. It remains to be established, however, whether these motifs have the same functions as they do in *T. brucei* or are fossils from an ancestral gene.

Why do these two species of African trypanosomes have completely different surface coats in the tsetse fly ? Procyclic forms of both *T. brucei* and *T. congolense* replicate in the midgut, where they have to contend with the same set of digestive enzymes and trypanocidal factors. In contrast, the epimastigote forms are found in the salivary glands and proboscis, respectively, where they then give rise to infective metacyclic forms. It is therefore possible that procyclins and GARPs also function as molecular zip codes that direct the trypanosomes to the correct tissue.

Aknowledgements

We are grateful to Etienne Pays, Magali Berberof, Christine Clayton, Dave Barry and Desikan Rangarajan for communicating unpublished data and to Dirk Dobbelaere for reading yet another manuscript on procyclin. The work in our laboratories is supported by a Helmut Horten Incentive award to I.R. and by grants from the Swiss National Science Foundation and the Jean Brachet Foundation.

REFERENCES

[1] Koch R. Remarks on trypanosome diseases. Brit Med J 1904; ii : 1445–1449.

[2] Bruce D., Hamerton A.E., Bateman H.R., Mackie F.P. The development of *Trypanosoma gambiense* in *Glossina palpalis.* Proc R Soc London; B81; 1909; 405–414.

[3] Bruce D., Hamerton A.E., Bateman H.R., Mackie F.P. The development of trypanosomes in tsetse flies. Proc R Soc London; B82; 1910; 368-388.

[4] Vickerman K. On the surface coat and flagellar adhesion in trypanosomes. J Cell Sci; 5; 1969; 163-193.

[5] Richardson J.P., Jenni L., Beecroft R.P., Pearson T.W. Procyclic tsetse fly midgut forms and culture forms of African trypanosomes share stage- and species-specific surface antigens identified by monoclonal antibodies. J Immunol; 136; 1986; 2259-2264.

[6] Roditi I., Carrington M., Turner M. Expression of a polypeptide containing a dipeptide repeat is confined to the insect stage of *Trypanosoma brucei.* Nature; 325; 1987; 272-274.

[7] Mowatt M.R., Clayton C.E. Developmental regulation of a novel repetitive protein of *Trypanosoma brucei.* Mol Cell Biol; 7; 1987; 2833-2844.

[8] Richardson J.P., Beecroft R.P., Tolson D.L., Liu M.K., Pearson T.W. Procyclin : an unusual immunodominant glycoprotein surface antigen from the procyclic stage of African trypanosomes. Mol Biochem Parasitol; 31; 1988; 203-216.

[9] Roditi I., Pearson T.W. The procyclin coat of African trypanosomes. Parasitol Today; 6; 1990; 79-82.

[10] Cross G.A.M. Antigenic variation in trypanosomes : secrets surface slowly. Bioessays; 18; 1996; 283-291.

[11] Roditi I., Schwarz H., Pearson T.W., Beecroft R.P., Liu M.K., Richardson J.P., Bühring H.-J., Pleiss J., Bülow R., Williams R.O., Overath P. Procyclin gene expression and loss of the variant surface glycoprotein during differentiation of *Trypanosoma brucei.* J Cell Biol; 108; 1989; 737-746.

[12] Ziegelbauer K, Quinten M, Schwarz H, Pearson TW, Overath P. Synchronous differentiation of *Trypanosoma bruceii* from bloodstream to procyclic forms in vitro. Eur J Biochem 1990; 192 : 373–80.

[13] Matthews K.R., Gull K. Cycles within cycles : the interplay between differentiation and cell division in *Trypanosoma brucei.* Parasitol Today; 10; 1994; 473-476.

[14] Vanhamme L., Pays E. Control of gene expression in trypanosomes. Microbiol Rev; 59; 1995; 223-240.

[15] Roditi, I. The VSG-Procyclin Switch. Parasitol Today 1996; 12 : 47–49.

[16] Borst P, Bitter W, Blundell P, et al. Control of VSG gene expression sites in *Trypanosoma brucei.* Mol Biochem Parasitol. 1998; 91 : 67–76.

[17] Cross G, Wirtz L, Navarro M. Regulation of *vsg* expression site transcription and switching in *Trypanosoma brucei.* Mol Biochem Parasitol 1998; 91 : 77–91.

[18] Barry JD, Graham SV, Fotheriingham M, Graham VS, Kobryn K, Wymer B. VSG gene control and infectivity strategy of metacyclic stage *Trypanosoma brucei.* Mol Biochem Parasitol 1998; 91 : 91–105.

[19] Vanhamme et al., this issue.

[20] Koenig E., Delius H., Carrington M., Williams R.O., Roditi I. Duplication and transcription of procyclin genes in *Trypanosoma brucei.* Nucleic Acids Res; 17; 1989; 8727-8739.

[21] Ruepp S, Furger A, Kurath U, Kunz Renggli C, Hemphill A, Brun R, Roditi I. Survival of *Trypanosoma brucei* in the tsetse fly is enhanced by the expression of specific forms of procyclin. J Cell Biol 1997; 137 : 1369–79.

[22] Mowatt M.R., Clayton C.E. Polymorphisms in the procyclic acidic repetitive protein (PARP) gene family of *Trypanosoma brucei.* Mol Cell Biol; 8; 1988; 4055-4062.

[23] Kooter J.M., Borst P. α-amanitin-insensitive transcription of variant surface glycoprotein genes provides further evidence for discontinous transcription in trypanosomes. Nucleic Acids Res; 12; 1984; 9457-9472.

[24] Rudenko G., Bishop D., Gottesdiener K., van der Ploeg L.H.T. Alpha-amanitin resistant transcription of protein coding genes in insect and bloodstream form *Trypanosoma brucei.* EMBO J; 8; 1989; 4259-4263.

[25] Rudenko G., LeBlanq S., Smith J., Lee M.G.S., Rattray A., van der Ploeg L.H.T. Procyclic acidic repetitive protein genes (PARP) genes located in an unusually small α-amanitin-resistant transcription unit : PARP promoter activity assayed by transient DNA transfection of *Trypanosoma brucei.* Mol Cell Biol; 10; 1990; 3492-3504.

[26] Sherman D.R., Janz L., Hug M., Clayton C. Anatomy of the parp gene promoter of *Trypanosoma brucei.* EMBO J; 10; 1991; 3379-3386.

[27] Brown S.D., Huang J., van der Ploeg L.H.T. The promoter for the procyclic acidic repetitive protein (PARP) genes of *Trypanosoma brucei* shares features with RNA polymerase I promoters. Mol Cell Biol; 12; 1992; 2644-2652.

[28] Janz L., Clayton C. The PARP and rRNA promoters of *Trypanosoma brucei* are composed of dissimilar sequence elements that are functionally interchangeable. Mol Cell Biol; 14; 1994; 5804-5811.

[29] Vanhamme L., Pays A., Tebabi P., Alexandre S., Pays E. Specific binding of proteins to the noncoding strand of a crucial element of the variant surface glycoprotein, procyclin and ribosomal promotors of *Trypanosoma brucei*. Mol Cell Biol; 15; 1995; 5598-5606.

[30] Rudenko G., Lee M.G.-S., van der Ploeg L.H.T. The PARP and VSG genes of *Trypanosoma brucei* do not resemble RNA polymerase II transcription units in sensitivity to Sarkosyl in nuclear run-on assays. Nucleic Acids Res; 20; 1992; 303-306.

[31] Grondal E.J.M., Evers R., Kosubek K., Cornelissen A.W.C.A. Characterisation of the RNA polymerases of *Trypanosoma brucei* trypanosomal RNAs are composed of transcripts derived from both RNA polymerase II and III. EMBO J; 8; 1989; 3383-3389.

[32] Sharp P.A. TATA-binding protein is a classless factor. Cell; 68; 1992; 819-821.

[33] Koenig-Martin E., Yamage M., Roditi I. A procyclin-associated gene in *Trypanosoma brucei* encodes a polypeptide related to ESAG 6 and 7. Mol Biochem Parasitol; 55; 1992; 135-146.

[34] Huang J., van der Ploeg L.H.T. Requirement of a polypyrimidine tract for *trans*-splicing in trypanosomes : discriminating the PARP promoter from the immediately adjacent 3' splice acceptor site. EMBO J; 10; 1991; 3877-3885.

[35] Metzenberg S., Agabian N. Human and fungal 3' splice sites are used by *Trypanosoma brucei* for *trans* splicing. Mol Biochem Parasitol; 83; 1996; 11-23.

[36] Graham S.V., Jefferies D., Barry J.D. A promotor directing alpha-amanitin-sensitive transcription of GARP, the major surface antigen of insect stage *Trypanosoma congolense*. Nucleic Acid Res; 24; 1996; 272-281.

[37] Matthews K.R., Tschudi C., Ullu E. A common pyrimidine-rich motif governs *trans*-splicing and polyadenylation of tubulin polycistronic pre-mRNA in trypanosomes. Genes Dev; 8; 1994; 491-501.

[38] Schürch N., Hehl A., Vassella E., Braun R., Roditi I. Accurate polyadenylation of procyclin mRNAs in *Trypanosoma brucei* is determined by pyrimidine-rich elements in the intergenic regions. Mol Cell Biol; 14; 1994; 3668-3675.

[39] Vassella E., Braun R., Roditi I. Control of polyadenylation and alternative splicing of transcripts from adjacent genes in a procyclin expression site : a dual role for polypyrimi-

dine tracts in trypanosomes ?. Nucleic Acids Res; 22; 1994; 1359-1364.

[40] Hug M., Hotz H.-R., Hartmann C., Clayton C. Hierarchies of RNA-processing signals in a trypanosome surface antigen mRNA precursor. Mol Cell Biol; 14; 1994; 7428-7435.

[41] Furger A., Schürch N., Kurath U, Roditi I. Elements in the 3' untranslated region of procyclin mRNA regulate expression in insect forms of *Trypanosoma brucei* by modulating RNA stability and translation. Mol Cell Biol 1997; 17 : 4372–80.

[42] Berberof M., Pays A., Lips S., Tebabi P., Pays E. Characterization of a transcriptional terminator the of the procyclin PARP A unit of *Trypanosoma brucei*. Mol Cell Biol; 16; 1996; 914-924.

[43] Ligtenberg M.J., Bitter W., Kieft R., Steverding D., Janssen H., Calafat J., Borst P. Reconstitution of a surface transferrin binding complex in insect form *Trypanosoma brucei*. EMBO J; 13; 1994; 2565-2573.

[44] Salmon D., Geuskens M., Hanocq F., Hanocq-Quertier J., Nolan D., Ruben L., Pays E. A novel heterodimeric transferrin receptor encoded by a pair of VSG expression site-associated genes in *Trypanosoma brucei*. Cell; 78; 1994; 75-86.

[45] Chaudhri M., Steverding D., Kittelberger D., Tjia S., Overath P. Expression of a glycosylphosphatidylinositol-anchored *Trypanosoma brucei* transferrin-binding protein complex in insect cells. Proc Natl Acad Sci USA; 91; 1994; 6443-6447.

[46] Koenig-Martin E. Ph.D. thesis. University of Tübingen, Germany, 1992.

[47] Berberof M., Pays A., Pays E. A similar gene is shared by both variant surface glycoprotein and procyclin gene transcription units of *Trypanosoma brucei*. Mol Cell Biol; 11; 1991; 1473-1479.

[48] Schneider A., Hemphill A., Wyler T., Seebeck T. Large microtubule-associated protein of *T. brucei* has tandemly repeated, near-identical sequences. Science; 241; 1988; 459-462.

[49] Pays E., Coquelet H., Tebabi P., Pays A., Jefferies D., Steinert M., Koenig E., Williams R.O., Roditi I. *Trypanosoma brucei* : constitutive activity of the VSG and procyclin promoters. EMBO J; 9; 1990; 3145-3151.

[50] Vanhamme L., Berberof M., Le Ray D., Pays E. Stimuli of differentiation regulate RNA elongation in the transcription units for the major stage-specific antigens of *Trypanosoma brucei*. Nucleic Acids Res; 23; 1995; 1862-1869.

[51] Ürményi T.P., van der Ploeg PARP promoter-mediated activation of a VSG expression site promoter in insect form

Trypanosoma brucei. Nucleic Acids Res; 23; 1995; 1010-1018.

[52] Jefferies D., Tebabi P., Pays E. Transient activity assays of the *Trypanosoma brucei* VSG gene promotor: control of gene expression at the post-transcriptional level. Mol Cell Biol; 11; 1991; 338-343.

[53] Hehl A., Vassella E., Braun R., Roditi I. A conserved stem-loop structure in the 3' untranslated region of procyclin mRNAs regulates expression in *Trypanosoma brucei*. Proc Natl Acad Sci USA; 91; 1994; 370-374.

[54] Clayton C., Hotz H.-R. Post-transcriptional control of PARP gene expression. Mol Biochem Parasitol; 77; 1996; 1-6.

[55] Schürch N., Furger A., Kurath U, Roditi I. Contributions of the procyclin 3' untranslated region and coding region to the regulation of expression in bloodstream forms of *Trypanosoma brucei*. Mol Biochem Parasitol 1997; 89: 109–21.

[56] Hans-Rudolf H, Biebinger S, Flaspohler J, Clayton C. PARP gene expression: control at many levels. Mol Biochem Parasitol 1998; 91: 131–43.

[57] Bayne R.A.L., Kilbride E.A., Lainson F.A., Tetley L., Barry J.D. A major surface antigen of procyclic stage *Trypanosoma congolense*. Mol Biochem Parasitol; 61; 1993; 295-310.

[58] Hehl A., Roditi I. The regulation of procyclin expression in *Trypanosoma brucei*: Making or breaking the rules?. Parasitol Today; 10; 1994; 442-445.

[59] Dorn P.L., Aman R.A., Boothroyd J.C. Inhibition of protein synthesis results in super-induction of procyclin (PARP) RNA levels. Mol Biochem Parasitol; 44; 1991; 133-139.

[60] Graham S.V., Barry J.D. Polysomal, procyclin mRNAs accumulate in bloodstream forms of monomorphic and pleomorphic trypanosomes treated with protein synthesis inhibitors. Mol Biochem Parasitol; 80; 1996; 179-191.

[61] Evans J.S., Levine B.A., Trayer I.P., Dorman C.J., Higgins C.F. Sequence-imposed structural restraints in the Ton B protein of *E. coli*. FEBS Lett; 208; 1986; 211-216.

[62] Otsu K., Willard H.F., Khanna V.K., Zorzato F., Green N.M., MacLennan D.H. Molecular cloning of cDNA encoding the Ca^{2+} release channel (ryanodine receptor) of rabbit cardiac muscle sarcoplasmic reticulum. J Biol Chem; 265; 1990; 13472-13483.

[63] Lafrenière R.G., Carrel L., Willard H.F. A novel transmembrane transporter encoded by the XPCT gene in Xq13.2. Hum Mol Genet; 3; 1994; 1133-1139.

[64] Geertman R., McMahon A., Sabban E. Cloning and characterisation of cDNAs for novel proteins with glutamic acid-proline dipeptide tandem repeats. Biochim Biophys Acta; 1306; 1996; 147-152.

[65] Latif F., Tory K., Gnarra J., Yao M., Duh F.-M., Orcutt M.L., et al. Identification of the von Hippel-Lindau disease tumor suppressor gene. Science; 260; 1993; 1317-1320.

[66] Ferguson M.A.F., Murray P., Rutherford H., McConville M.J. A simple purification of procyclic acidic repetitive protein and demonstration of a sialylated glycosyl-phosphatidylinositol membrane anchor. Biochem J; 291; 1993; 51-55.

[67] Bütikofer P, Ruepp S, Boschung M, Roditi I. «GPEET» procyclin is the major surface glycoprotein of *Trypanosoma brucei brucei* procyclic culture forms. Biochem J 1997; 326 : 415–23.

[68] Treumann A, Zitzmann N, Hülsmeier A, Prescott AR, Almond A, Sheelah J, Ferguson MAJ. Structural characterisation of two forms of procyclic acidic repetitive protein expressed by procyclic forms of *Trypanosoma brucei*. J Mol Biol 1997; 269 : 529–47.

[69] Pontes de Carvalho L.C., Tomlinson S., Vandekerckhove F., Bienen E.J., Clarkson A.B., Jiang M.-S., Hart G.W., Nussenzweig V. Characterization of a novel *trans*-sialidase of *Trypanosoma brucei* procyclic trypomastigotes and identification of procyclin as the main sialic acid acceptor. J Exp Med; 177; 1993; 465-474.

[70] Engstler M., Reuter G., Schauer R. The developmentally regulated *trans*-sialidase from *Trypanosoma brucei* sialylates the procyclic acidic repetitive protein. Mol Biochem Parasitol; 61; 1993; 1-13.

[71] Clayton C.E., Mowatt M.R. The procyclic acid repetitive proteins of *Trypanosoma brucei*: purification and post-translational modification. J Biol Chem; 264; 1989; 15088-15093.

[72] Maudlin I., Welburn S.C. Maturation of trypanosome infections in tsetse. Exp Parasitol; 79; 1994; 202-205.

[73] Maudlin I., Welburn S.C. The role of lectins and trypanosome genotype in the maturation of midgut infections in *Glossina morsitans*. Trop Med Parasitol; 39; 1988; 56-58.

[74] Welburn S., Dale C., Ellis D., Beecroft R., Pearson T.W. Apoptosis in procyclic *Trypanosoma brucei rhodesiense* in vitro. Cell Death Differ; 3; 1996; 229-236.

[75] Ten Asbroek A.L.M.A., Ouellette M., Borst P. Targeted insertion of the neomycin phosphotransferase gene into the tubulin gene cluster of *Trypanosoma brucei*. Nature; 348; 1990; 174-175.

[76] Beecroft R.P., Roditi I., Pearson T.W. Identification and characterization of a major surface glycoprotein from procyclic stage *Trypanosoma congolense*. Mol Biochem Parasitol; 61; 1993; 285-294.

[77] Hehl A., Pearson T.W., Barry J.D., Braun R., Roditi I. Expression of GARP, a major surface glycoprotein of *Trypanosoma*

congolense, on the surface of *Trypanosoma brucei* : characterisation and use as a surface marker. Mol Biochem Parasitol; 70; 1995; 45-58.

[78] Majiwa P.A.O., Masake R.A., Nantulya V.M., Hamers R., Matthyssens G. *Trypanosoma (Nannomonas) congolense :*

identification of two karyotypic groups. EMBO J; 4; 1985; 3307-3313.

[79] Garside L.H., Gibson W.C. Molecular characterisation of trypanosome species and subgroups with subgenus *Nannomonas*. Parasitology; 111; 1995; 301-312.

9

PARP gene expression : control at many levels

Hans-Rudolf Hotz,
Susanne Biebinger,
John Flaspohler,
Christine Clayton

Zentrum fur Molekulare Biologie, Im Nevenheimer Feld 282, 6900 Heidelberg, Germany

Keywords : Gene expression; Procyclic acidic repetitive protein; *Trypanosoma brucei*

1 • Introduction

The procyclic acidic repetitive proteins (PARPs) or procyclins are the major constituents of the surface of *Trypanosoma brucei* procyclic forms. The mature proteins consist largely of Glutamate-Proline (EP) or Gly-Pro-Glu-Glu-Thr repeats [1] and are linked to the membrane by an unusual glycosyl phosphatidylinositol (GPI) anchor [2]. The functional significance of the different repeats are discussed by Isabel Roditi elsewhere in this volume.

There is probably very strong selection against expression of PARP in bloodstream forms, and indeed, it has never been detected there. It is known that when PARP and VSG are simultaneously expressed, the PARP is accessible to antibodies [3], so that its expression in bloodstream forms would probably induce an effective immune response.

The most recent measurements, made using reporter gene constructs, indicate that PARP expression in bloodstream forms is down-regulated relative to procyclic forms at at least three levels :

1. Transcription is down-regulated 5–10-fold ([4] and Refs. therein).

2. Sequences in the 3'-untranslated region (3'-UTR) induce rapid degradation of some of the RNA, yielding 11-fold post-transcriptional down-regulation of mRNA levels.

3. The same 3'-UTR sequences inhibit translation at least 10-fold. All three factors acting simultaneously could thus result in at least 1000-fold down-regulation of PARP in bloodstream forms. If each procyclic parasite contains 10^6–10^7 molecules of PARP [5], bloodstream forms should have less than 10^4 molecules per cell. Additional controls might be :

4. Inhibition of translation by the *PARP* coding region

5. Inefficient processing or trafficking of the protein in the secretory pathway (for example, failure to recognise the GPI-anchor addition signal).

In this review we will concentrate on the first three points.

2 ● Transcription

2.1 Structure of the *PARP* loci

The *PARP* genes are arranged as direct tandem repeats with the promoter immediately upstream (Fig. 1).

There are two or three *PARP* genes per locus [6, 7] ; like nearly all trypanosomatid genes, they are transcribed in a polycistronic fashion, and mature mRNAs are generated by polyadenylation and *trans*-splicing [8]. The overwhelming weight of evidence indicates that the *PARP* genes, like the VSG genes, are transcribed by RNA polymerase I [9, 10]. One or two additional unrelated downstream genes are co-transcribed, and a terminator has been mapped for one of the loci [11]. Upstream of the *PARP* loci are polymerase II transcription units with the same orientation as the *PARP* locus; this transcription terminates within a few hundred base-pairs of *PARP* transcriptional initiation [12].

FIGURE 1

Organisation of the PARP B locus.

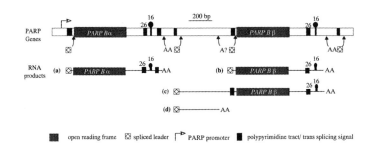

2.2 Structure of polymerase I promoters

PARP, VSG and rRNA (*RRN*) promoters have dissimilar sequences, although conservation within the different promoter classes is quite strong. If the PARP and VSG promoters evolved from the RRN promoters, divergence must have been very extensive before becoming fixed by gene conversion. An alternative is that each promoter class evolved independently.

Despite the dissimilarity in the primary sequences, deletion and mutation analyses revealed that for each polymerase I promoter type, the essential «core» promoter region spans about 10 base-pairs centred around position − 30 relative to transcription initiation [13–19]. The *PARP* and *RRN* promoters (but not the *VSG* promoters) also have a second sequence at around position −70 that enhances transcriptional activity [13–15]. A variety of hybrid promoters is active [15, 20], implying that at least some of the transcription factors involved are either common to both promoters, or share compatible functional domains. The results of attempts to detect such factors by DNA-binding assays have so far not been encouraging. We found evidence for weak but sequence-specific binding to double-stranded *PARP* promoter DNA [21], but others found evidence only for binding to single strands [19, 22].

The initiation site sequence was reported to be critical for *RRN* and *VSG* promoter activity [8, 23, 24]. In particular, it was suggested that an A residue was necessary at the start site. Point mutations at the

FIGURE 2

Comparison of transcription initiation sites of selected *VSG, RRN,* and *PARP* promoters. Sequences and start sites (bent arrows) of different promoters are as indicated, and point mutations are indicated by arrows beneath the *RRN* and *PARP* A promoter sequences. The mutations of the *RRN* promoter reduced activity by 90–98%, whereas none of the PARP promoter mutations had any significant effect on activity. Data are taken from: P_{RRN}: [23, 25]; $P_{PARP\ B}$: [14]; $P_{PARP\ A}$: [13] and results of J. Flaspohler; P_{MVAT4} (metacyclic VSG promoter reactivated in bloodstream forms): [16]; P_{mVSG} (metacyclic VSG promoter activated in metacyclic trypanosomes: [26]; $P_{VSG\ (ds)}$ (downstream start site of a VSG bloodstream form expression site): [25]; $P_{VSG\ (AnTat\ 1.3)}$ (start site of AnTat 1.3 expression site): [27]; $P_{VSG\ (us)}$ (upstream start site of a VSG bloodstream form expression site): [25].

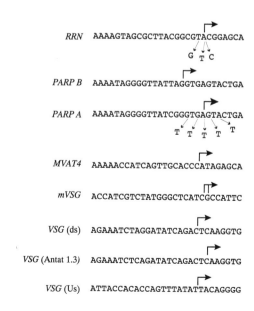

initiation site of an the *RRN* promoter (T → G at position − 1, or A → T or A → C at position +1) were aufficient to reduce reporter gene expression 10–50-fold (Fig. 2).

The *PARP* promoter is singularly insensitive in comparison. Linker-scanner mutations covering the start site had relatively minor effects [13, 14], and point mutations similar to those performed with the *RRN* promoter had no effect whatsoever (Fig. 2). Preliminary RNAase protection results suggested, though, that these mutations did affect the precise position of initiation (J. Flaspohler, unpublished results). Other results also hint that the position of initation may be not be as inflexible as initially thought. The positions of initiation mapped for the *PARP* A and *PARP* B promoters were different [13, 14] as were initiation points reported for different *VSG* promoters [16, 25–27] (Fig. 2).

2.3 Why polymerase 1 ?

We will probably never know how *PARP* and *VSG* genes came to be transcribed by RNA polymerase I. In other eukaryotes, expression of protein-coding genes using polymerases other than RNA polymerase II is very rare, as polymerase II initiation is required in order to put the 5' cap on the RNA. The cap plays a major role in RNA export to the cytosol, stability, and translation; only some viral RNAs, with special internal translation entry sites, can circumvent this requirement. In trypanosomatids, the cap is present on the spliced leader, so that capping of mRNAs is coupled to *trans*-splicing but independent of the transcribing polymerase [28]. Since *trans*-splicing is found in all Kinetoplastids whereas use of RNA polymerase I to transcribe protein-coding genes has so far been reported only for the salivarian trypanosomes, we can probably assume that the development of *trans*-splicing preceded the use of polymerase I for *VSG* and *PARP*.

Given that transcription of protein-coding genes by RNA polymerase I should be possible in all *trans*-splicing organisms, why has it only been detected in salivarian trypanosomes ? Although protein expression from the ribosomal RNA promoter is possible in *Trypanosoma cruzi* [29] there is no evidence for transcription of protein coding genes by polymerase I, despite the fact that genes for a major surface antigen are, like those encoding VSG, telomeric [30]. Leaving aside the real possibility that such transcription has merely not yet been detected, the most obvious difference between salivarian trypanosomes and the other kinetoplastids is the phenomenon of antigenic variation. For effective antigenic variation, it is absolutely necessary that only one *VSG* gene be expressed at a time, but that this gene should yield sufficient VSG to completely cover the trypanosome surface — estimated at up to 10% of total cell protein. In addition, transcription of the *VSG* gene should be subject to very strong control. To understand why these conditions can only be met by RNA polymerase I, a brief divergence to the subject of trypanosomatid RNA polymerase II is necessary.

Accumulated evidence suggests that trypanosomatid RNA polymerase II initiation is very weak, astonishingly non-specific, and subject to no discernable regulation [8, 31]. Developmentally-regulated genes show no regulation at the level of transcription; and genes showing drastically different regulation are co-transcribed. No transcription unit has been fully mapped and gaps in polymerase II transcription seem only to occur at positions where other polymerases are active [12, 32]. In *Leishmania*, transcription of plasmids bearing no trypanosomatid sequence whatsoever was observed [33] and strand specificity may be mediated via termination [34]. Attempts in several laboratories (including ours) to isolate RNA polymerase II promoters from these organisms have been crowned only by conspicuous failure; the only two candidate trypanosomatid polymerase II promoters described [35, 36] had very low activity. The model that is most consistent with the data is that polymerase II transcription initiates at many very weak sites within polycistronic transcription units.

RNA polymerase I promoters have two clear advantages for VSG transcription : they yield strong initiation which is subject to regulation. Moreover, elongation by RNA polymerase I can be developmentally controlled. The expression of reporter genes integrated downstream of *RRN, PARP* and *VSG* promoters is 20 times higher than that of identical constructs integrated in the tubulin, actin or aldolase loci ([4] and C. Hartmann, ZMBH, unpublished results). Control of *VSG* transcription is discussed extensively elsewhere in this volume : initiation is regulated during antigenic variation, by a mechanism that can also control rRNA promoter activity; and both elongation and transcription are probably down-regulated in procyclics [27, 37–39]. In contrast with *VSG*, several *PARP* genes (8–10) are expressed simultaneously. The high expression needed to coat the parasite could probably be obtained through gene amplification, without recourse to polymerase I. Is use of polymerase I an evolutionary accident, or does it confer a selective advantage ? The one obvious advantage is the regulatability of the *PARP* promoter.

2.4   Control of RNA polymerase I transcription

All RNA polymerase I promoters can be regulated by chromosomal context, but there are clear differences in the patterns seen. The only one that is regulated in transient assays is a metacyclic *VSG* promoter [26]; for all others, regulation is seen only in a chromosomal context. The *PARP* promoter is the only one that is down-regulated in bloodstream forms when integrated in a ribosomal RNA spacer [4]. *RRN* and bloodstream *VSG* promoters are not regulated in this context [4, 38, 39].

In addition to the intrinsic regulatablility of the *PARP* promoter, other sequences within the locus may also suppress bloodstream-form transcription, as not only the *PARP*, but also the *RRN* promoter, are down-regulated in bloodstream forms when integrated there [4, 37]. The mechanism of this regulation is somewhat controversial. Our results were most consistent with regulation of transcriptional initiation [4] but it is also clear that transcription from the *PARP* promoter is attenuated within pBR322-derived plasmid sequences [10], and that this is exacerbated in bloodstream forms [4, 37].

The *PARP* promoter may also have special activating properties in procyclic trypanosomes. For example, it can promote RNA polymerase I transcription from within an RNA polymerase II transcription unit, but the *VSG* and *RRN* promoters cannot [40, 41] unless they are activated by a *PARP* promoter integrated nearby [20, 41].

3 • Processing

3.1 *PARP* mRNA processing

The *PARP* genes are arranged as direct tandem repeats with the promoter immediately upstream and a gap of several hundred bp between the polyadenylation site of the upstream (alpha) gene and the *trans*-splice acceptor site of the downstream (beta) gene (Fig. 1). *Trans*-splicing of the *PARP* transcripts is directed by polypyrimidine tracts located immediately upstream of the splice acceptor AG [42]. However, the intergenic region and 3'-UTRs have many other polypyrimidine tracts which, if placed upstream of a reporter gene, can also direct *trans*-splicing (thin black blocks in Fig. 1) [43]–45]. In kinetoplastids polyadenylation is mechanistically [46] and specially [43, 47–49] linked to *trans*-splicing. Polyadenylation occurs preferentially at one or more A residues, approximately (for *T. brucei*) 100 bases upstream of a *trans*-splice signal [43, 48, 49]. This means we have two ways to detect *trans*-splicing signals. We can — as for higher eukaryotic cells — deduce the presence of a signal from the structure of the *trans*-spliced product, but in addition, the presence of a polyadenylated mRNA betrays the presence of an active *trans*-splicing signal downstream of the poly(A) site even if the corresponding *trans*-spliced product is undetectable. In the case of *PARP*, a *trans*-splicing signal in the intergenic region directs *PARP* alpha polyadenylation (Fig. 1, a) [43], and another site is responsible for *PARP* beta polyadenylation (Fig. 2, b) [45, 49]. Correspondingly spliced RNAs can also be detected (e.g. RNA (c) in Fig. 1), but neither is likely to be functional as an mRNA [43, 45, 49]. In theory, a small non-coding intergenic RNA should also be synthesised (Fig. 1, d), but this has never been detected.

3.2 How are processing sites chosen ?

Splice site choice is in general a poorly-understood phenomenon. We have used constructs containing two open reading frames (Fig. 3a) to analyse splice acceptor site choice in trypanosomes. The constructs contains a chloramphenicol acyltransferase (*CAT*) gene followed by a hygromycin resistance *HYG* gene.

The two open reading frames are separated by a 3'-UTR followed by a *trans*-splicing signal and 5'-UTR. The construct is set up so that polyadenylation of the *CAT* mRNA occurs at the normal polyadenylation site within the 3'-UTR sequence [40, 50]. If a second *trans*-splicing signal is inserted, however, polyadenylation of the *CAT* mRNA shifts downstream; addition of a third signal results in even longer *CAT* mRNAs [40, 50]. Preliminary results inducate that the pattern of polyadenylation is dictated more by the constellation of possible splice sites than by the presence of a downstream open reading frame (C. Hartmann, ZMBH, unpublished results). We have as yet no idea how the «last» splice site in a series is recognised.

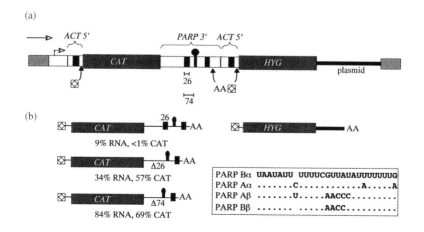

(a)

(b)

FIGURE 3

(a) Structure of a bicistronic plasmid used to analyse the regulation mediated by 3'-UTRs. Symbols are the same as those used in Fig. 1. The structures of RNA products from the wild-type construct, and from deletion mutants, with corresponding levels of *CAT* mRNA and CAT activity, are indicated; (b) sequences of 26mers from different *PARP* 3'-UTRs.

4 • Export and degradation

4.1 Regulation by 3'-UTRs

After the development of trypanosomatid transfection assays it rapidly became apparent that the level of reporter gene expression was drastically affected by the nature of the 3' sequence [24]. In particular, the pattern of expression seen for developmentally-regulated genes could be mimicked by placing their 3'-UTRs downstream of reporter genes or selectable markers [40, 51–58]. The regulation mediated by the *PARP* 3'-UTR is particularly strong and is illustrated in Fig. 4.

The dicistronic contruct described above (Fig. 3a), containing *CAT* and *HYG* genes, was integrated into the tubulin locus of bloodstream or procyclic trypanosomes. In the construct, the *HYG* gene is preceded by an actin (*ACT*) gene 5'-UTR and *trans*-splicing signal (together labelled *ACT*-5'). The nature of the 3'-UTR on the preceding *CAT* transcript can be changed at will. Using the *ACT* 3'-UTR (*ACT*-3') expression is similar in both life cycle stages (Fig. 4); this construct is a useful control (values for mRNA abundance and CAT activity set at 100%). The *PARP* 3'-UTR (*PARP*-3') gives approximately 100% CAT activity and RNA in procyclic forms, but 9% *CAT* mRNA and less than 1% CAT activity in bloodstream forms. The discrepancy between levels of *CAT*- *PARP*-3' RNA and CAT activity indicates that the *PARP* 3'-UTR down-regulates not only mRNA levels, but also translation. The aldolase (*ALD*) 3'-UTR (as an additional control) mediates opposite effects, giving up-regulation in bloodstream forms. The *HYG* mRNA is unchanged throughout, showing that the transcription is similar for all constructs.

FIGURE 4

Effects of different 3'-UTRs on levels of poly(A)+ mRNA and *CAT* gene expression. Northern blots of poly(A)+ RNA were probed with *CAT*, *ACT* and *HYG* probes, the latter two probes serving as controls. B, bloodstream form; P, procyclic.

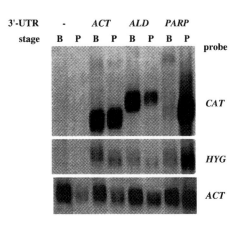

4.2 A conserved 26mer is necessary for regulation

We used deletion mutagenesis analysis to determine which sequences in the *PARP* 3'-UTR are responsible for developmental regulation (Fig. 3). Although all *PARP* gene 3'-UTRs are of similar length, only two regions show any sequence conservation. One is a 16mer that is predicted to form a stem-loop structure; deletion or mutation of the 16mer reduces translation about 3-fold in procyclic forms [59] and bloodstream forms [44] but the sequence appears to play no direct role in developmental regulation [44]. The other conserved region is an interrupted polypyrimidine tract, consisting of two stretches of oligo(U) separated by a less conserved spacer (Fig. 3b). This 26mer is absolutely required for developmental regulation mediated by both *PARP* B alpha and *PARP* B beta 3'-UTRs. Precise deletion of the 26mer (to give the *CAT*- *PARP* Δ26-3' RNA, Fig. 3a) raised CAT activity and *CAT* mRNA levels in bloodstream forms but had no effect in procyclics [44]. Complete deletion of the sequence preceding the 26mer had only marginal effects on expression, indicating that it was not directly involved in regulation. In order to raise CAT activity to levels approaching the control, it was necessary to delete 76 bases, including the 26mer and 50 bases downstream, from the *PARP*-alpha 3' (Fig. 3a). Mutation of only three of the U residues in one of the U tracts was sufficient to raise CAT activity and mRNA to at least 20% [44], indicating the the function of the 26mer is very sequence-specific.

Although this 26mer is necessary for regulation, it is not sufficient. It does not, for example, reduce CAT expression if it is placed between the *CAT* gene and the beginning of an *ACT*-3'. (Compare this result with that mentioned earlier : if a *PARP*-3' is deleted from the 5' side, so that the 26mer is placed immediately downstream of a *CAT* gene but the downstream portion of the 3'-UTR is retained, regulation is intact.) Thus, the context of the 26mer is important for regulation. One possible explanation could be that the surrounding sequences affect 26mer secondary structure. Computer-predicted structures of the *PARP* alpha and *PARP* beta 3'-UTRs partially support this idea. The most favoured structures for the relevant regions of the *PARP* alpha and beta 3'-UTRs are shown in Fig. 5.

The 16mer stem-loop (shown as a thick dotted line) is predicted to sit at the end of a long stem, and the 26mer is predicted to be largely free of base-pair interactions. The predicted structures of the 5'-halves of the 3'-UTRs, which are not required for control, do not resemble each other at all (not shown).

FIGURE 5

Predicted structures, made using the MFold programme, for 3'-halves of two *PARP* 3'-UTRs. One structure is shown for the *PARP* alpha sequence, and two structures with similar energies for *PARP* beta. Perfect base-pairs are indicated with connecting lines and G-U base-pairs with dots. The 16mer is indicated as a thick dotted line. The conserved (U)n sequences of the 26mer are thick black lines, and the beginning and central regions as lines of medium thickness.

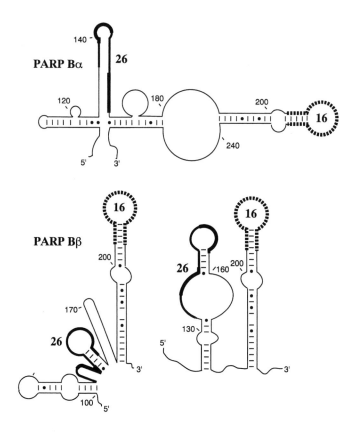

If these predicted structures bear any relationship to intracellular reality, the 26mer will be free to interact with controlling factors without interference from other parts of the 3'-UTR.

4.3 The 26mer stimulates degradation in bloodstream forms

The *PARP-3'* could regulate the mRNA in several ways : by affecting processing, export from the nucleus, or stability. Such controls are not mutually exclusive and could interact : for example, uncapped RNAs are not exported from the nucleus, and uncapping in the cytosol is a prelude to degradation. We have so far only examined RNA degradation in detail. We incubated trypanosomes with inhibitors of transcription (actinomycin D or chloroquine) or with an inhibitor that prevents *trans*-splicing (sinefungin) and assayed the amount of surviving *ACT, PARP,* or *CAT* mRNA. In procyclic forms, *ACT, PARP, CAT- ACT-3', CAT- PARP-3',* and *CAT- PARP Δ26-3'* mRNAs all had half-lives of between 90 and 120 min [44]. In bloodstream forms, the *ACT* and *CAT- ACT-3'* mRNAs had half-lives of 20 min [44], degradation commencing 10–15 min after addition of inhibitor. In general, mRNA turnover is faster in bloodstream forms than in procyclic forms [60]; this probably reflects the higher growth temperature (and presumably faster transcription), shorter cell-cycle time, and smaller volume of bloodstream forms. The patterns of *PARP* and *CAT-PARP-3'* mRNA degradation were similar, and clearly distinct from the pattern seen with the control RNAs. The kinetics were biphasic, with rapid initial degradation followed by a slower component. RNA prepared from cells treated with inhibitor immediately before cell centrifugation and harvest (an interval of 8–10 min) had less than half as much *CAT-PARP-3'* or *PARP* mRNA as cells that received no drug. The half-life of the remaining RNA could not be accurately measured because of its low abundance, but it appeared to be similar to that of the *ACT* controls. Importantly, *CAT-PARP Δ26-3'* mRNA behaved exactly like the *ACT* controls. Thus, the 26mer causes instability of some *PARP* and *CAT-PARP-3'* RNAs.

The biphasic nature of the degradation kinetics implies that there may be two subpopulations of *PARP-3'* RNAs, one of which is protected (or specially separated) from the degradation mechanism. Several possible explanations come to mind, not all of them mutually exclusive. Each has precedents in higher eukaryotes (including yeast).

4.4 Retention in the nucleus by splicing factors ?

One explanation of the biphasic kinetics is that the unstable RNA subpopulation is retained in the nucleus and the stable portion is in the cytoplasm. This would imply that it is newly-synthesised RNA that is preferentially degraded by a nucleus-specific mechanism. In higher eukaryotes, binding of splicing factors to unprocessed RNAs can inhibit their export from the nucleus, leading to rapid degradation [61, 62]. The 26mer can act as a splicing signal when placed upstream of an open reading frame, but — at least in transient assays — the splicing is not developmentally regulated. This does not support the idea that the 26mer binds *trans*-splicing factors in the bloodstream form, but not the procyclic form nucleus. Also, preliminary results of a mutational analysis of the 26mer revealed no correlation of splicing potential with regulatory activity [63]. The remaining option is that there is a factor in the procyclic (but not bloodstream-form) nucleus that binds to the 26mer, shielding it from recognition by active splicing factors. Such a factor might not be detected in transient assays because the transiently-expressed product mRNA precursor might be present in large excess.

4.5 Is degradation connected with (or prevented by) translation ?

Another possibility is that there are two populations of *PARP* RNA in the cytosol : localised in different parts of the cytosol, or perhaps on and off polysomes. Incubation of bloodstream trypanosomes with protein synthesis inhibitors results in a slight rise in several RNAs, but *PARP* RNAs are particularly strongly affected [64]. One explanation — that there is an RNAase associated with polysomes — can be discounted because both puromycin and cycloheximide have the same effect. The induced mRNA is cytosolic and polysome-associated [64]. We do not yet know the location of *PARP* or *CAT- PARP*-3' mRNA in untreated bloodstream trypanosomes, as we have been unable to detect it after fractionation. We made one mutant of the 26mer that abolished translational repression without affecting the level of mRNA [44, 63], so translational repression and RNA instability are not inextricably linked.

4.6 Degradation initiated by a site-specific endonuclease

One of the paradigms of 3'-UTR-mediated post-transcriptional regulation in higher eukaryotic cells is the transferrin mRNA [65]. The responsible sequence, the iron regulatory element (IRE) forms a stem-loop that is sensitive to a specific endonuclease [66]. This is bound by a regulatory protein (IRP) that is structurally related to aconitase, and binds iron. In the absence of iron, the IRP binds the IRE, protecting the mRNA from the endonuclease. In the presence of iron, the IRP dissociates from the IRE, allowing degradation of the transferrin mRNA [65]. The presence of a related mechanism for *PARP* would be consistent with the predicited exposed state of the 26mer in the secondary structure. This would require expression in bloodstream forms of an endonuclease that can attack the 26mer (Fig. 6a).

To achieve regulation, the endonuclease could be absent in procyclics. Alternatively the endonuclease might be constitutively expressed, but competed by a procyclic-specific 26mer-binding protein (Fig. 6b). This mechanism implies the presence of a specific cleavage product, which might be detectable by appropriately sensitive assays.

During differentiation of bloodstream forms into procyclic forms in vitro, *PARP* becomes detectable (by immunofluorescence using monoclonal antibodies) within 4 h in pleomorphic parasites [67]. This early appearance could be due to release of translational

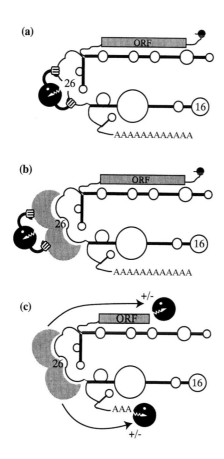

(a)

(b)

(c)

FIGURE 6

Alternative regulation mechanisms. The entire PARP alpha 3'-UTR is shown schematically, and to scale; thin lines are single strands and thick lines are double strands. The poly(A) tail (AAAAA), the open reading frame (grey box, ORF) and the 5'-cap (self explanatory) are not to scale: (a) action of a hypothetical site-specific endonuclease, cutting the 26mer; (b) protection against the hypothetical endonuclease by a hypothetical procyclic-specific 26mer binding protein; (c) action of a hypothetical 26mer-binding protein on deadenylation (below) or decapping and/or 5' → 3' exonuclease action (above).

control, or to synthesis of new RNA, or both [37, 68]. The rise in RNA, also detectable within 4 h, could be mediated either by loss of the RNAase, or rapid synthesis of a binding protein, or both. The existence of an unstable, bloodstream-form specific *PARP*-mRNA-specific RNAase is one possible explanation for the rapid increase in the RNA after protein synthesis inhibition on bloodstream forms [64, 69] — or it could be a secondary effect, as initiation of differentiation is associated anyway with a pause in protein synthesis [70].

An additional possibility is that the hypothetical endonuclease or 26mer-binding proteins might be constitutively present, but regulated by post-translation modifications such as phosphorylation. This would allow a very rapid response to a change in environmental conditions and would thwart any attempts to isolate the responsible gene by differential library screen approaches!

4.7 The deadenylation/decapping pathway

A common degradation pathway in yeast, that affects many RNAs but can be accelerated by specific 3'-UTR sequences, starts with deadenylation, followed by decapping, and finally degradation by a $5' \rightarrow 3'$ exonuclease [71, 72]. A 26mer-binding protein might stimulate or inhibit enzymes involved in this process (Fig. 6c). So far, however, it seems unlikely that this mechanism is involved in the rapid component of *PARP* mRNA degradation. Because deadenylation has to be complete before degradation of the body of the RNA can be degraded, the first thing that happens after inhibition of transcription is that the RNA becomes shorter, but remains at the same abundance [73]. Poly(A) tails on steady-state ACT, PGK and *PARP* mRNAs are 150–200 bases long (S. Krieger, unpublished). After incubation of trypanosomes with RNA synthesis inhibitors, there is indeed a delay before degradation of *ACT* mRNAs commences. During this time, poly(A) tails on PARP, ACT and other RNAs are trimmed to less than 50 bases, irrespective of the abundance of the respective transcripts (S. Krieger, unpublished). This suggests that deadenylation followed by decapping may be the default mechanism for RNA degradation.

5 • Control of translation

Given that detectable amounts of *PARP*-3' mRNA are present in bloodstream trypanosomes, some mechanism has to prevent its expression. Although differential regulation of *PARP* processing in the secretory pathway may well occur, there is also an element of control that is completely independent of post-translational events. The presence of the *PARP*-3' on the *CAT* mRNA strongly inhibited expression of CAT, which is a soluble cytosolic protein. After inhibition of protein synthesis with cycloheximide, the *PARP* mRNA that accumulates has been shown to be stalled on polysomes [64], implying that it is cytoplasmic (not nuclear) and that the 26mer does not prevent initiation of translation. Neither the subcellular location of *P ARP*-3' mRNA, nor its association with ribosomes, have yet been determined in untreated bloodstream forms : such experiments have so far been precluded by the low abundance of the RNAs concerned. All we know so far is that the 26mer plays a role in translation inhibition and that this effect is not dependent on the presence of the 16mer.

This sort of control is definitely not unique to *PARP*. It is probably involved in control of phosphoglycerate kinase mRNAs in *T. brucei* [74], and of hsp83 mRNAs in *Leishmania mexicana* [52, 75]. In higher eukaryotes and yeast, translation can also affect mRNA levels. For example the introduction of premature termination codons in some RNAs (but not others) results in instability, and sequences in the 3'-UTR can influence translation by interacting with the translational initiation complex.

6 ● Conclusion

PARP gene expression is controlled at nearly every level that has been studied so far : transcriptional initiation and elongation; RNA turnover; and translation. Although there is as yet no evidence for control of RNA processing, such a mechanism may be linked with RNA degradation. As the GPI anchor added to *PARP* in procyclic forms is different from that on VSG [2], it is quite possible that *PARP* trafficking in the secretory pathway will turn out to be regulated too.

Almost nothing is known about RNA degradation in trypanosomes. Since all polymerase II transcripts are regulated by post-transcriptional mechanisms, and since the 3'-UTRs on many RNAs have already been shown to play a crucial role in this regulation, degradation of RNA is likely to be one of the most important control points in stage-specific gene expression. The very strong regulation of the PARP mRNA makes it an ideal model for the study of this process.

R E F E R E N C E S

[1] Clayton CE, Fueri J, Mowatt M. The procyclic surface protein of *Trypanosoma brucei*. In : Molecular and Immunological Aspects of Parasitism. New Orleans : American Association for the Advancement of Science, 1990.

[2] McConville MJ. In : Smith DF, Parsons M, editors. Molecular Biology of Parasitic Protozoa. IRL Press : Oxford, 1996 : 205–228.

[3] Roditi I., Schwartz H., Pearson T.W., Beecroft R.P., Liu M.K., Richardson J.P., Buring H.-J., Pleiss J., Bulow R., Williams R.O., Overath P. Procyclin gene expression and loss of the variant surface glycoprotein during differentiation of *Trypanosoma brucei*. J Cell Biol; 108; 1989; 737-746.

[4] Biebinger S., Rettenmaier S., Flaspohler J., Hartmann C., Pena-Diaz J., Wirtz L.E., Hotz H.R., Barry J.D., Clayton C.E. The PARP promoter of *Trypanosoma brucei* is developmentally regulated in a chromosomal context. Nucleic Acids Res; 24; 1996; 1202-1211.

[5] Clayton C.E., Mowatt M.R. The procyclic acidic repetitive proteins of *Trypanosoma brucei* : purification and post-translational modification. J Biol Chem; 264; 1989; 15088-15093.

[6] Hehl A., Roditi I. The regulation of procyclin expression in *Trypanosoma brucei* : making or breaking the rules. Parasitol Today; 10; 1994; 442-445.

[7] Clayton CE. In : Moldave K, Cohn W, editors. Progress in Nucleic Acid Research and Molecular Biology. San Diego (CA) : Academic Press, 1992 : 37–66.

[8] Vanhamme L., Pays E. Control of gene expression in trypanosomes. Microbiol Rev; 59; 1995; 223-240.

[9] Chung H.-M., Lee M.G.-S., Van der Ploeg L.H.T. RNA polymerase I mediated protein-coding gene expression in *Trypanosoma brucei*. Parasitol Today; 8; 1992; 414-418.

[10] Chung H.-M.M., Lee M.G.-S., Dietrich P., Huang J., van der Ploeg L.H.T. Disruption of the largest subunit RNA polymerase II genes in *Trypanosoma brucei*. Mol Cell Biol; 13; 1993; 3734-3743.

[11] Berberof M., Pays A., Lips S., Tebabi P., Pays E. Characterization of a transcription terminator of the procyclin PARP A unit of *Trypanosoma brucei*. Mol Cell Biol; 16; 1996; 914-924.

[12] Clayton C.E., Fueri J.P., Itzhaki J.E., Bellofatto V., Wisdom G.S., Vijayasarathy S., Mowatt M.R. Transcription of the procyclic acidic repetitive protein genes of *Trypanosoma brucei*. Mol Cell Biol; 10; 1990; 3036-3047.

[13] Sherman D., Janz L., Hug M., Clayton C.E. Anatomy of the procyclic acidic repetitive protein promoter of *Trypanosoma brucei*. EMBO J; 10; 1991; 3379-3386.

[14] Brown S.D., Huang J., Van der Ploeg L.H.T. The promoter for the procyclic acidic repetitive protein (*PARP*) genes of *Trypanosoma brucei* shares features with RNA polymerase I promoters. Mol Cell Biol; 12; 1992; 2644-2652.

[15] Janz L., Clayton C. The PARP and rRNA promoters of *Trypanosoma brucei* are composed of dissimilar sequence elements that are functionally interchangeable. Mol Cell Biol; 14; 1994; 5804-5811.

[16] Alarcon C.M., Son H.J., Hall T., Donelson J.E. A moncistronic transcript for a trypanosome variant surface glycoprotein. Mol Cell Biol; 14; 1994; 5579-5591.

[17] Nagoshi Y.L., Alarcon C.M., Donelson J.E. The putative promoter for a metacyclic VSG gene in African trypanosomes. Mol Biochem Parasitol; 72; 1995; 33-45.

[18] Pham V.P., Qi C.C., Gottesdiener K.M. A detailed mutational analysis of the VSG gene expression site promoter. Mol Biochem Parasitol; 75; 1996; 241-254.

[19] Vanhamme L., Pays A., Tebabi P., Alexandre S., Pays E. Specific binding of proteins to the non-coding strand of a crucial element of the variant surface glycoprotein, procyclin, and ribosomal promoters of *Trypanosoma brucei*. Mol Cell Biol; 15; 1995; 5598-5606.

[20] Qi C.C., Urmenyi T., Gottesdiener K.M. Analysis of a hybrid PARP/VSG ES promoter in procyclic trypanosomes. Mol Biochem Parasitol; 77; 1996; 147-160.

[21] Janz L., Hug M., Clayton C. Factors that bind to RNA polymerase I promoter sequences of *Trypanosoma brucei*. Mol Biochem Parasitol; 65; 1994; 99-108.

[22] Brown S.D., Van der Ploeg L.H.T. Single-stranded DNA-protein binding in the procyclic acidic repetitive protein (PARP) promoter of *Trypanosoma brucei*. Mol Biochem Parasitol; 65; 1994; 109-122.

[23] Rudenko G., Chung H.-M.M., Pham V.P., Van der Ploeg L.H.T. RNA polymerase I can mediate expression of CAT and protein-coding genes in *Trypanosoma brucei*. EMBO J; 10; 1991; 3387-3397.

[24] Zomerdijk J.C.B.M., Ouellette M., ten Asbroek A.L.M.A., Kieft R., Bommer A.M.M., Clayton C.E., Borst P. Active and inactive versions of a promoter for a variant surface glyco-

protein gene expression site in *Trypanosoma brucei*. EMBO J; 9; 1990; 2791-2801.

[25] Zomerdijk J.C.B.M., Kieft R., Shiels P., Borst P. Alpha-amanitin resistant transcription units in trypanosomes : a comparison of promoter sequences for a VSG gene expression site and for ribosomal RNA genes. Nucleic Acids Res; 19; 1991; 5153-5158.

[26] Graham S.V., Barry J.D. Transcriptional regulation of metacyclic variant surface glycoprotein gene expression during the life cycle of *Trypanosoma brucei*. Mol Cell Biol; 15; 1995; 5945-5956.

[27] Pays E., Vanhamme L., Berberof M. Genetic controls for the expression of surface antigens in African trypanosomes. Annu Rev Microbiol; 48; 1994; 25-52.

[28] Wirtz L.E., Hartmann C., Clayton C.E. Gene expression mediated by bacteriophage T3 and T7 RNA polymerases in transgenic trypanosomes. Nucleic Acids Res; 22; 1994; 3887-3894.

[29] Tyler-Cross R., Short S.L., Floeter-Winter L.M., Buck G.A. Transient expression mediated by the *Trypanosoma cruci* rRNA promoter. Mol Biochem Parasitol; 72; 1995; 23-31.

[30] Peterson D.S., Fouts D.L., Manning J.E. The 85-kDa surface antigen gene of *Trypanosoma cruzi* is telomeric and a member of a multigene familiy. EMBO J; 8; 1989; 3911-3916.

[31] Graham S.V. Mechanisms of stage-regulated gene expression in Kinetoplastida. Parasitol Today; 11; 1995; 217-223.

[32] Fantoni A., Dare A.O., Tschudi C. RNA polymerase III-mediated transcription of the tryanosome U2 small nuclear RNA gene is controlled by both intragenic and extragenic regulatory elements. Mol Cell Biol; 14; 1994; 2021-2028.

[33] de Lafaille M.A.C., Laban A., Wirth D.F. Gene expression in *Leishmania* : analysis of essential 5' DNA sequences. Proc Natl Acad Sci USA; 89; 1992; 2703-2707.

[34] Wong A.K., Curotto de Lafaille C., Wirth D.F. Identification of a *cis* acting gene regulatory element from the lemdr locus of *Leishmania enriettii*. Proc Natl Acad Sci USA; 269; 1994; 26497-26502.

[35] Lee M.G.-S. An RNA polymerase II promoter in the hsp70 locus of *Trypanosoma brucei*. Mol Cell Biol; 16; 1996; 1220-1230.

[36] Ben Amar M.F., Jefferies D., Pays A., Bakalara N., Kendall G., Pays E. The actin gene promoter of *Trypanosoma brucei*. Nucleic Acids Res; 19; 1991; 5857-5862.

[37] Vanhamme L., Berberof M., Le Ray D., Pays E. Stimuli of differentiation regulate RNA elongation in the transcription units for the major stage specific antigens of *Trypanosoma brucei*. Nucleic Acids Res; 23; 1995; 1862-1869.

[38] Rudenko G., Blundell P.A., Taylor M.C., Kieft R., Borst P. VSG gene expression site control in insect form *Trypanosoma brucei*. EMBO J; 13; 1994; 5470-5482.

[39] Rudenko G., Blundell P.A., Dirks-Mulder A., Kieft R., Borst P. A ribosomal DNA promoter replacing the promoter of a telomeric VSG expression site can be efficiently switched on and off in *T. brucei*. Cell; 83; 1995; 547-553.

[40] Hotz H.-R., Lorenz P., Fischer R., Krieger S., Clayton C.E. Developmental regulation of hexose transporter mRNAs in *Trypanosoma brucei*. Mol Biochem Parasitol; 75; 1995; 1-14.

[41] Urmenyi T.P., van der Ploeg L.H.T. PARP promoter-mediated activation of a VSG expression site promoter in insect form *Trypanosoma brucei*. Nucleic Acids Res; 23; 1995; 1010-1018.

[42] Huang J., van der Ploeg L.H.T. Requirement of a poly-pyrimidine tract for *trans*-splicing in trypanosomes : discriminating the PARP promoter from the immediately adjacent 3' splice acceptor site. EMBO J; 10; 1991; 3877-3885.

[43] Hug M., Hotz H.R., Hartmann C., Clayton C.E. Hierarchies of RNA processing signals in a trypanosome surface antigen mRNA precursor. Mol Cell Biol; 14; 1994; 7428-7435.

[44] Hotz H-R, Hartman C, Huober K, Hug M, Clayton CE. Mechanisms of developmental regulation in *Trypanosoma brucei* : A polypyrimidine tract 3'-untranslated region of a trypanosome surface protein mRNA affects RNA abundance and translation. Nucl Acids Res 1997; 25 : 3017–25.

[45] Vassella E., Braun R., Roditi I. Control of polyadenylation and alternative splicing of transcripts from adjacent genes in a procyclin expression site : a dual role for polypyrimidine tracts in trypanosomes. Nucleic Acids Res; 22; 1994; 13591364.

[46] Ullu E., Matthews K.R., Tschudi C. Temporal order of RNA processing reactions in trypanosomes : rapid *trans*-splicing precedes polyadenylation of newly synthesized tubulin transcripts. Mol Cell Biol; 13; 1993; 720-725.

[47] LeBowitz J.H., Smith H.Q., Rusche L., Beverley S.M. Coupling of poly(A) site selection and *trans*-splicing in *Leishmania*. Genes Dev; 7; 1993; 996-1007.

[48] Matthews K.R., Tschudi C., Ullu E. A common pyrimidine-rich motif governs *trans*-splicing and polyadenylation of tubulin polycistronic pre-mRNA in trypanosomes. Genes Dev; 8; 1994; 491-501.

[49] Schurch N., Hehl A., Vassella E., Braun R., Roditi I. Accurate polyadenylation of procyclin mRNAs in *Trypanosoma brucei* is determined by pyrimidine-rich elements in the intergenic regions. Mol Cell Biol; 14; 1994; 3668-3675.

[50] Hotz H-R. Postranskriptionelle Genregulation in *Trypanosoma brucei*. PhD thesis. Heidelberg : Universitat Heidelberg, 1996.

[51] Hug M., Carruthers V., Sherman D., Hartmann C., Cross G.A.M., Clayton C.E. A possible role for the 3'-untranslated region in developmental regulation in *Trypanosoma brucei*. Mol Biochem Parasitol; 61; 1993; 87-96.

[52] Aly R., Argaman M., Halman S., Shapira M. A regulatory role for the 5' and 3' untranslated regions in differential expression of hsp83 in *Leishmania*. Nucleic Acids Res; 22; 1994; 2922-2929.

[53] Berberof M., Vanhamme L., Tebabi P., Pays A., Jefferies D., Welburn S., Pays E. The 3'-terminal region of the mRNAs for VSG and procyclin can confer stage specificity to gene expression in *T. brucei*. EMBO J; 14; 1995; 2925-2934.

[54] Blattner J., Clayton C.E. The 3'-untranslated regions from the *Trypanosoma brucei* phosphoglycerate kinase genes mediate developmental regulation. Gene; 162; 1995; 153-156.

[55] Nozaki T., Cross G.A.M. Effects of 3'-untranslated and intergenic regions on gene expression in *Trypanosoma cruzi*. Mol Biochem Parasitol; 75; 1995; 5568.

[56] Ramamoorthy R., Swihart K.G., McCoy J.J., Wilson M.E., Donelson J.E. Intergenic regions between tandem gp63 genes influence the differential expression of gp63 RNAs in *Leishmania chagasi*. J Biol Chem; 270; 1995; 12133-12139.

[57] Charest H., Zhang W.-W., Matlashewski G. The developmental expression of *Leishmania donovani* A2 amastigote-specific genes is post-transcriptionally mediated and involves elements in the 3'-untranslated region. J Biol Chem; 271; 1996; 17081-17090.

[58] Hausler T., Clayton C.E. Post-transcriptional control of hsp 70 mRNA in *Trypanosoma brucei*. Mol Biochem Parasitol; 76; 1996; 57-72.

[59] Hehl A., Vassella E., Braun R., Roditi I. A conserved stem-loop structure in the 3' untranslated region of procyclin mRNAs regulates expression in *Trypanosoma brucei*. Proc Natl Acad Sci USA; 91; 1994; 370-374.

[60] Ehlers B., Czichos J., Overath P. RNA turnover in *Trypanosoma brucei*. Mol Cell Biol; 7; 1987; 1242-1249.

[61] Legrain P., Rosbash M. Some *cis* and *trans*-acting mutants for splicing target pre-mRNA to the cytoplasm. Cell; 57; 1989; 573-583.

[62] Chang D.D., Sharp P.A. Regulation by HIV Rev depends upon regulation of splice sites. Cell; 59; 1989; 789-795.

[63] Huober K. Posttranskriptionelle Regulation der Genexpression in *Trypanosoma brucei*. Diploma Thesis. Heidelberg : University of Heidelberg, 1996.

[64] Graham S.V., Barry J.D. Polysomal, procyclin mRNAs accumulate in bloodstream forms of monomorphic and pleomorphic trypanosomes treated with protein synthesis inhibitors. Mol Biochem Parasitol; 80; 1996; 179-192.

[65] Mullner E.W., Neupert B., Kuhn L.C. A specific mRNA binding factor regulates the iron-dependent stability of cytoplasmic transferrin receptor mRNA. Cell; 58; 1989; 373-382.

[66] Leibold E.A., Laudano A., Yu Y. Structural requirements of ironresponsive elements for binding of the protein involved in both transferrin receptor and ferritin mRNA post-transcriptional regulation. Nucleic Acids Res; 18; 1990; 1819-1824.

[67] Ziegelbauer K., Quinten M., Schwarz H., Pearson T.W., Overath P. Synchronous differentiation of *Trypanosoma brucei* bloodstream to procyclic forms in vitro. Eur J Biochem; 192; 1990; 373-378.

[68] Pays E., Hanocq-Quertier J., Hanocq F., Van Assel S., Nolan D., Rolin S. Abrupt RNA changes precede the first cell division during the differentiation of *Trypanosoma brucei* bloodstream forms into procyclic forms in vitro. Mol Biochem Parasitol; 61; 1993; 107-114.

[69] Dorn P.L., Aman R.A., Boothroyd J.C. Inhibition of protein synthesis results in super-induction of procyclin (PARP) RNA levels. Mol Biochem Parasitol; 44; 1991; 133-140.

[70] Bass K.E., Wang C.C. Transient inhibition of protein synthesis accompanies differentiation of *Trypanosoma brucei* from bloodstream from procyclic form. Mol Biochem Parasitol; 56; 1992; 129-140.

[71] Caponigro G., Parker R. Mechanisms and control of mRNA turnover in *Saccharomyces cerevisiae*. Microbiol Rev; 60; 1996; 233-249.

[72] Beelman C.A., Parker R. Degradation of mRNA in eukaryotes. Cell; 81; 1995; 179-184.

[73] Caponigro G., Parker R. mRNA turnover in yeast promoted by the MAT alpha 1 instability element. Nucleic Acids Res; 24; 1996; 4304-4312.

[74] Parsons M., Hill T. Elevated phosphoglycerate kinase mRNA but not protein in monomorphic *Trypanosoma brucei* : implications for stage-regulation and post-transcriptional control. Mol Biochem Parasitol; 33; 1989; 215-228.

[75] Zilberstein D., Shapira M. The role of pH and temperature in the development of *Leishmania* parasites. Annu Rev Microbiol; 48; 1994; 499-570.

10

Abstract

Trypanosoma brucei, in common with the other African trypanosomes, exhibits unusual cell-surface molecular architecture. The bloodstream form of the parasite is coated with a continuous layer of approximately five million variant surface glycoprotein (VSG) dimers that provide the parasite with a macromolecular diffusion barrier to guard against lysis by the alternative complement pathway. The procyclic form of the parasite has a more diffuse cell-surface coat made up of approximately 2.5 million copies of procyclic acidic repetitive protein (PARP). Within the VSG and PARP coats exist lower-abundance surface glycoproteins such as receptors and nutrient transporters. Both the VSG molecules and the PARP molecules are attached to the membrane via glycosyl-phosphatidylinositol (GPI) membrane anchors and the VSGs and one form of PARP are *N*-glycosylated. In this article, the structures of the *N*-glycans and the GPI anchors of *T. brucei* VSGs and PARPs are reviewed and simple models of the surfaces of bloodstream and procyclic trypomastigotes are presented. © 1998 Francqui Foundation. Published by Elsevier Science B.V. All rights reserved.

Keywords: *Trypanosoma brucei*; Variant surface glycoprotein; Procyclic acidic repetitive protein; *N*-glycosylation; Glycosylphosphatidylinositol

The glycosylation of the variant surface glycoproteins and procyclic acidic repetitive proteins of *Trypanosoma brucei*

Angela Mehlert [a],
Nicole Zitzmann [a],
Julia M. Richardson [b],
Achim Treumann[1] [a],
Michael A.J. Ferguson

[a] *Department of Biochemistry, University of Dundee, Dundee DD1 4HN, UK*

[b] *Centre for Biomolecular Science, St. Andrews University, KY16 9ST, UK*

1. Present address: Institute of Comprehensive Medical Science, Fujita Health University, Japan.

1 • The surface of bloodstream form *Trypanosoma brucei*

The bloodstream forms of the African trypanosomes express an unusual surface coat [1] which is composed of about ten million copies of variant surface glycoprotein (VSG) [2] arranged as a dense monolayer of homodimers on the parasite surface. The VSG coat acts a macromolecular diffusion barrier that prevents the approach of macromolecules, such as the components of the alternative complement pathway, to the plasma membrane while allowing the free diffusion of small nutrient molecules to underlying transmembrane transporter systems. The trypanosome genome contains several hundred VSG genes that encode immunologically distinct VSGs that are expressed one at a time by an individual cell. The sequential expression of different VSG genes (antigenic variation) enables the parasite population to evade specific humoral immune attack; the mechanism of antigenic variation is reviewed in some of the accompanying articles.

Each VSG monomer has a molecular weight of approximately 55 kDa. The amino-terminal domains of the VSGs represent about 75% of the mature polypeptide sequences and show relatively little primary sequence homology [3], thereby allowing the VSGs their unique immunological identities. However, X-ray crystallographic studies indicate that they fold into similar elongated shapes, with two extended α-helical bundles per monomer [4], that pack into dense monolayer coat arrays. This arrangement allows the coat to be quite thick (15 nm) and means that only a limited subset of VSG B-cell epitopes are exposed on the surface of the living trypanosome. The C-terminal domains of the VSGs display more sequence homology and most VSGs may be grouped into two main (class-1 and class-2), and one minor (class-3), sub-types based on these sequences [3], however, the three-dimensional structures of these domains have not been solved.

The VSG molecules are finally attached to the plasma membrane through a covalent linkage from the C-terminal amino acid α-carboxyl group to a glycosylphosphatidylinositol (GPI) membrane anchor [5]. The mature VSG GPI anchors contain the core structure of ethanolamine–HPO_4 – 6Man $\alpha1$ – 2Man $\alpha1$ – 6Man $\alpha1$ – 4GlcN $\alpha1$ – 6PI, common to all GPI membrane anchors, but this is modified in the class-1 and class-2 VSGs by galactose side chains that are unique to VSGs (Fig. 1).

The predicted three-dimensional structure of the complete anchor of the class-1 VSG MITat.1.4 suggests that it forms a dense plate-like structure of carbohydrate upon which the VSG polypeptide sits [6].

The *N*-linked glycans of several VSGs have been solved by Zamze and co-workers. Each VSG variant contains one, two or three *N*-linked oligosaccharides [7, 8]. The class-1 VSGs contain one conserved *N*-glycosylation site about 50 residues from the mature C-terminus that is occupied by oligomannose structures ($Man_{9-5}GlcNAc_2$) with $Man_7GlcNAc_2$ being the most abundant species [7] (Fig. 1). The class-2 VSGs generally contain two glycosylation sites, one 5 or 6 resi-

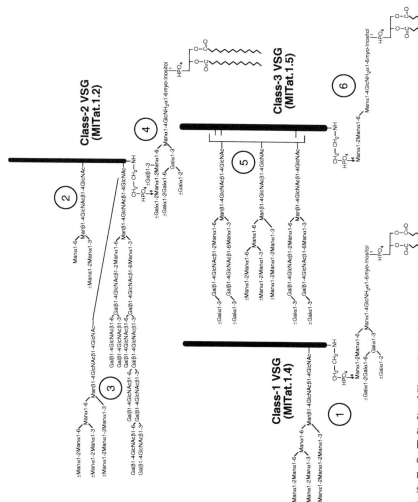

FIGURE 1

The structures of the GPI anchors and *N*-linked glycans of *T. brucei* bloodstream form VSGs. The structures of the *N*-linked glycans [7] and GPI-anchors [5, 27] of two class-1 VSGs (MITat.1.4 and MITat.1.6) have been solved. The data show that both sets of structures are highly conserved (1). The structures of the *N*-linked oligosaccharides of two class-2 VSGs (MITat.1.2 and MITat.1.7) [8] and the GPI anchor of MITat.1.2 (Mehlert, Richardson and Ferguson, unpublished data) have been solved. The data show that the *N*-glycans at the internal glycosylation site are, mainly, unusual small Man$_{3-4}$GlcNAc$_2$ structures (2) whereas the C-terminal site is a mixture of Man$_{9-7}$GlcNAc$_2$ oligomannose structures and larger polydisperse polylactosamine-containing glycans, of which a representative structure is shown (3). The GPI anchor of MITat.1.2 can contain Gal residues attached to all three Man residues of the GPI core (4). The structures of the *N*-glycans [8] and GPI anchor [28] of the class-3 VSG MITat.1.5 have been solved. The *N*-glycans are a mixture of oligomannose structures and complex biantennary structures, that lack sialic acid and fucose but which contain terminal Gal α1–3Gal structures (5). The relative positions of the various structures on the MITat.1.5 polypeptide are unknown [8]. This VSG has a very simple GPI anchor that lacks any Gal residues (6).

dues from the mature C-terminus and the other about 170 residues from the mature C-terminus. The C-terminal site is occupied by a mixture of oligomannose structures (Man$_{9-7}$GlcNAc$_2$), similar to those found on the class-1 VSGs, and larger polylactosmine-containing structures (Fig. 1). The internal site is occupied by unusually small structures like Man$_{4-3}$GlcNAc$_2$ and GlcNAcMan$_3$GlcNAc$_2$ as well as, in some cases, regular biantennary complex glycans (Fig. 1) [8]. The one characterised class-3 VSG (MITat.1.5) contains three potential *N*-glycosylation sites (at 123, 356 and 377 residues from the mature C-terminus) occupied by a mixture of oligomannose (Man$_{9-5}$GlcNAc$_2$) and complex biantennary structures (Fig. 1) [8]. In both the class-2 and class-3 VSGs, the complex and polylactosamine glycans can be substituted with terminal Gal residues in α1–3 linkage. The significance of the variation in the *N*-glycans is unclear. However, in the class-2 VSG (MlTat.1.2) the relatively small internal *N*-glycans at Asn296 can be seen in the crystal structure to occupy similar space to that occupied by an *α*-helix of peptide in a class-1 VSG structure [4], suggesting that, at this site, carbohydrate can substitute for protein within the overall VSG fold. In addition, the relatively large oligomannose and polylactosamine-containing *N*-glycans very close to the C-termini of the class-2 VSGs presumably must, together with the GPI-anchor carbohydrate, contribute significantly to the glycocalyx immediately adjacent to the plasma membrane (Fig. 3). The observed differences in GPI-anchor galactosylation and *N*-glycan number and structure appear to correlate with VSG sub-class (Fig. 1). It seems possible, therefore, that carbohydrate is used as space-filling material to compensate for differences in VSG three-dimensional structure and to ensure the barrier characteristics of different VSG coats.

2 • The surface of procyclic form *Trypanosoma brucei*

The surface of the procyclic form of *T. brucei*, that lives in the tsetse fly mid-gut, is covered with a more diffuse coat made up of glycoproteins called procyclins or procyclic acidic repetitive proteins (PARPs). Most trypanosome clones contain four pairs of PARP genes that encode three PARP types : two with repeat domains of -Glu-Pro- (EP-PARPs), one of which contains an *N*-glycosylation site adjacent to the polyanionic EP-repeat domain, and one with a repeat domain of -Gly-Pro-Glu-Glu-Thr- (GPEET-PARP) [9, 10]. Both *N*-glycosylated EP-PARP and GPEET-PARP have been isolated from tissue culture procyclics and structurally characterised [11, 12]. Both forms are believed to adopt highly extended rod-like structures [11, 13] and both contain GPI anchors with an unusual lipid structure and large polydisperse carbohydrate side chains made of branched polylactosamine repeats (Fig. 2) [11, 14, 15].

When the parasites are grown in culture, the *β*-galactose termini of these side chains are substituted with sialic acid through the action of a cell surface *trans*-sialidase enzyme that transfers *α*2–3-linked sialic acid from fetal calf serum glycoconjugates [16, 17]. The significance of *trans*-sialylation in *T. brucei* procyclics, and the extent to which it occurs in the tsetse fly, are unclear. Overall, the PARP coat may be considered as a dense GPI glycocalyx immediately adjacent to the membrane above which are projected the highly extended polyanionic rod-like structures of the PARP polypeptides (Fig. 3).

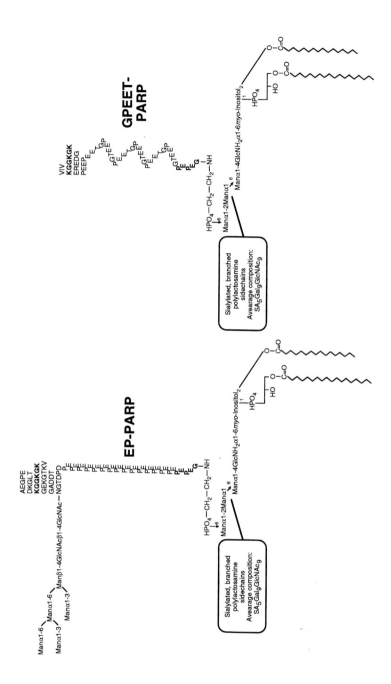

FIGURE 2

The structures of the GPI anchors and *N*-linked glycans of *T. brucei* procyclic form PARPs. The *N*-glycosylated form of EP-PARP contains a single type of Man$_5$GlcNAc$_2$ *N*-glycan [11]. The GPI anchors of EP-PARP and GPEET-PARP are substituted with polydisperse branched structures ranging from five to 30 lactosamine (Galβ 1–4GlcNAc) repeats that terminate with α2–3-linked sialic acid residues [11, 15].

FIGURE 3

Simple models of the surfaces of blood-stream and procyclic forms of *T. brucei*. Only the most abundant molecules are shown. The membrane projection is approximately to scale and represents a section of plasma membrane of about 20×20 nm. The shape of the N-terminal domain of the VSG dimer is taken from [4] (1). The shape of the C-terminal domain is unknown (2). The VSG dimers sit on top of a glycocolyx made up of the glycans of the two GPI anchors [6] (3) and, for the class-2 VSGs, the C-terminal *N*-linked glycan. This glycocalyx must be relatively sparse for the class-3 VSG where the GPI glycan is relatively small (Fig. 1). The shape of EP-PARP is based on the predicted dimensions of the $(DP)_2(EP)_{29}$ polyanionic rod-like domain [13] (4). This form of PARP contains a single $Man_5GlcNAc_2$ *N*-linked glycan [11] (5) and a polydisperse branched polylactosamine side chain attached to the GPI anchor [11, 15] (6). The other form of PARP (GPEET-PARP, Fig. 2) is also a highly elongated molecule, though probably not as extended as EP-PARP, and it contains identical GPI anchor structures but no *N*-linked glycan [11].

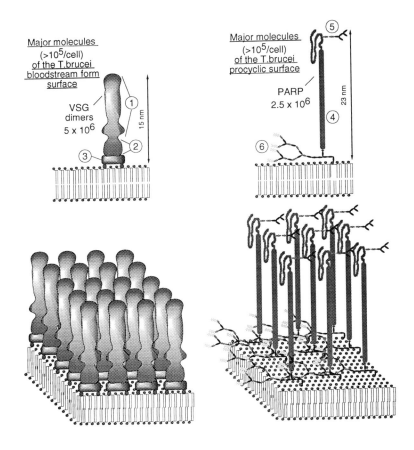

The significance of the three different PARP forms, described above, is unclear. However, when strain 427 bloodstream form trypanosomes are transformed into procyclics in vitro the cells generally express predominantly *N*-glycosylated EP-PARP that is gradually replaced by GPEET-PARP over a period of months [11]. The expression of the non- *N*-glycosylated form of EP-PARP at the protein-level is yet to be demonstrated. It will be interesting to analyse which forms of PARP are being expressed by trypanosomes during their complex life-cycle within the tsetse fly.

The occupancy of the single *N*-glycosylation site of EP-PARP with only a single type of *N*-glycan ($Man_5GlcNAc_2$, Fig. 2) is noteworthy. This lack of micro-heterogeneity at an *N*-glycosylation site is not unique but it is quite rare. Recently, tsetse fly lectins have been suggested to be involved in controlling the parasite population in the tsetse fly [18, 19] and it is likely that the PARPs would serve as the principle ligands for such molecules.

3 ● The relationships between GPI anchor and *N*-glycan biosynthesis in bloodstream and procyclic trypanosomes

The presence of exclusively $Man_5GlcNAc_2$ in EP-PARP would suggest that procyclic trypanosomes do not process their *N*-linked glycans beyond trimming them down to this structure by the action of ER α-mannosidase and Golgi α-mannosidase I [20]. The absence of a GlcNAc-transferase I activity would then preclude any further processing of this structure [20]. The situation is clearly more complex in bloodstream forms that can make a variety of complex and polylactosmine-containing *N*-linked glycans. These structures require the further processing of the $Man_5GlcNAc_2$ intermediate structure to $Man_3GlcNAc_2$ by Golgi α-mannosidase II and the subsequent action of a number of Golgi glycosyltransferases [20]. The different *N*-glycosylation patterns observed for the different VSG variants [7, 8] is likely to be due to the location of the individual VSG glycosylation sites in the VSG molecules and the local three-dimensional structure around those glycosylation sites. Thus, glycosylation sites in similar places (e.g. the single internal glycosylation site for the class-1 VSGs and the C-terminal and internal glycosylation sites of the class-2 VSGs) carry similar arrays of glycan structures [7, 8]. It is less likely that *N*-glycan processing of VSGs is modulated by changing the expression of the processing enzymes (exoglycosidases and glycosyltransferases) since (a) none of the expression-site associated genes (ESAGs) appear to encode this type of protein and (b) biochemical studies suggest that trypanosomes belonging to all three VSG sub-classes contain similar *N*-glycan processing glycosyltransferase activities [21].

The unusual GPI-anchor lipid structure on PARP (Fig. 2) can be easily explained in terms of the current model of GPI-anchor biosynthesis in *T. brucei* [22–24] if one postulates that fatty acid remodelling does not occur in the procyclic forms beyond the removal of one fatty acid from the *sn*-2-position of the PI moiety. The radical differences in GPI-anchor carbohydrate side-chains between the VSGs and the PARPs is less easy to explain. Bloodstream form trypanosomes clearly have the enzymes required for polylactosamine synthesis (see the class-2 VSG *N*-glycan structures) and yet, unlike procyclic trypanosomes, they do not add these structures to their VSG GPI-anchors. Possible explanations are (a) that they lack key glycosyltransferase activities which add a structure to the conserved GPI trimannosyl core that is required for polylactosamine addition or (b) that the action of the αGal-transferases responsible for initiating the characteristic VSG GPI αGal-branch block polylactosamine synthesis. In support of (a) there does appear to be a novel (but unsolved) structure immediately between the trimannosyl core and the polylactosamine repeats in PARP [11, 15] and, in support of (b), there is evidence that the addition of αGal residues begins in the endoplasmic reticulum [25]. Finally, the presence of sialic acid as a terminal residue on the polylactosamine-repeats of the PARP anchor, but not on the termini of the VSG N-glycan polylactosamine repeats, can be explained by the stage-specific expression of the *T. brucei trans*-sialidase responsible for the addition of sialic acid at the cell surface [16, 17].

The changes in the carbohydrate processing machinery between the bloodstream and procyclic forms suggested above are consistent with the recent observation that the expression of VSG in procyclic forms gives rise to a VSG with oligomannose N-linked glycans and a PARP-type of GPI anchor [26].

Acknowledgements

This work was supported by The Wellcome Trust. Nicole Zitzmann is a Wellcome Trust PhD student. Mike Ferguson is a Howard Hughes International Research Scholar.

R E F E R E N C E S

[1] Vickerman K., Luckins A.G. Localization of variable antigens in the surface coat of *Trypanosoma brucei* using ferritin-conjugated antibody. Nature; 224; 1969; 1125-1126.

[2] Cross G.A.M. Identification, purification and properties of clone-specific glycoprotein antigens constituting the surface coat of *Trypanosoma brucei*. Parasitology; 71; 1975; 393-417.

[3] Carrington M., Miller N., Blum M., Roditi I., Wiley D., Turner M. Variant specific glycoprotein of *Trypanosoma brucei* consists of two domains each having an independently conserved pattern of cysteine residues. J Mol Biol; 221; 1991; 823-835.

[4] Blum M.L., Down J.A., Gurnett A.M., Carrington M., Turner M.J., Wiley D.C. A structural motif in the variant surface glycoproteins of *Trypanosoma brucei*. Nature; 362; 1993; 603-609.

[5] Ferguson M.A.J., Homans S.W., Dwek R.A., Rademacher T.W. Glycosyl-phosphatidylinositol moiety that anchors *Trypanosoma brucei* variant surface glycoprotein to the membrane. Science; 239; 1988; 753-759.

[6] Homans S.W., Edge C.J., Ferguson M.A.J., Dwek R.A., Rademacher T.W. Solution structure of the glycosylphosphatidylinositol membrane anchor glycan of *Trypanosoma brucei* variant surface glycoprotein. Biochemistry; 28; 1989; 2881-2887.

[7] Zamze S.E., Wooten E.W., Ashford D.A., Ferguson M.A.J., Dwek R.A., Rademacher T.W. Characterisation of the asparagine-linked oligosaccharides from *Trypanosoma brucei* type-1 variant surface glycoproteins. Eur J Biochem; 187; 1990; 657-663.

[8] Zamze S.E., Ashford D.A., Wooten E.W., Rademacher T.W., Dwek R.A. Structural characterization of the asparagine-linked oligosaccharides from *Trypanosoma brucei* type II and type III variant surface glycoproteins. J Biol Chem; 266; 1991; 20244-20261.

[9] Roditi I., Carrington M., Turner M. Expression of a polypeptide containing a dipeptide repeat is confined to the insect stage of *Trypanosoma brucei*. Nature; 325; 1987; 272-274.

[10] Mowatt M.R., Clayton C.E. Polymorphism in the procyclic acidic repetitive protein gene family of *Trypanosoma brucei*. Mol Cell Biol; 8; 1988; 4055-4062.

[11] Treumann A., Zitzmann N., Hülsmeier A., Prescott A.R., Almond A., Sheehan J., Ferguson M.A.J. Structural characterisation of two forms of procyclic acidic repetitive protein

expressed by procyclic forms of *Trypanosoma brucei*. J Mol Biol; 269; 1997; 529-547.

[12] Butikofer P, Ruepp S, Boschung M, Roditi I. GPEETprocyclin is the major surface protein of *Trypanosoma brucei* 427 procyclic culture forms. Biochem J 1997; 326 : 415–23.

[13] Roditi I., Schwarz H., Pearson T.W., Beecroft R.P., Liu M.K., Richardson J.P., Buhring H.-J., Pleiss J., Bulow R., Williams R.O., Overath P. Procyclin gene expression and loss of the variant surface glycoprotein during differentiation of *Trypanosoma brucei*. J Cell Biol; 108; 1989; 737-746.

[14] Field M.C., Menon A.K., Cross G.A.M. A glycosylphosphatidylinositol protein anchor from procyclic stage *Trypanosoma brucei* : lipid structure and biosynthesis. EMBO J; 10; 1991; 2731-2739.

[15] Ferguson M.A.J., Murray P., Rutherford H., McConville M.J. A simple purification of procyclic acidic repetitive protein and demonstration of a sialylated glycosylphosphatidylinositol membrane anchor. Biochem J; 291; 1993; 51-55.

[16] Engstler M., Reuter G., Schauer R. The developmentally regulated *trans*-sialidase from *Trypanosoma brucei* sialylates the procyclic acidic repetitive protein. Mol Biochem Parasitol; 61; 1993; 1-14.

[17] Schenkman S., Eichinger D., Pereira M.A., Nussenzweig V. Structural and functional properties of *Trypanosoma trans*-sialidase. Annu Rev Microbiol; 48; 1994; 499-523.

[18] Maudlin I., Welburn S.C. Maturation of trypanosome infections in tsetse. Exp Parasitol; 79; 1994; 202-205.

[19] Welburn S.C., Dale C., Ellis D., Beecroft R., Pearson T.W. Apoptosis in procyclic *Trypanosoma brucei rhodesiense* in vitro. Cell Death Differ; 3; 1996; 229-236.

[20] Kornfeld R., Kornfeld S. Assembly of asparagine-linked oligosaccharides. Annu Rev Biochem; 54; 1985; 631-664.

[21] Pingel S., Duszenko M. Identification of two distinct galactosyltransferase activities acting on the variant surface glycoprotein of *Trypanosoma brucei*. Biochem J; 283; 1992; 479-485.

[22] Field M.C., Menon A.K., Cross G.A.M. Developmental variation of glycosylphosphatidylinositol membrane anchors in *Trypanosoma brucei*. In vitro biosynthesis of intermediates in the construction of the GPI-anchor of the major procyclic surface glycoprotein. J Biol Chem; 267; 1992; 5324-5329.

[23] Englund P.T. The structure and biosynthesis of glycosyl phosphatidylinositol protein anchors. Annu Rev Biochem; 62; 1993; 121-138.

[24] Guther M.L.S., Ferguson M.A.J. The role of inositol-acylation and inositol-deacylation in GPI biosynthesis in *Trypanosoma brucei*. EMBO J; 14; 1995; 3080-3093.

[25] Mayor S., Menon A.K., Cross G.A.M. Galactose-containing glycosylphosphatidylinositols in *Trypanosoma brucei*. J Biol Chem; 267; 1992; 754-761.

[26] Paturiaux-Hanocq F., Zitzmann N., Hanocq-Quertier J., Vanhamme L., Rolin S., Geuskens M., Ferguson M.A.J., Pays E. Expression of a variant surface glycoprotein of *Trypanosoma gambiense* in procyclic forms of *Trypanosoma brucei* shows that the cell-type dictates the nature of the glycosylphosphatidylinositol membrane anchor attached to the glycoprotein. Biochem J; 324; 1997; 885-895.

[27] Strang A.-M., Allen A.K., Holder A.A., van Halbeek H. The carbohydrate structures of *Trypanosoma brucei* MITat.1.6 variant surface glycoprotein. Biochem Biophys Res Commun; 196; 1993; 1430-1439.

[28] Guther MLS, Ferguson MAJ. The micro-analysis of glycosylphosphatidylinositol glycans. In : Hounsell EF, editor. Glycoprotein Analysis in Biomedicine (Methods in Molecular Biology Series). Clifton (NJ) : Humana, 1993 : 99–117.

11

Glycosyl phosphatidylinositol myristoylation in African trypanosomes

Karl A. Werbovetz,
Paul T. Englund

Department of Biological Chemistry, Johns Hopkins University School of Medicine, Baltimore, MD 21205, USA.

1 • Introduction

The variant surface glycoprotein (VSG) of *Trypanosoma brucei* plays a vital role in the survival of this parasite within its host. In a process of antigenic variation the parasite switches expression from one VSG to another, and thereby evades the host's immune response ([1] for review). The VSG forms a coat covering the entire surface of the parasite, with roughly 10^7 VSG molecules tightly packed in a monolayer. Each VSG molecule is attached to the bloodstream-form *T. brucei* cell surface by a glycosyl phosphatidylinositol (GPI) anchor ([2] for review). GPI anchors are also used for cell surface tethering of proteins by other eukaryotes, and all protein-linked GPI anchors have the same glycan core structure : Ethanolamine-*p*-6-Manα1-2-Manα1-6-Manα1-4-GlcN [3]. This core structure is linked at its reducing end to either a phosphatidylinositol or an inositol-phospho-ceramide. The *T. brucei* VSG GPI is unique, however, in that both fatty acids in the diacylglycerol portion of its phosphatidylinositol are myristate. The specificity for myristoylation is high, as the initial chemical analysis showed no hint of any other fatty acid besides myristate [4].

It is intriguing that the trypanosome chooses to incorporate myristate into its GPI anchor because this parasite cannot synthesize fatty acids de novo and must therefore import its entire supply from the host [5,6]. Myristate is a relatively rare fatty acid in the blood of mammals, comprising only about 1% of the total fatty acyl residues. In addition, there is no detectable β-oxidation of the more abundant longer chain fatty acids such as palmitate and stearate, so it is unlikely that trypanosomes obtain significant quantities of myristate by chain shortening [6]. The total myristate concentration (including free fatty acid, phospholipid, triglyceride, and cholesterol ester) is only about 27 μM in rat serum [6]. To grow to a cell density of 2×10^9 parasites ml^{-1} (a parasitemia commonly attained in an infected rat) and fully myristoylate its 10^7 VSG molecules, the trypanosome requires roughly two to three times more myristate than is available in normal rat serum. Obviously the supply of myristate in the blood must be replenished during the several days needed for the parasite to reach this maximal density. In this regard it is interesting that the mammalian very low density lipoprotein (VLDL) concentration increases strikingly during a trypanosome infection [7], due to suppression of the host lipoprotein lipase by tumor necrosis factor (see [8] for a review of tumor necrosis factor). This excess lipoprotein could provide needed myristate. Also, human infections with *T. brucei* involve much lower parasitemias, reducing the requirement for myristate. Nevertheless, at least in some circumstances the trypanosome may face a dilemma when attempting to myristoylate its VSG in that it must salvage large amounts of this fatty acid in an environment where little is available. Therefore trypanosomes may have developed sophisticated cellular machinery for uptake and processing of myristate. We describe in this review work over the past several years which has provided support for this hypothesis.

2 • Specific high-affinity pathways for myristate incorporation into trypanosomal GPI

In 1990 our laboratory reported a novel mechanism for incorporation of myristate into the VSG anchor [9]. Using a trypanosomal cell-free system consisting of washed parasite membranes we found that GPI precursors are initially biosynthesized with heterogeneous fatty acyl residues having a chain length longer than that of myristate. Specific deacylation—reacylation reactions then occur in which these more hydrophobic fatty acids are sequentially replaced by myristate. Myristoyl-coenzyme A (CoA) is the fatty acid donor. This process, termed fatty acid remodeling, is shown schematically in Fig. 1. It is likely that these reactions occur in the endoplasmic reticulum (ER), the site of GPI precursor synthesis and of attachment of the GPI to the newly synthesized VSG.

We subsequently discovered a second, alternative, GPI myristoylation pathway. This reaction, termed myristate exchange, occurs on glycolipid A (the GPI precursor) [10], but the major substrate appears to be GPIs already linked to VSG [11]. Exchange occurs at both positions on a GPI glycerol. Like remodeling, exchange is specific for myristate, involves deacylation and reacylation, and utilizes myristoyl-CoA as a fatty acyl donor. Both exchange and remodeling reactions also have low Km values for myristoyl-CoA, around 10 nM, probably reflecting the fact that myristate is present in low concentration. Despite these similarities, there is good evidence that remodeling and exchange are distinct processes. Remodeling and exchange occur in different subcellular compartments, with exchange probably occurring in a compartment downstream from the ER (possibly the Golgi) [10]. Another distinction is that they have different sensitivities to inhibitors (e.g., remodeling reactions, but not those of exchange, are inhibited by EDTA and EGTA). Therefore the two reactions likely utilize different enzymatic machinery. The anchor on newly synthesized VSG is not the only substrate for exchange. An additional substrate is the GPI on mature VSG [11]. Presumably this VSG, derived from the plasma membrane, is transported to the exchange compartment in an endocytic reaction. After exchange, it is apparently recycled back to the cell surface.

What is the biological function of myristate exchange ? Although still speculative, we think that exchange is a backup or proofreading mechanism, providing insurance that all VSG GPIs are fully myristoylated. If a GPI escaped myristoylation in the ER, it could still be myristoylated by exchange, either as it traversed the secretory pathway or possibly after recycling from the cell surface. The exchange machinery could even be used to repair a GPI that had lost a myristate by spurious phospholipase action. The fact that trypanosomes have two pathways for GPI myristoylation underscores the importance of myristate to this parasite.

3 • Trypanosome strategies for myristate utilization

Chemical analysis of bloodstream-form trypanosomes prepared from infected rat blood revealed that about 90% of the myristate is present in VSG [6]. The rest is distributed among various phospholipids and triglycerides, and less than 1% is present in GPI precursors. The significance of this finding is that trypanosomes do not store large amounts of myristate, and therefore they must import it into the cell as quickly as they can use it for assembling GPI anchors.

Given this result, it was surprising to find that incubation of cultured bloodstream-form parasites with [3H]myristate resulted in most of the radioactivity being incorporated into phospholipids [6]. In a 60 min labeling only a few percent of the radioactivity was incorporated into GPIs or VSG. An explanation of this paradox came from the finding that much of the [³H]myristate was elongated, with the majority of the elongated fatty acid being in the form of palmitate or stearate. This process would obviously be wasteful to the parasite under conditions when myristate was scarce. Further experiments showed that elongation depended upon the radiolabeling conditions. Elongation was extensive in medium containing 5% serum. Under these conditions the added [³H]myristate was 1—2 μM, close to its physiological concentration as a free fatty acid in blood, but there was starvation for other fatty acids. Thus elongation of the [³H]myristate was favored. When the culture medium was supplemented with palmitate and stearate to their physiological concentrations, elongation was reduced and a larger fraction of [³H]myristate was incorporated into GPIs. When trypanosomes were incubated with [³H]myristate in whole blood, there was no elongation and most of the myristate was used for GPI biosynthesis. These findings indicate that trypanosomes have evolved highly efficient mechanisms for directing myristate into the GPI biosynthetic pathway.

Another important aspect of trypanosomal myristate utilization is the uptake of myristate into the cell. The process of cellular fatty acid uptake in general is unclear, and one possible mechanism involves simple diffusion through the plasma membrane. In addition, a recent report described a putative fatty acid transporter in adipocyte plasma membranes [12]. Trypanosomes may possess such transporters which prefer myristate over other fatty acids. An additional crucial step in processing myristate is the intracellular formation of myristoyl-CoA, the direct substrate for GPI myristoylation [9,13]. A fatty acyl-CoA synthase is the enzyme responsible for myristoyl-CoA formation. We have recently purified to near homogeneity a major fatty acyl-CoA synthase from a *T. brucei* membrane fraction. Prelimi-

FIGURE 1

Fatty acid remodeling in bloodstream-form African trypanosomes. The reaction scheme indicates the order of deacylation—reacylation reactions observed by which glycolipid A', the initial product of GPI biosynthesis, is remodeled to the dimyristoylated GPI precursor glycolipid A. Components shown are ethanolamine (open squares), phosphate (filled circles), mannose (open circles), glucosamine (shaded circles), inositol (open hexagons), and fatty acyl groups. The fatty acids of glycolipid A' are stearate in the *sn*-1 position and a mixture of longer, mostly unsaturated fatty acids in the *sn*-2 position [34].

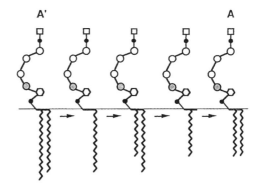

nary assays show a preference for myristate over other fatty acid substrates. The enzyme produces nearly twice as much myristoyl-CoA as palmitoyl-CoA and greater than five fold more myristoyl-CoA than stearoyl-CoA when assayed with radiolabeled fatty acids under our conditions (K. Werbovetz, unpublished observations). This specificity is intriguing in that the lipids of *T. brucei* contain at least 10—20 times more palmitate and stearate than myristate [6].

4 • Is free fatty acid the only source of myristate for the trypanosome ?

Free fatty acids constitute less than 5% of the total fatty acyl residues in mammalian blood, the rest being present in other lipids [14,15]. It is likely that these other lipid species also provide myristate to the trypanosome. Another source of myristate that is efficiently utilized by *T. brucei* is lysophosphatidylcholine (LPC) [13,16—18]. This species is important because LPC is present in relatively high concentrations (100—250 μM) in human plasma [19], and the concentration of myristoyl-LPC (M-LPC) is comparable to that of free myristate [20]. It has been reported that trypanosomes metabolize LPC by two routes : acylation by endogenous acyl-CoA to form phosphatidylcholine or hydrolysis by a phospholipase to form free fatty acid [18]. Of particular importance to GPI myristoylation was the finding that the fatty acyl residue of M-LPC was incorporated into VSG. In an investigation of the mechanism of GPI myristoylation from an M-LPC substrate, we found that trypanosomes use myristate and M-LPC with equal efficiency for GPI labeling in live cells in serum-free medium and in a cell-free system [13]. In live cells, M-LPC is efficiently hydrolyzed, generating extracellular free myristate. This species is then taken up by the trypanosome, converted into myristoyl-CoA, and incorporated into GPIs and VSG. Labeling experiments performed in the presence of serum suggest, however, that myristate may be the favored donor for GPI myristoylation over M-LPC under physiological conditions.

Judging from their efficient utilization, myristate and M-LPC are probably vital donors for GPI myristoylation during a trypanosome infection. Nevertheless, *T. brucei* is likely to require more myristate than is available as free fatty acid or LPC to grow to a cell density commonly attained in the blood of an infected rat, as mentioned earlier. Since myristoylated species of phosphatidylcholine, cholesterol ester, and triglycerides are present in blood at concentrations higher than those of free fatty acids or M-LPC [14,15,20], these species may also be important sources of myristate for GPI anchors. Such lipids are carried in the blood by lipoproteins. Bloodstream-form trypanosomes possess receptors for low density lipoprotein (LDL) in their flagellar pocket, and they

FIGURE 2

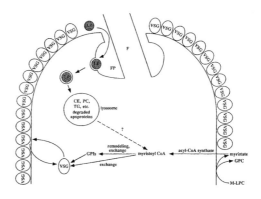

Model for myristate uptake and GPI myristoylation in bloodstream-form *T. brucei*. Solid arrows indicate processes that have been demonstrated experimentally; dashed arrow indicates a hypothetical pathway. Abbreviations: CE, cholesterol ester; F, flagellum; FP, flagellar pocket; GPC, glycerophosphorylcholine; M-LPC, myristoyllysophosphatidylcholine; PC, phosphatidylcholine; TG, triglyceride. VSG is also found in the flagellar pocket, which is the site of its exocytosis and endocytosis. See text for details.

take up LDL by receptor-mediated endocytosis [21,22]. Recently, the utilization of LDL-associated cholesterol ester and sphingomyelin for the synthesis of other trypanosomal lipid species was demonstrated [23]. As mentioned in the introduction, the concentration of mammalian VLDL rises during a trypanosome infection [7], further suggesting that lipoproteins are an important source of lipids for bloodstream-form trypanosomes. Binding studies indicate that trypanosomes possess high density lipoprotein (HDL) receptors and take up HDL as well [24,25], and therefore they may also acquire lipids from this source.

In short, the acquisition of myristate for incorporation into trypanosomal GPIs has been demonstrated from free myristate and M-LPC, both of which are available from the host. Evidence also suggests that lipoproteins could be an important myristate source for bloodstream-form *T. brucei* as well. A model for myristate acquisition by the trypanosome which accounts for these observations is shown in Fig. 2

5 ● Trypanocidal activity of myristate analogs

Attacking parasite myristate metabolism provides an exciting approach to the development of much-needed antitrypanosomal drugs. For example, the myristate analog 11-oxatetradecanoic acid (O-11) was incorporated into VSG and the GPI precursor, and it was selectively toxic to bloodstream-form *T. brucei* growing in culture. This analog killed the bloodstream-form parasites under conditions where procyclic trypanosomes or cultured mammalian cells (both of which do not possess myristoylated GPI anchors) were unaffected [26]. O-11 was also found to be toxic to several *T. evansi* isolates [27].

In subsequent studies 244 additional myristate analogs, which differed from myristate by the presence of heteroatom or functional group substitutions in the hydrocarbon chain, were tested for trypanocidal activity [28]. Some compounds proved to be about ten fold more active than O-11.

Based on the results of the screen described above, three of the most toxic myristate analogs and their corresponding LPC analogs were synthesized and tested against several pathogenic strains of African trypanosomes in a serum-rich medium [29]. Each of these agents was toxic to the trypanosomes tested, including *T. b. rhodesiense* clinical isolates. The three most active compounds (5-oxotetradecanoic acid, its LPC derivative, and the LPC derivative of 9-tetradecynoic acid; each with IC50 values in the range of 1—10 μM) were selected for further study in a murine model of African trypanosomiasis. In studies conducted so far, the analogs did not appear to be toxic to the host, but no clear-cut antitrypanosomal effects were observed either. It is likely that rapid metabolism of the analogs and their LPC derivatives accounts for their ineffectiveness in model infections. Better methods for delivering the myristate analogs to the parasite must be developed if these compounds are to be effective as antitrypanosomal drugs.

6 • Why myristate ?

Some insight into this question can be obtained by considering the properties of *N*-myristoyl proteins, a well studied class of polypeptides found in all eukaryotes (probably including trypanosomes [28] and Lisa Godsel and David Engman, personal communication). The *N*-myristoyl proteins include many important cellular constituents such as components of signal transduction pathways (e.g., protein kinases and phosphatases and G proteins). These molecules have a single myristate linked to an N-terminal glycine, and a crucial question is why myristate is chosen for this role rather than one of the more abundant fatty acids. One possible answer is that a relatively short fatty acid, such as myristate, permits reversible association with cellular membranes. In support of this hypothesis, studies of the interaction of model fatty acyl peptides with phospholipid vesicles revealed that the free energy of binding depends upon the length of the acyl chain [30]. Myristoyl chains allow reversible binding whereas longer fatty acyl chains confer much higher affinities. One example of a reversibly binding *N*-myristoyl protein is recoverin, a molecule involved in visual signal transduction which binds to rod outer segment membranes in the retina [31]. Membrane binding of recoverin is controlled by Ca^{2+}. This cation induces a conformational change in the protein which apparently extrudes the myristate, allowing membrane binding. Removal of Ca^{2+} reverses the conformational change and the protein dissociates from the membrane. Recoverin was the first example of a protein in which membrane binding was regulated by a «myristate switch», controlled by Ca^{2+}. There are other proteins in which the myristate switch is controlled by phosphorylation or GTP binding (reviewed in [32]).

Does myristoylation of VSG allow reversible binding of this protein to the plasma membrane ? In fact there is a report that co-culturing of trypanosomes with sheep erythrocytes results in transfer, via diffusion through the aqueous phase, of small amounts of VSG to the surface of the erythrocytes. These cells then become sensitive to antiVSG-mediated complement lysis, and this lysis was proposed to contribute to the anemia associated with trypanosomiasis [33]. Although the presence of two myristates on the VSG anchor would seem to provide nearly irreversible binding of the protein to the parasite's plasma membrane, it is possible that an endogenous phospholipase occasionally removes one myristate, thus facilitating release of the protein and transfer to the erythrocyte. Although VSG release could be a possible function for GPI myristoylation, it would seem unlikely to require the high myristoylation specificity found in the trypanosome. Therefore, there are likely to be other reasons as well. Perhaps a fully myristoylated GPI anchor is required to control certain biophysical properties of the plasma membrane. Determination of the function of myristate in the trypanosome VSG without question is one of the most exciting challenges for future research.

Acknowledgements

The research in our laboratory was supported by NIH grant AI21334. KAW was supported by NIH postdoctoral fellowship AI08917. We also thank Alvaro Acosta-Serrano, Kuo-Yuan Hwa, David Jiang, Yasu Morita, Jayne Raper, and Theresa Shapiro for many discussions and for critical review of the manuscript.

REFERENCES

[1] Cross, G.A.M. (1990) Cellular and genetic asp,ects of antigenic variation in trypanosomes. Annu. Rev. Immunol. 8, 83—110.

[2] Englund, P.T. (1993) The structure and biosynthesis of glycosyl phosphatidylinositol protein anchors. Annu. Rev. Biochem. 62, 121—138.

[3] Ferguson, M.A.J., Homans, S.W., Dwek, R.A., and Rademacher, T.W. (1988) Glycosyl-phosphatidylinositol moiety that anchors *Trypanosoma brucei* variant surface glycoprotein to the membrane. Science 239, 753—759.

[4] Ferguson, M.A. and Cross, G.A.M. (1984) Myristylation of the membrane form of a *Trypanosoma brucei* variant surface glycoprotein. J. Biol. Chem. 259, 3011—3015.

[5] Dixon, H., Ginger, C. D., and Williamson, J. (1971) The lipid metabolism of blood and culture forms of *Trypanosoma lewisi* and *Trypanosoma rhodesiense*. Comp. Biochem. Physiol. B 39, 247—266.

[6] Doering, T.L., Pessin, M.S., Hoff, E.F., Hart, G.W., Raben, D.M., and Englund, P.T. (1993) Trypanosome metabolism of myristate, the fatty acid required for the variant surface glycoprotein membrane anchor. J. Biol. Chem. 268, 9215—9222.

[7] Rouzer, C.A. and Cerami, A. (1980) Hypertriglyceridemia associated with *Trypanosoma brucei brucei* infection in rabbits : Role of defective triglyceride removal. Mol. Biochem. Parasitol. 2, 31—38.

[8] Beutler, B. and Cerami, A. (1988) Tumor necrosis, cachexia, shock, and inflammation : a common mediator. Annu. Rev. Biochem. 57, 505—518.

[9] Masterson, W.J., Raper, J., Doering, T.L., Hart, G.W., and Englund, P.T. (1990) Fatty acid remodeling : a novel reaction sequence in the biosynthesis of trypanosome glycosyl phosphatidylinositol membrane anchors. Cell 62, 73—80.

[10] Buxbaum, L.U., Raper, J., Opperdoes, F.R., and Englund, P.T. (1994) Myristate exchange : a second glycosyl phosphatidylinositol myristoylation reaction in African trypanosomes. J. Biol. Chem. 269, 30212—30220.

[11] Buxbaum, L.U., Milne, K.G., Werbovetz, K.A., and Englund, P.T. (1996) Myristate exchange on the *Trypanosoma brucei* variant surface glycoprotein. Proc. Natl. Acad. Sci. USA 93, 1178—1183.

[12] Schaffer, J. and Lodish, H.F. (1994) Expression cloning and characterization of a novel adipocyte long chain fatty acid transport protein. Cell 79, 427—436.

[13] Werbovetz, K.A. and Englund, P.T. (1996) Lipid metabolism in *Trypanosoma brucei* : Utilization of myristate and myristoyllysophosphatidylcholine for myristoylation of glycosyl phosphatidylinositols. Biochem. J. 318, 575—581.

[14] Goodman, D.S. and Shiratori, T. (1964) Fatty acid composition of human plasma lipoprotein fractions. J. Lipid Res. 5, 307—313.

[15] Hallgren, B., Stenhagen, S., Svanborg, A., and Svennerholm, L. (1960) Gas chromatographic analysis of the fatty acid composition of the plasma lipids in normal and diabetic subjects. J. Clin. Invest. 39, 1424—1434.

[16] Samad, A., Licht, B., Stalmach, M.E., and Mellors, A. (1988) Metabolism of phospholipids and lysophospholipids by *Trypanosoma brucei*. Mol. Biochem. Parasitol. 29, 159—169.

[17] Mellors, A. and Samad, A. (1989) The acquisition of lipids by African trypanosomes. Parasitol. Today 5, 239—244.

[18] Bowes, A.E., Samad, A.H., Jiang, P., Weaver, B., and Mellors, A. (1993) The acquisition of lysophosphatidylcholine by African trypanosomes. J. Biol. Chem. 268, 13885—13892.

[19] Nye, W.H.R., Waterhouse, C., and Marinetti, G.V. (1961) The phosphatides of human plasma. I. Normal values determined by paper and column chromatography. J. Clin. Invest. 40, 1194—1201.

[20] Ruitenbeek, W. (1978) The fatty acid composition of various lipid fractions isolated from erythrocytes and blood plasma of patients with Duchenne and congenital myotonic muscular dystrophy. Clin. Chim. Acta 89, 99—110.

[21] Coppens, I., Bastin, P., Courtoy, P.J., Baudhuin, P., and Opperdoes, F.R. (1991) A rapid method purifies a glycoprotein of *M*r 145000 as the LDL receptor of *Trypanosoma brucei brucei*. Biochem. Biophys. Res. Commun. 178, 185—191.

[22] Coppens, I., Baudhuin, P., Opperdoes, F.R., and Courtoy, P.J. (1988) Receptors for the host low density lipoproteins on the hemoflagellate *Trypanosoma brucei* : Purification and involvement in the growth of the parasite. Proc. Natl. Acad. Sci. USA 85, 6753—6757.

[23] Coppens, I., Levade, T., and Courtoy, P.J. (1995) Host plasma low density lipoprotein particles as an essential source of lipids for the bloodstream forms of *Trypanosoma brucei*. J. Biol. Chem. 270, 5736—5741.

[24] Hagar, K.M., Pierce, M.A., Moore, D.R., Tytler, E.M., Esko, J.D., and Hajduk, S.L. (1994) Endocytosis of a cytotoxic human high density lipoprotein results in disruption of acidic intracellular vesicles and subsequent killing of African trypanosomes. J. Cell Biol. 126, 155—167.

[25] Gillet, M.P.T. and Owen, J.S. (1992) Characteristics of the binding of human and bovine high-density lipoproteins by bloodstream forms of the African trypanosome, *Trypanosoma brucei brucei*. Biochim. Biophys. Acta 1123, 239—248.

[26] Doering, T.L., Raper, J., Buxbaum, L.U., Adams, S.P., Gordon, J.I., Hart, G.W., and Englund, P.T. (1991) An analog of myristic acid with selective toxicity for African trypanosomes. Science 252, 1851—1854.

[27] Ross, C.A. and Taylor, A.M. (1994) Trypanocidal activity of a myristic acid analog in axenic cultures of *Trypanosoma evansi*. Parasitol. Res. 80, 147—153.

[28] Doering, T.L., Lu, T., Werbovetz, K.A., Gokel, G.W., Hart, G.W., Gordon, J.I., and Englund, P.T. (1994) Toxicity of myristic acid analogs toward African trypanosomes. Proc. Natl. Acad. Sci. USA 91, 9735—9739.

[29] Werbovetz, K.A., Bacchi, C.J., and Englund, P.T. (1996) Myristate and myristoyllysophosphatidylcholine analogs as trypanocides. Mol. Biochem. Parasitol. 81, 115—118.

[30] Peitzsch, R.M. and McLaughlin, S. (1993) Binding of acylated peptides and fatty acids to phospholipid vesicles : Pertinence to myristoylated proteins. Biochemistry 32, 10436—10443.

[31] Zozulya, S. and Stryer, L. (1992) Calcium-myristoyl protein switch. Proc. Natl. Acad. Sci. USA. 89, 11569—11573.

[32] Johnson, D.R., Bhatnager, R.S., Knoll, L.J., and Gordon, J.I. (1994) Genetic and biochemical studies of protein *N*-myristoylation. Annu. Rev. Biochem. 63, 869—914.

[33] Rifkin, M.R. and Landsberger, F.R. (1990) Trypanosome variant surface glycoprotein transfer to target membranes : A model for the pathogenesis of trypanosomiasis. Proc. Natl. Acad. Sci. USA 87, 801—805.

[34] Doering, T.L., Pessin, M.S., Hart, G.W., Raben, D.M., and Englund, P.T. (1994) The fatty acids in unremodelled trypanosome glycosyl-phosphatidylinositols. Biochem. J. 299, 741—746.

12

The properties and function of the glycosylphosphatidylinositolphospholipase C in *Trypanosoma brucei*

Mark Carrington,
Nicola Carnall,
Mandy S. Crow,
Anne Gaud,
Maria B. Redpath,
Christine L. Wasunna,
Helena Webb

Department of Biochemistry, Tennis Court Road, Cambridge CB2 1QW, UK

Abstract

The purpose of this review is to consider recent results obtained concerning the properties and function of the glycosylphosphatidylinositol-phospholipase C (GPI-PLC) in *Trypanosoma brucei*. A mutagenesis study that provides evidence that the GPI-PLC is more closely related to bacterial PI-PLCs than previously realised is described. The variant specific glycoprotein (VSG), which dominates the surface of the mammalian stages of the trypanosome, is almost certainly the major substrate of the GPI-PLC. The hydrolysis of the GPI-anchor of the VSG under stress conditions and hypotonic lysis is well established. To investigate whether this hydrolysis of the GPI-anchor plays any role during the life cycle a GPI-PLC null mutant has been made. The phenotype indicates that the gene is non-essential, but its absence alters the course of infection in mice. © 1998 Francqui Foundation. Published by Elsevier Science B.V. All rights reserved.

Keywords: Glycosylphosphatidylinositol; Phospholipase; *Trypanosoma brucei*; Variant specific glycoprotein; Targeted gene deletion

1 • The cell surface of the bloodstream form trypanosome

The ability of *Trypanosoma brucei* to form a persistent infection in a mammalian host whilst remaining continually exposed to immune attack results from the remarkable properties exhibited by the trypanosome cell surface. The trypanosome presents a single polypeptide, the variant specific glycoprotein (VSG), to the immune system. Antigenic variation, which results from a switch in the VSG gene being expressed, allows the trypanosomes to express VSGs with different primary sequences to the host immune system, and thus avoid antibody mediated lysis. The rate of switching, which varies from 10^{-2} to 10^{-6} per cell division depending on the isolate [1], means that it is the infection rather than an individual trypanosome that persists.

In addition to a central role in antigenic variation, different VSGs must have the ability to pack to form a barrier to prevent host antibodies gaining access to conserved proteins on the cell surface. When the three dimensional structures of two VSG N-terminal domains were solved by X-ray crystallography it became clear that there is a stunning conservation of secondary and tertiary structure [2]. It is probable that the conservation of structure results from a requirement to form a physical barrier to host antibodies. It is assumed the VSG dimers are closely packed on the cell surface to form the protective barrier. There are estimates, but no direct measurements, of the mean distance between dimers. The most detailed estimate of the spacing of VSG dimers (5.75 nm) comes from an estimate of the packing density of the VSG, itself derived from a measurement of the mean number of VSG molecules per trypanosome and an estimate of the surface area [3]. The proximity of the VSG dimers to each other in the surface coat, at least in the N-terminal domain, is limited by the widest part which is at the base, nearest the cell surface, and is shown in Fig. 1. In one dimension these «hips» at the base of the N-terminal domain are significantly wider than the rest of the molecule and result in a gap between the dimers. This gap is particularly apparent in the middle of the VSG layer and is reduced but still

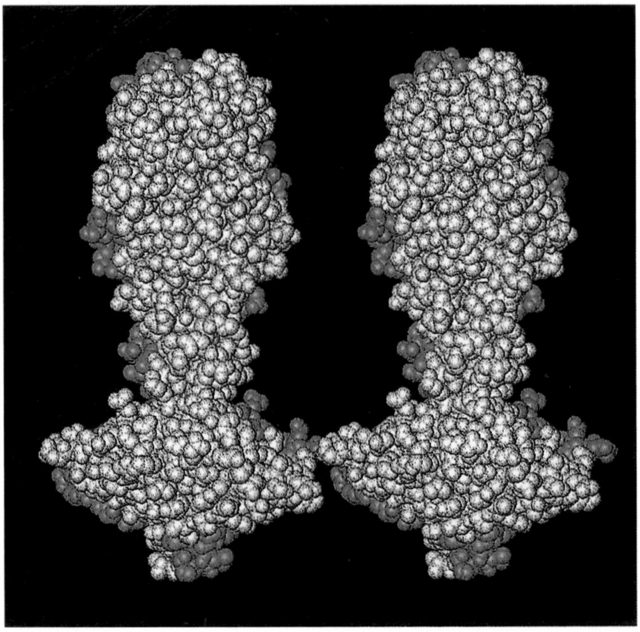

FIGURE 1

The N-terminal domains of two dimers of MITat 1.2 showing the estimated mean spacing on the cell surface (5.7 nm) [28]. Within each dimer one monomer is white and the other green. The figure was prepared using the programme Quanta.

pronounced at the top of the VSG. Importantly, the gap appears to be too small to allow the penetration of immunoglobulins. The model is very tentative in the absence of firm information on the structure of the C-terminal domain but does appear to explain why immunoglobulins cannot penetrate the VSG monolayer.

The attachment of the VSG to the cell surface is through a covalent bond between the C-terminal carboxyl group and a glycosylphosphatidylinositol (GPI) [4]. As would be expected from such a membrane attachment, the VSG is free to diffuse in the plane of the membrane [5] so any model of the VSG monolayer can only represent a moment in a dynamic process.

In addition to acting as a barrier to host antibodies the VSG monolayer must also permit the uptake of nutrients. Small molecules such as sugars and amino acids are unlikely to be significantly retarded by the VSG layer but, as immunoglobulins cannot penetrate the VSG monolayer, it is probable that other proteins of comparable size are also excluded. However, some large proteins, such as transferrin, are essential growth factors for trypanosomes [6]. The transferrin receptor is encoded by the ESAG6 and ESAG7 genes [7] the products of which form a heterodimer located in the flagellar pocket [8, 9], an invagination near the base of the flagellum that is resistant to antibody mediated attack, possibly through exclusion of effector cells. It is believed that other receptors also reside in the flagellar pocket [10]. Like the VSG, the transferrin receptor is linked to the cell surface by covalent linkage to a GPI [7]. The structure of other receptors is not so well known but it appears likely that some others are also GPI-linked.

Outside the flagellar pocket there are a range of ISGs of unknown function [11–15]. The ISGs are attached to the membrane through a membrane spanning helix with a small cytoplasmic domain and there are approximately 50 000 copies of ISG 75; 70 000 copies of ISG 65 [11]. It is not known whether there are any GPI-linked ISGs as the isolation procedures used would probably not have identified these [11, 13]. It has been suggested that ISGs may reside in the gap between VSGs [15], although it has also been proposed that the secondary and tertiary structure of the ISGs and transferrin receptor resemble that of the VSG N-terminal domain [16] which may preclude it occupying the gaps between VSGs. The structures, or even the dimensions of an ISG and VSG C-terminal domain are urgently needed to improve the model of the cell surface.

In summary, the cell surface of the bloodstream trypanosome is dominated by the VSG, there are more than 100 VSG molecules for each ISG. An exception to this is the flagellar pocket where there is probably a greater mixture of proteins present, but these remain minor components relative to the cell surface as a whole. Any large scale release of VSG from the surface of a living cell would strip the trypanosome of an essential protective layer.

2 • The GPI-phospholipase C

T. brucei contains an endogenous phospholipase C (PLC) known as the GPI-phospholipase C (GPI-PLC) [17–19] that hydrolyses the GPI-anchor on the VSG, releasing dimyristyl glycerol [20]. The result of this hydrolysis is to convert the hydrophobic membrane form VSG to a water soluble VSG [21]. Hypotonic lysis [21] or stress [22, 23] results in the shedding of the VSG from the membrane. This conversion can be detected immunologically as it results in the exposure of the cross-reacting determinant (CRD) [21, 24], an epitope contained in the residue of the anchor left attached to the VSG after phospholipase C hydrolysis.

As well as the VSG, the majority of the precursors of the GPI anchor are also substrates for the GPI-PLC in vitro ([25] for a review on GPI biosynthesis). Recently, it has been shown that *T. brucei* GPI-PLC can hydrolyse phosphatidylinositol (PI) under certain assay conditions [26]. However, the enzyme is active against GPI under a wider range of assay conditions, and the K_m for PI (37 μM) is one to two orders of magnitude higher than that for GPI-linked proteins (0.4–0.7 μM for VSG [17, 27], 0.8 μM for acetylcholine esterase [26]). The K_m values are significant as the number of VSG and PI molecules per trypanosome is roughly equivalent; 1.1×10^7 molecules of the VSG [28] and approximately 2.7×10^7 molecules of PI [29, 30], so under most conditions of cell lysis the PLC would first act on the endogenous GPI. However, the observation that the PLC is active against both GPI and PI has added to the confusion concerning its function.

The *T. brucei* GPI-PLC has some sequence identity with bacterial PI-specific PLCs in the N-terminal half of the polypeptide [31]. Furthermore the bacterial PI-PLCs can hydrolyse GPI substrates [32]. However, bacterial PI-PLCs and *T. brucei* GPI-PLC have been distinguished by a number of characteristics. Most noticeable amongst these is the inhibition of GPI-PLC, but not bacterial PI-PLCs, by some sulphydryl reagents, most effectively by Zn^{2+} and *p*-chloromercuryl-phenylsulphonic acid (pCMPSA) [22, 33, 34]. The bacterial enzymes have been classified as type II PLCs and the *T. brucei* GPI-PLC as a type III [35, 36].

PI-PLCs from bacteria are related to one another. Some are closely related, such as those from *Bacillus cereus* and *Bacillus thuringiensis* which differ by only eight amino acids [37]; others, such as the PI-PLC from *Listeria monocytogenes* [36], are divergent having only 25% identity with *B. cereus* PI-PLC. The solution of the structure of the *B. cereus* PI-PLC complexed with myo-inositol has allowed the identification of putative active site residues [38]. All but one of the residues found to be in contact with the myo-inositol, are conserved in the *L. monocytogenes* PI-PLC despite an overall sequence identity of only 25%, suggesting a similar active site and catalytic mechanism for these enzymes [38].

3 • The GPI-PLC is closely related to bacterial PI-PLCs

The observation that the GPI-PLC is inhibited by sulphydryl reagents suggested that a cysteine was essential for activity. If active GPI-PLC could be expressed in *E. coli* then this hypothesis could be tested directly by mutagenesis of each of the eight cysteine residues to serine. The production of active GPI-PLC in *E. coli* was achieved by inducing expression at 20 °C [39], expression at higher temperatures resulted in the production of insoluble aggregates. The specific activity of the recombinant protein was approximately 5-fold lower than estimates for the native protein, although the cause of this difference is not clear. Surprisingly the activity of each of the eight individual cysteine to serine mutants was similar to that of the wild type enzyme [39]. This result indicates that there is no cysteine which is essential for catalysis and could be reconciled with the observed inhibition of the activity of GPI-PLC by sulphydryl reagents if it is proposed that the modification of a cysteine by pCMPSA blocked the access of the substrate to the active site. However, all eight of the mutants were still inhibited by pCMPSA to a degree similar to that of the wild type enzyme [39]. To explain this result it is necessary to propose a model in which only one of two cysteines have to be modified to block access to the active site. At this stage it is probably correct to judge that such a model is beginning to seem like clutching at straws, especially when a second observation is highlighted. The use of pCMPSA has been predominantly in the preparation of VSG with an intact GPI-anchor, it is used at a concentration of 5 mM and is totally effective inferring that it totally inhibits the GPI-PLC. However, 5 mM pCMPSA does not completely inhibit either native or recombinant GPI-PLC when the purified enzyme is assayed [18, 39]. This suggests that the pCMPSA may be acting at more than one point during the preparation of intact VSG.

One further mutant was then made based on the identification of the residues that interact with myo-inositol in the *B. cereus* PI-PLC.

FIGURE 2

Alignment of the PI-PLC from *Bacillus cereus* with GPI-PLC from *Trypanosoma brucei* and the PI-PLC from *Listeria monocytogenes*. The six residues that interact with the myo-inositol in the *B. cereus* PI-PLC and the additional histidine proposed to be involved in catalysis [38] are shown in bold. The proposed homologous residues are also shown in bold and all identities are marked by an asterisk. Tb, *Trypanosoma brucei* GPI-PLC; Bc, *Bacillus cereus* PI-PLC; Lm, *Listeria monocytogenes* PI-PLC.

```
Tb    MFGGVKWSPQSWMSDTRSSIEKKCIGQVYMVGAHNAGTHGIQMFSPFGL   49
           **        **       *       * *  **      *
Bc    ASSVNELENWSKWMQPIPDSIPLARIS...IPGTHDSGTFKLQN......   41
           **  **   **  *    ******
Lm    NKPIKNSVTTKQWMSALPDTTNLAALS...IPGTHDTMSYNGDI......   41


Tb    DAPEKLRSLPPYVTFLLRFLTVGVSSRWGRCQNLSIRQLLDHGVRYLDLR   99
                          **  *    *     *** *   * *
Bc    ....................PIKQVWGMTQEYDFRYQMDHGARIFDIR     69
                          **       *   * *    *** *
Lm    ...................TWTLTKPLAQTQTMSLYQQLEAGIRYIDIR    71


Tb    MNISPDQENKIYTTHFH..ISVPLQEVLKDVKDFLTTPASANEFVILDFL  147
         *   *    *  *    * * *     * * *     *
Bc    GRLTDDNT..IVLHHGPLYLYVTLHEFINEAKQFLKDNPSETIIMSLKKE  117
            **    *** *   *      **** ** ***** ** *
Lm    ...AKDNL...NIYHGPIFLNASLSGVLETITQFLKKNPKETIIMRLKDE  115


Tb    ....HFYGFNESHTMKRFVEELQALEEFYIPTTVSLTTPLCNLWQSTRRI  193
                          *                     *
Bc    ...YEDMKGAEDSFSSTFEKKYFVDPIFLKTEGNIKLGDARGKIVLLKRY  164
                         *              * * **** **
Lm    QMSNDSFDYRIQPLINIYKDYFYTTPRTDTSNKIPTLKDVRGKILLLSEN  165


Tb    FLVVRPYVEYPYARLRSVALKSIWVNQMELNDLLDRLEELMTRDLEDVSI  243
            *         ***    *
Bc    SGSNEPGGYNNFYWPDNETFT.TTVNQNANVTVQDKYKV.SYDEKVKSIK  212
                          **        ** *   *    * *  *
Lm    .....HTKKPLVINSRKFGMQFGAPNQV....IQDDYNGPSVKTKFKEIV  206


Tb    GGVPSKMYVTQAIGTPRNNDFAVAACCGACPGSHPDLYSAAKHKNPHLLK  293
                   *                *       *        **
Bc    DTMDETMNNSEDLNHLYINFTSLSSGGTA..WNSPYYYASYI..NPEIAN  258
             *  * * * *
Lm    ...QTAYQASKADNKLFLNHISATSLTFTPRQYAAA..........LNN  242


Tb    WFYDLNVNGVMRGERVTIRRGNNTHGNILLLDFVQEGTCTVKGVDKPMNA  343
Bc    YIKQKNPARVGWVIQDYINEKWSPLLYQEVIRANKSLIKE          298
        *                       *        *
Lm    KVEQFVLNSTSEKVRGLGILIMDFPEKQTIKNIIKNNKFN          282


Tb    VALCVHLNTNQTARS                                    358
```

An alignment of the GPI-PLC with the PI-PLCs from *B. cereus* and *L. monocytogenes* showed that the majority of these residues were conserved (Fig. 2).

This suggested that the reaction mechanism is the same and would be dependent on a histidine [38]. This histidine was mutated to glutamic acid and, like the same mutation in the *B. cereus* PI-PLC [38], this resulted in a totally inactive enzyme [39]. This result indicates that the GPI-PLC is related to the bacterial PI-PLCs and is consistent with the recent observation that it can also catalyse the hydrolysis of PI [26] as the bacterial PI-PLCs also have dual substrate specificity [32].

There are still many questions remaining about the properties of the GPI-PLC. It requires detergent to be soluble in both the native and recombinant form [39, 40]. There is no obvious sequence in the primary structure that would be responsible for this membrane association, there is no signal sequence, and the means of membrane attachment remains unclear.

The localisation of the GPI-PLC within the trypanosome is strictly regulated. The importance of this became apparent when the *T. brucei* GPI-PLC was ectopically expressed in *Leishmania major* [41] with the result that the major GPI-linked cell surface protein (gp63) was secreted instead of remaining attached to the cell surface. This was probably the result of the degradation of the GPI-anchor precursors, which are synthesised on the cytoplasmic face of the endoplasmic reticulum [42], before they are flipped to the lumenal surface prior to addition to gp63. Presumably, in *T. brucei*, the GPI-PLC is localised away from the GPI synthesis and the localisation signals are not recognised in *L. major*. The conclusion above is consistent with the reported localisation of the GPI-PLC to the cytoplasmic face of vesicles with the cytoplasm [43], distinct from the endoplasmic reticulum. However, this location itself leads to the question as to how the GPI-PLC gains access to the VSG on the outside of the cell, for example during the shedding of VSG under stress conditions [22, 23], as the two would be on opposite sides of the membrane if conventional mechanisms of membrane fusion occur. Since it has been established that the VSG and GPI-PLC have to be in the same membrane for catalysis to occur [17], and presumably on the same face, then it is fair to conclude that something unusual is afoot. Whether this involves translocating the GPI-PLC across a membrane or not remains to be clarified.

4 • The function of the GPI-PLC

It is important to realise the amount of the different potential GPI-PLC substrates present within the cell to enable the measured activity of the GPI-PLC to be placed in context. There are roughly 3×10^4 molecules of the enzyme [18]. At an estimated turnover rate of 100–700 mfVSG molecules min^{-1} under assay conditions [18, 27] there is sufficient GPI-PLC to release the entire surface coat in a few minutes, as occurs on hypotonic lysis of trypanosomes. The rate of VSG synthesis, at a cell doubling time of 5 h, is ~4×10^4 min^{-1}, and the rate of synthesis of the GPI-anchor precursor, which occurs at ten times the rate of VSG synthesis [44] is ~4×10^5 min^{-1}. Table 1 compares the activity of the GPI-PLC with the amount and rate of synthesis of various potential substrates.

TABLE 1

Comparison of GPI-PLC copy number and activity with potential substrates

GPI-PLC	3×10^4/cell
GPI-PLC turnover	1.5×10^7/min/cell
VSG	1.1×10^7/cell
VSG synthesis	4×10^4/min/cell
GPI synthesis	4×10^5/min/cell
PI	2.7×10^7/cell
transferrin receptor (ESAG 6/7)	3×10^3/cell

The origins of these numbers are in the text, except the copy number of the transferrin receptor [7]. There is no reason to believe that the GPI-PLC has a single substrate in vivo, however the enzyme activity per cell means that the VSG is the only substrate present in amounts sufficient to account for the quantity of enzyme present. There is further circumstantial evidence that the VSG is a substrate; the VSG and GPI-PLC show the same developmentally regulated expression, being found in bloodstream but not in procyclic trypanosomes [34, 45, 46]. GPI-PLC expression also coincides with GPI-anchor sensitivity to GPI-PLC cleavage; all GPI anchors analysed to date in procyclic trypanosomes are GPI-PLC resistant [47, 48]. In the case of the major surface protein, procyclin, this is due to palmitoylation of the inositol ring [47].

A low rate of VSG release from trypanosomes has been observed in cultures of bloodstream forms, and clearly demonstrated not to result from lysis of a subset of the population [49]. In addition, release of VSG can be induced under stress conditions that do not lyse trypanosomes [23]. Both of these observations suggest that GPI-PLC acts on VSG in intact trypanosomes, not just on cell lysis.

The ability of the GPI-PLC to catalyse the shedding of the VSG coat in vitro, and the co-temporal expression of the two proteins, has led to models that suggest an important role for the enzyme in the developmental changes that involve alterations in expression of cell surface proteins [31]. There are three circumstances when a trypanosome must replace its surface VSG and therefore when a specific VSG shedding activity, such as GPI-PLC, might be invoked. The first occurs within a few days after entry into a mammalian host when all cells exchange the metacyclic VSG, expressed in the insect salivary gland, for a bloodstream form VSG [50]. The second occasion may arise in the individual trypanosomes undergoing antigenic variation. In both cases, a passive exchange of new for old VSG, based on measurements of VSG turnover [49] in combination with growth and dilution, would take several generations, so a process for more rapid exchange has obvious advantages in a host which is mounting an immune response to the old VSG. As antigenic variation occurs in a very small fraction of the population it has not been possible to determine whether this occurs. The third is on the differentiation of bloodstream to procyclic trypanosomes that occurs on ingestion by the insect vector and involves the replacement of surface VSG with procyclin [51]. Although the increase in rate of VSG shedding on this differentiation can be fully explained by the activation or induction of a specific protease [52], the fate of the GPI-linked C-terminal peptide remains unresolved.

5 • Deletion of the GPI-PLC gene

The direct approach of making a GPI-PLC null mutant was taken to try and resolve the questions about the function of the enzyme [53]. There is one copy of the GPI-PLC gene per haploid genome and both alleles were completely deleted by two successive rounds of targeted gene deletion using selectable markers to replace the GPI-PLC gene. The deletions were performed in cultured procyclic forms as these do not normally express the GPI-PLC so deletion of the gene should not result in any selection pressure. Procyclic forms of the GPI-PLC null mutant (PLC$^-$) were then cycled through tsetse flies and recovered as bloodstream forms in immunosuppressed mice. The successful transmission of PLC$^-$ trypanosomes through to bloodstream forms indicated that GPI-PLC activity is not necessary for these life cycle transitions.

Before further experiments to analyse the growth and behaviour of the PLC$^-$ trypanosomes were performed, attempts were made to determine whether there was a second PLC activity that might hide any phenotype in the PLC$^-$ bloodstream forms. Two sets of assays were performed, both using the VSG as a substrate. In the first, lysates were made from PLC$^-$ cells and assayed for release of ^{3}H into an organic phase from [^{3}H]myristyl-VSG [34]. The PLC$^-$ lysate was indistinguishable from background, which was 0.3% of the wild type activity. In the second assay the exposure of the cross reacting determinant on hypotonic lysis was determined. The action of a PLC on the GPI-anchor of the VSG results in the release of dimyristyl glycerol and the formation of an inositol 1,2 cyclic phosphate. The appearance of this residual anchor can be visualised by Western blotting with anti-CRD immunoglobulins. Two such assays are shown in Fig. 3, the VSG in the PLC$^-$ trypanosomes remained anti-CRD negative whether hypotonic or Triton X-100 lysis was used.

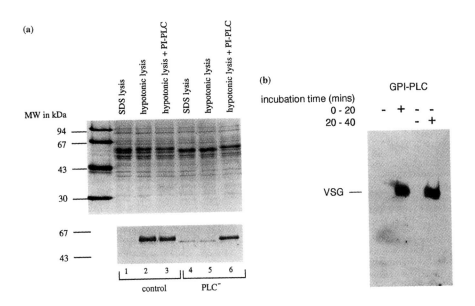

FIGURE 3

Test for redundant PLC activity in PLC⁻ and control bloodstream trypanosomes. (a) Cell extracts were prepared by SDS lysis, hypotonic lysis and with addition of exogenous *B. cereus* PI-PLC to the hypotonic lysate. Control cell extracts were loaded in lanes 1–3, the equivalent PLC⁻ trypanosome extracts in lanes 4–6. The upper panel shows a Coomassie blue-stained gel (2×10^6 cells per track). Beneath is an equivalent gel (2×10^5 cells per track) which has been Western blotted and probed with an anti-CRD polyclonal antibody. (b) Trypanosome extracts were prepared by Triton lysis and incubated at 37 °C in the absence or presence of GPI-PLC. The hydrolysis of the VSG by the GPI-PLC was monitored by Western blotting the whole reaction using anti-CRD.

However, on the addition of exogenous PLC the VSG became anti-CRD positive whether it was added at the start of the assay or after 20 min (Fig. 3). This experiment provides further evidence that there is no other enzyme that metabolises the GPI-anchor on a substantial scale but also that a normal, PLC susceptible, GPI-anchor is present on the VSG in PLC⁻ trypanosomes. It would be almost certainly a mistake to believe that there are no enzymes present in the PLC⁻ trypanosomes that can metabolise the GPI-anchor; for example there are the enzymes that catalyse fatty acid remodelling [54] or putative PLCs involved in signal transduction; the point is that these activities are very small compared to the wild type GPI-PLC and are undetectable in the assays normally used for the GPI-PLC.

The PLC⁻ trypanosomes were grown in immunosuppressed mice and induced to differentiate to procyclic forms both in vitro [55] and by feeding tsetse flies with blood from the mice. In both cases differentiation to procyclic forms occurred and in vitro the kinetics of VSG loss, procyclin appearance and cell division was indistinguishable from wild type [53]. This result showed that the PLC⁻ trypanosomes could complete the life cycle and that the GPI-PLC was not needed for the differentiation of bloodstream form to procyclic trypanosomes.

The final set of experiments showed that PLC⁻ trypanosomes were able to maintain a persistent infection in immunologically competent mice and undergo antigenic variation [53]. This result clearly showed that the GPI-PLC was not needed for either the switch from a metacyclic to bloodstream form VSG or for subsequent antigenic variation.

However, the mice infected with the PLC⁻ trypanosomes lived for more than twice as long as, and the first peak of parasitaemia of PLC⁻ trypanosomes was significantly lower than in, mice infected with control trypanosomes. To try and determine whether this difference was due to the absence of the GPI-PLC gene an attempt was made to rescue the PLC⁻ trypanosomes by returning a copy of the GPI-PLC gene to the tubulin locus. Unfortunately, the levels of expression and activity of GPI-PLC in these trypanosomes were lower than wild type trypanosomes. The reasons for this are not clear but are almost certainly due to the poorly understood mechanisms of post-transcriptional regulation of gene expression that predominate for most genes in trypanosomes, despite the lower levels of expression, there was some rescue of the phenotype [53]. This last result is consistent with the proposal that the altered growth characteristics of the PLC⁻ trypanosomes were due to the absence of the GPI-PLC gene.

The PLC⁻ trypanosomes are attenuated compared to wild type. It is worth considering the possibilities as to why this might occur and then to describe some experiments that might distinguish between them. The simplest observed phenotype is the reduced parasitaemia in the first peak around day 6 of the infection. This reduction was independent of passage number of the innoculum and still occurred if 10-fold more PLC⁻ than control trypanosomes were used to infect the mice [53]. The reduction in parasitaemia at the first peak can only be explained by a reduced rate of growth of the PLC⁻ trypanosomes or a more efficient clearance of PLC⁻ trypanosomes by the host immune system, or both. The first possibility can be tested by measuring the rate of growth in culture or in irradiated mice. This is not quite as easy as it seems as the PLC⁻ trypanosomes are pleomorphic and it is difficult to obtain a population which are exactly equivalent to a control. However, subjective observations on the growth of the monomorphic population in irradiated mice suggest that the growth rate is not unusually slow (MC, unpublished), although this remains to be accurately quantified. The second possibility is that the PLC⁻ trypanosomes are cleared more rapidly by the host immune system. It should be borne in mind that the first peak of parasitaemia occurs at least 2 days after anti-VSG immunoglobulins can be detected in the sera of infected mice. Presumably, the concentration of immunoglobulins has to exceed a certain value before the trypanosomes are lysed. One model that provides a possible explanation as to how trypanosomes interfere with antibody mediated lysis is that, as lysis begins, the trypanosomes release VSG, through the action of GPI-PLC, into the blood of the host. The huge amount of VSG released (1×10^6 trypanosomes release 1 μg of VSG) competes with the remaining living trypanosomes for antibody binding. However, PLC⁻ trypanosomes are unable to release VSG on lysis and provide less of a distraction to the host immune system. One satisfying aspect of this model is that it provides an explanation for the ability of the trypanosome to shed the entire VSG coat in a very short time and why this is stimulated by stress conditions. The model leads to certain predictions that need to be tested. The more rapid clearance of trypanosomes by the host immune system would lead to the first peak of parasitaemia being narrower than a comparable peak produced by wild type trypanosomes. Second, on comparing PLC⁻ and wild type, the amount of circulating VSG should be lower in the PLC⁻ trypanosomes.

Any analysis of parasitaemia after the first peak is far more complicated as the subsequent behaviour of the host immune system will be affected by previous events. Mice infected with PLC⁻ trypanosomes lived longer than mice infected with control trypanosomes and had a lower parasite burden [53]. Most mice died after immuno-suppression had set in and there was an inadequate response to the infection, this took longer in mice infected with PLC⁻ trypanosomes. In the simplest model, one perfectly feasible explanation of this is that because of a reduced growth rate, or more rapid clearance, of PLC⁻ trypanosomes the parasite burden is reduced and the onset of the lethal immunosuppression takes longer. Since the mechanism of immunosuppression that occurs during a *T. brucei* infection is not understood it is difficult to speculate as to how this may be delayed by a mechanism not related to parasite burden but related instead to the presence of GPI-PLC in the trypanosomes. Alternatively, there could be a more sophisticated interaction within the trypanosome population to limit the growth rate of the population [56] that possibly involves VSG shedding. It is more difficult to test these models, especially before the cause of the reduction in first peak parasitaemia of PLC⁻ trypanosomes has been determined.

The «stress» conditions that induce VSG shedding cover a range of different treatments from a reduction to pH 5.5 [23] to local anaesthetics [57]. The cell remains intact during the shedding and there is no release of cytoplasmic contents. Does the shedding observed in vitro represent an event that occurs in vivo ? If such a loss of the VSG coat were to occur in vivo then the underlying ISGs would be immediately exposed to the host immune system, and since infection sera contain anti-ISG immunoglobulins the trypanosoma would become susceptible to attack by the host immune system. A more probable explanation is that the conditions that induce shedding mimic the early events in host antibody mediated lysis of the trypanosome and this triggers the activation or translocation of the GPI-PLC so that it has access to the VSG. If true, this would be consistent with the role for the GPI-PLC in release of VSG to divert the host immune system from live trypanosomes expressing the same VSG.

6 • Unanswered questions

The action of the GPI-PLC on the VSG on cell rupture has been the main focus of this review, but it would be rash to exclude the possibility of other substrates or hydrolysis of the VSG at other times. The function of the slow release of VSG produced by the action of a PLC that has been observed in cultured trypanosomes [49] is not understood. The mechanism by which transferrin enters the cytoplasm of trypanosome after binding to a GPI-anchored receptor is not clear, particularly whether the receptor is released from a membrane and how the occupancy of the receptor is signalled across the plasma membrane. Does the GPI-PLC hydrolyse the GPI-anchor of any other protein, such as an ESAG ? Whatever the roles of the GPI-PLC turns out to be, the viability of the null mutant indicates that is not essential.

There are other questions that remain unanswered about the properties and role of the phospholipase C, how does it associate with membranes, and how is it translocated across a membrane to gain access to the VSG. The answers will provide fundamental insights into the regulation of activity and location of proteins in *T. brucei.*

Acknowledgements

This work was funded by the Wellcome Trust. Studentships were sponsored by the MRC (HW), the BBSRC (NC and MSC), the Sir Jules Thorn Charitable Trust (AG) and the Cambridge Commonwealth Trust (CW).

REFERENCES

[1] Turner C.M.R., Barry J.D. High frequency of antigenic variation in *Trypanosoma brucei rhodesiense* populations. Parasitology; 99; 1989; 67-75.

[2] Blum M.L., Down J.A., Gurnett A.M., Carrington M., Turner M.J., Wiley D. A structural motif in the variant surface glycoproteins of *Trypanosoma brucei.* Nature; 362; 1993; 603-609.

[3] Jackson D.G., Voorheis H.P. Release of the variable surface coat glycoprotein from *Trypanosoma brucei* requires the cleavage of a phosphate ester. J Biol Chem; 260; 1985; 5179-5183.

[4] Ferguson M.A.J., Homans S.W., Dwek R.A., Rademacher T.W. Glycosylphosphatidylinositol moiety that anchors *Trypanosoma brucei* variant surface glycoprotein to the membrane. Science; 239; 1988; 753-759.

[5] Bülow R., Overath P., Davoust J. Rapid lateral diffusion of the variant surface glycoprotein in the coat of *Trypanosoma brucei.* Biochemistry; 27; 1988; 2384-2388.

[6] Schell D., Borowy N.K., Overath P. Transferrin is a growth factor for the bloodstream form of *Trypanosoma brucei.* Parasitol Res; 77; 1991; 558-560.

[7] Schell D., Evers R., Preis D., Ziegelbauer K., Kiefer H., Lottspeich F., Cornelissen A.W.C.A., Overath P. A transferrin-binding protein of *Trypanosoma brucei* is encoded by one of the genes in the variant surface glycoprotein expression site. EMBO J; 10; 1991; 1061-1066.

[8] Salmon D., Geuskens M., Hanocq F., Hanocq-Quertier J., Nolan D., Ruben L., Pays E. A novel heterodimeric transferrin receptor encoded by a pair of VSG expression site-associated genes in *T. brucei.* Cell; 78; 1994; 75-86.

[9] Steverding D., Stierhof Y., Chaudhri M., Ligtenberg M., Schell D., Beck-Sickinger A.G., Overath P. ESAG 6 and 7 products of *Trypanosoma brucei* form a transferrin binding protein. Eur J Cell Biol; 64; 1994; 78-87.

[10] Webster P., Russell D.G. The flagellar pocket of Trypanosomatids. Parasitol Today; 9; 1993; 201-206.

[11] Ziegelbauer K., Overath P. Identification of Invariant Surface Glycoproteins in the bloodstream stage of *Trypanosoma brucei.* J Biol Chem; 267; 1992; 10791-10796.

[12] Ziegelbauer K., Multhaup G., Overath P. Molecular characterization of two invariant surface glycoproteins specific for the bloodstream stage of *Trypanosoma brucei.* J Biol Chem; 267; 1992; 10797-10803.

[13] Jackson D.G., Windle H.J., Voorheis H.P. The identification, purification, and characterization of two invariant surface glycoproteins located beneath the surface coat barrier of bloodstream forms of *Trypanosoma brucei.* J Biol Chem; 268; 1993; 8085-8095.

[14] Ziegelbauer K., Overath P. Organization of two invariant surface glycoproteins in the surface coat of *Trypanosoma brucei.* Infect Immun; 61; 1993; 4540-4545.

[15] Overath P., Chaudhri M., Steverding D., Ziegelbauer K. Invariant surface glycoproteins in bloodstream forms of *Trypanosoma brucei.* Parasitol Today; 10; 1994; 53-58.

[16] Carrington M., Boothroyd J. Implications of conserved structural motifs in disparate trypanosome surface proteins. Mol Biochem Parasitol; 81; 1996; 119-126.

[17] Bulow R., Overath P. Purification and characterization of the membrane-form variant surface glycoprotein hydrolase of *Trypanosoma brucei.* J Biol Chem; 261; 1986; 11918-11923.

[18] Hereld D., Krakow J.L., Bangs J.D., Hart G.W., Englund P.T. A phospholipase C from *Trypanosoma brucei* which selectively cleaves the glycolipid on the variant surface glycoprotein. J Biol Chem; 261; 1986; 13813-13818.

[19] Fox J.A., Druszenko M., Ferguson M.A.J., Low M.G., Cross G.A.M. Purification and characterization of a novel glycanphosphatidylinositol specific phospholipase C from *Trypanosoma brucei.* J Biol Chem; 261; 1986; 15767-15771.

[20] Ferguson M.A.J., Low M.G., Cross G.A.M. Glycosyl-sn-1,2-dimyristylphosphatidylinositol is covalently linked to *Trypanosoma brucei* variant surface glycoprotein. J Biol Chem; 260; 1985; 14547-14555.

[21] Cardoso de Almeida M.L., Turner M.J. The membrane form of variant surface glycoproteins of *Trypanosoma brucei.* Nature; 302; 1983; 349-353.

[22] Voorheis H.P., Bowles D.J., Smith G.A. Characteristics of the release of the surface coat protein from bloodstream forms of *Trypanosoma brucei.* J Biol Chem; 257; 1982; 2300-2304.

[23] Rolin S., Hanocq-Quertier J., Paturiaux-Hanocq F., Nolan D., Salmon D., Webb H., Carrington M., Voorheis P., Pays E. Simultaneous but independent activation of adenylate cyclase and glycosylphosphatidylinositol-phospholipase C under stress conditions in *Trypanosoma brucei.* J Biol Chem; 271; 1996; 10844-10852.

[24] Holder A.A., Cross G.A.M. Glycopeptides from variant surface glycoproteins of *Trypanosoma brucei.* C-terminal location of antigenically cross-reacting carbohydrate moitities. Mol Biochem Parasitol; 2; 1981; 135-150.

[25] McConville M.J., Ferguson M.A.J. The structure, biosynthesis and function of glycosylated phosphatidyinositols in the parasitic protozoa and higher eukaryotes. Biochem J; 294; 1993; 305-324.

[26] Bütikofer P., Boschung M., Brodbeck U., Menon A.K. Phosphatidylinositol hydrolysis by *Trypanosoma brucei* glycosylphosphatidylinositol phospholipase C. J Biol Chem; 271; 1996; 15533-15541.

[27] Mensa-Wilmot K., Englund P.T. Glycosyl phosphatidylinositol-specific phospholipase C of *Trypanosoma brucei :* expression in *Escherichia coli.* Mol Biochem Parasitol; 56; 1992; 311-322.

[28] Jackson D.G., Owen M.J., Voorheis H.P. A new method for the rapid purification of both the membrane-bound and released forms of the variant surface glycoprotein from *Trypanosoma brucei.* Biochem J; 230; 1985; 195-202.

[29] Carroll M., McCrorie P. Lipid composition of bloodstream forms of *Trypanosoma brucei brucei*. Comp Biochem Physiol; 83B; 1986; 647-651.

[30] Voorheis H.P., Martin B.R. «Swell dialysis» demonstrates that adenylate cyclase in *Trypanosoma brucei* is regulated by calcium ions. Eur J Biochem; 113; 1980; 223-227.

[31] Carrington M., Walters D., Webb H. The biology of the glycosylphosphatidylinositol-specific phospholipase C of *Trypanosoma brucei*. Cell Biol Int; 15; 1991; 1101-1114.

[32] Ikezawa H. Bacterial PI-PLCs — unique properties and usefulness in studies on GPI anchors. Cell Biol Int; 15; 1991; 1115-1131.

[33] Turner M.J., Cardoso de Almeida M.L., Gurnett A.M., Raper J., Ward J. Biosynthesis, attachment and release of variant surface glycoproteins of the African trypanosome. Curr Top Microbiol Immunol; 117; 1985; 23-55.

[34] Bülow R., Overath P. Synthesis of a hydrolase for the membrane form variant surface glycoprotein is repressed during transformation of *Trypanosoma brucei*. FEBS Lett; 187; 1985; 105-110.

[35] Low M.G., Saltiel A.R. Structural and functional roles of glycosyl-phosphatidylinositol in membranes. Science; 239; 1988; 268-275.

[36] Mengaud J., Braun-Breton C., Cossart P. Identification of phosphatidylinositol-specific phospholipase C activity in *Listeria monocytogenes*: a novel type of virulence factor. Mol Microbiol; 5; 1991; 367-372.

[37] Kuppe A., Evans L.M., McMillen D.A., Griffith O.H. Phosphatidylinositol-specific phospholipase C of *Bacillus cereus*: cloning, sequencing, and relationship to other phospholipases. J Bacteriol; 171; 1989; 6077-6083.

[38] Heinz D.W., Ryan M., Bullock T.L., Griffith O.H. Crystal structure of the phosphatidylinositol-specific phospholipase C from *Bacillus cereus* in complex with myo-inositol. EMBO J; 14; 1995; 3855-3863.

[39] Carnall N, Webb H, Carrington M. Mutagenesis study of the GPI-phospholipase C of *Trypanosoma brucei*. Mol Biochem Parasitol in press.

[40] Mensa-Wilmot K., Morris J.C., Al-Qahtani A., Englund P.T. Purification and use of recombinant glycosylphosphatidylinositol-phospholipase C. Methods Enzymol; 250; 1995; 641-655.

[41] Mensa-Wilmot K., LeBowitz J.H., Chang K.-P., Al-Qahtani A., McGwire B.S., Tucker S., Morris J.C. A glycosylphosphatidylinositol (GPI)-negative phenotype produced in *Leishmania major* by GPI phospholipase C from *Trypanosoma*

brucei: topography of two GPI pathways. J Cell Biol; 124; 1994; 935-947.

[42] Menon A.K., Vidugiriene J. Topology of GPI biosynthesis in the endoplasmic reticulum. Braz J Med Biol Res; 27; 1994; 167-175.

[43] Bülow R., Griffiths G., Webster P., Stierhof Y.-D., Opperdoes F., Overath P. Intracellular location of the glycosylphosphatidylinositol-specific phospholipase C of *Trypanosoma brucei*. J Cell Sci; 93; 1989; 233-240.

[44] Masterson W.J., Ferguson M.A.J. Phenylmethanesulphonyl fluoride inhibits GPI anchor biosynthesis in the African trypanosome. EMBO J; 10; 1991; 2041-2045.

[45] Carrington M., Bülow R., Reinke H., Overath P. Sequence and expression of the glycosylphosphatidylinositol-specific phospholipase C of *Trypanosoma brucei*. Mol Biochem Parasitol; 33; 1989; 289-296.

[46] Mensa-Wilmot K., Hereld D., Englund P.T. Genomic organisation, chromosomal localisation, and developmentally regulated expression of the glycosylphosphatidylinositol-specific phospholipase C of *Trypanosoma brucei*. Mol Cell Biol; 10; 1990; 720-726.

[47] Field M.C., Menon A.K., Cross G.A.M. A glycosylphosphatidylinositol protein anchor from procyclic stage *Trypanosoma brucei*: lipid structure and biosynthesis. EMBO J; 10; 1991; 2731-2739.

[48] Engstler M., Reuter G., Schauer R. Purification and characterisation of a novel sialidase found in procyclic culture forms of *Trypanosoma brucei*. Mol Biochem Parasitol; 54; 1992; 21-30.

[49] Bulow R., Nonnengasser C., Overath P. The release of the variable surface glycoprotein on the transformation of *Trypanosoma brucei* from bloodstream to procyclic form. Mol Biochem Parasitol; 32; 1989; 85-92.

[50] Esser K.M., Schoenbechler M.J. Expression of two variant surface glycoproteins genes on two individual African trypanosomes during antigen switching. Science; 229; 1985; 190-192.

[51] Roditi I., Schwartz H., Pearson T.W., Beecroft R.P., Liu M.K., Richardson J.P., Buhring H.-J., Pleiss J., Bulow R., Williams R.O., Overath P. Procyclin gene expression and loss of the variant surface glycoprotein during differentiation of *Trypanosoma brucei*. J Cell Biol; 108; 1989; 737-746.

[52] Ziegelbauer K., Stahl B., Karas M., Stierhof Y.-D., Overath P. Proteolytic release of cell surface proteins during differentiation of *Trypanosoma brucei*. Biochemistry; 32; 1993; 3737-3742.

[53] Webb H, Carnall N, Vanhamme L, Rolin S, Van Den Abbeele J, Welbum S, Pays E, Carrington M. The GPI phospholipase C of *Trypanosoma brucei* is non-essential but influences parasitaemia in mice. J Cell Biol 1997; 139 : 103–14.

[54] Masterson W.J., Raper J., Doering T.L., Hart G.W., Englund P.T. Fatty acid remodelling : a novel reaction sequence in the biosynthesis of trypanosome glycosyl phosphatidylinositol membrane anchors. Cell; 62; 1990; 73-80.

[55] Ziegelbauer K., Quinten M., Schwarz H., Pearson T., Overath P. Synchronous differentiation of *Trypanosoma brucei* from bloodstream to procyclic forms in vitro. Eur J Biochem; 192; 1990; 373-378.

[56] Turner C.M.R., Aslam N., Angus S.D. Inhibition of growth of *Trypanosoma brucei* parasites in chronic infections. Parasitol Res; 82; 1996; 61-66.

[57] Jackson D.G., Voorheis H.P. Release of the variant surface glycoprotein from *Trypanosoma brucei* is simulated by the local anaesthetic benzyl alcohol. Biochem Soc Trans; 13; 1985; 494-495.

13

Both IgM and IgG anti-VSG antibodies initiate a cycle of aggregation– disaggregation of bloodstream forms of *Trypanosoma brucei* without damage to the parasite [1]

Ciaran O'Beirne,
Christine M. Lowry,
H. Paul Voorheis

Department of Biochemistry, Trinity College, Dublin 2, Ireland

1. *Abbreviations* : CPT-cAMP, 8-(4-chlorophenylthio)adenosine-3',5'-cyclic monophosphate; DIDS, 4,4'-diisothiocyanostilbene-2,2'-disulphonate; NEM, *N*-ethylmaleimide; PMSF, phenyl-methanesulphonyl fluoride; TMB-8, 3,4,5-trimethoxybenzoic acid 8-(diethylamio)octyl ester.

Abstract

Bloodstream forms of *Trypanosoma brucei,* when aggregated in the presence of either acute immune plasma, acute immune serum, purified IgM anti-VSG antibodies or purified IgG anti-VSG antibodies, subsequently disaggregated with a $t_{1/2}$ for disaggregation of 15 min at 37 °C as long as the trypanosomes were metabolically active at the beginning of the experiment and maintained during the experiment in a suitable supporting medium. The $t_{1/2}$ for disaggregation was found to be directly dependent upon temperature and inversely proportional to the antibody concentration. The trypanosomes were always motile and metabolically active during aggregation and after disaggregation and were fully infective for a mammalian host following disaggregation as well as able to grow and divide normally during axenic culture. The disaggregation was strictly energy dependent and was inhibited when intracellular ATP levels were reduced by salicylhydroxamic acid or following addition of oligomycin while respiring glucose. In addition the process of disaggregation was dependent upon normal endosomal activity as evidenced by its sensitivity to a wide variety of inhibitors of various endosomal functions. Disaggregation was not due to separation of immunoglobulin chains by either disulphide reduction or disulphide exchange reactions and gross proteolytic cleavage of the immunoglobulins attached to the surface of the parasite was not detected. In addition, gross cleavage or release of the VSG from the surface of the cell did not occur during disaggregation but proteolytic cleavage of a small proportion of either the VSG or the immunoglobulins could not be eliminated from consideration. Finally the mechanism of disaggregation was found to be a regulated process, independent of Ca^{2+} movements but dependent upon the activity of protein kinase C or related kinases and inhibited by the activity of protein kinase A as evidenced by the effects of a panel of inhibitors and cAMP analogues on the process of disaggregation. The mechanism of disaggregation displayed by trypanosomes aggregated by anti-VSG antibody is proposed to form part of the parasite's defence against the host immune system and functions to aid survival of trypanosomes in the presence of antibody in the host prior to the occurrence of a VSG switching event.© 1998 Francqui Foundation. Published by Elsevier Science B.V. All rights reserved.

Keywords : *Trypanosoma brucei;* Variant surface glycoprotein; Antibodies; Aggregation; Disaggregation; Endosome; CyclicAMP; Protein kinase; Proteolysis

1 • Introduction

Polyclonal antibodies contain a variety of individual antibodies of different specificities and avidities that can bind to the various accessible epitopes on their target antigen. In the presence of an excess of antigen most antigen–antibody complexes are small and contain only a single antibody molecule with an antigen bound to each of its combining sites within the limits of the usual steric constraints, while in the presence of an excess of antibody most complexes consist of a single molecule of antigen with antibodies bound to each of its accessible epitopes. Neither of these conditions are conducive to the formation of extensive cross-linked lattices. However, in those cases where there are equal molar concentrations of accessible antigen epitopes and sterically functional antibody combining sites, known as the equivalence point, extensive non-covalent but stable cross-linking occurs between the antigen and antibody leading to the formation of large aggregates of antigen–antibody complexes and subsequent precipitation of these complexes.

This general principle for the formation of antigen–antibody complexes also extends to whole cells, which usually have a great number of different antigens and, therefore, epitopes, leading to agglutination of the cells by surface antigen specific antibodies. Furthermore, the formation of these cellular aggregates is of importance in the effective clearance of these complexes and the invading pathogen from which they arise by the phagocytic cells of the host. Most phagocytic cells have receptors for the direct binding of the Fc portion of IgG antibody. In addition, while most phagocytic cells from a wide range of hosts lack specific Fc receptors for IgM antibody, they do have complement receptors for the indirect binding of IgM antibody, which is mediated through the attachment of the complement component, C3b, to the Fc portion of IgM.

Antibody mediated agglutination of trypanosomes was first described at the turn of the century by Laveran and Mesnil [1] in a study of *Trypanosoma lewisi*. In subsequent studies the agglutination reaction was used for a variety of experimental purposes ranging from a diagnostic test for trypanosomiasis [2–4] to the detection of new variants that arise during antigenic variation [5–9]. The fate of trypanosomes aggregated by anti-sera was first addressed in two descriptive accounts by Laveran and Mesnil [10, 11] and later summarized in their classic treatise [12]. These workers reported that *T. lewisi,* when aggregated, remained motile and then eventually disaggregated by an unknown mechanism in a temperature dependent fashion after which they were found to be still infective for a mammalian host. Their observations were quickly confirmed by Francis [13] for the case of weakly agglutinating sera. Subsequently, Laveran and Mesnil [12] also observed a cycle of anti-sera mediated aggregation–disaggregation of *Trypanosoma brucei* without apparent damage to the trypanosomes. However, Cunningham and Vickerman [6] reported that the strains of trypanosomes that they studied, which were used directly from frozen stabilates and, consequently, may have been metabolically compromised, aggregated but did not disaggregate and then eventually lysed. Many other workers have apparently not directly studied the fate of the agglutinated trypanosomes. More recently, Takayanagi et al. [14, 15] have reported that trypanosomes agglutinated by IgG antibody can disaggregate following addition of complement to the aggregated cells without any apparent deleterious effects on the cells. Previous unpublished results in our own laboratory have also shown that bloodstream forms of *T. brucei*, agglutinated by acute immune serum, can disaggregate while remaining intact and motile. No complement was added in our studies and when the acute immune serum was first heated for 30 min at 56 °C, both aggregation and subsequent disaggregation still occurred, which confirms a similar observation by Laveran and Mesnil [12].

The aim of this study was 4-fold : (1) to confirm the original finding of Laveran and Mesnil [10] that healthy bloodstream form trypanosomes, agglutinated by acute immune serum, could disaggregate; (2) to identify and isolate the serum component(s) responsible for the observed aggregation–disaggregation; (3) to investigate the viability of the aggregated cells following disaggregation; and (4) to begin to characterize the mechanism responsible for the observed disaggregation in order to understand better how these organisms defend themselves against their host's immune defences prior to the onset of VSG switching.

2 • Materials and methods

2.1 Source of cells

Trypanosoma brucei MITat 1.1 [16] was used throughout this study and, in a few designated cases for checking the specificity of antibodies, both MITat 1.4 and MITat 1.5 were also used.

2.2 Purification of *T. brucei* from infected blood

Trypanosomes were isolated from blood according to the method of Lanham [17] incorporating several minor modifications [18, 19]. The cell density of each stock suspension was determined by

FIGURE 1

The effect of the concentration of acute immune serum and the effect of temperature on agglutination and the cycle of aggregation–disaggregation of bloodstream forms of *T. brucei*. Bloodstream forms of *T. brucei* (MITat 1.1) were incubated (10^7 ml^{-1}) in isosmotic Tes buffer (pH 7.5, 37 °C) containing glucose (10 mM). In panel (a) acute (day 6 post-immunization) immune serum (50 mg protein ml^{-1})) was added to the cells at the dilutions indicated (■). After a 1 min incubation samples of the medium were withdrawn and the number of free, unaggregated cells determined microscopically. In panel (b) either acute immune serum (■) (4 μl stock antisera ml^{-1} final incubation, stock antisera adjusted to 2.12 mg protein ml^{-1}) or non-immune serum (□) (4 μl non-immune serum ml^{-1} final incubation, non-immune serum adjusted to 2.12 mg protein ml^{-1}) was added to the cells and at the times indicated samples (10 μl) of the incubation medium were withdrawn and the number of free cells determined microscopically. In panel (c) suspensions of cells (2×10^7 ml^{-1}) were incubated in the presence of acute immune serum (diluted 1 : 200) at either 4 (□), 18 (■), 28 (○) or 37 °C (●). At the times indicated samples (10 μl) of the incubation medium were withdrawn and the number of free cells counted microscopically. In each case the results are representative experiments selected from a group of experiments performed on three separate occasions.

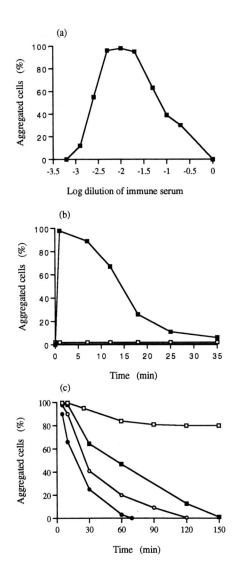

counting samples, which had been diluted 1 : 200 in isosmotic Tes buffer (Tes, 30 mM; Na_2HPO_4, 16 mM; NaH_2PO_4, 1.2 mM; NaCl, 120 mM; KCl, 5 mM; $MgSO_4$, 3 mM; adenosine, 0.1 mM; glucose 10 mM; pH 7.5), using an improved Neubauer haemocytometer with a silvered stage and a Zeiss light microscope.

2.3 Culturing of bloodstream forms of *T. brucei*

Bloodstream forms of *T. brucei* were cultured in the absence of feeder cells, except for an adaption stage, and in the absence of added antibiotics in Iscove's modified Dulbecco's medium according to previously published methods [20–22] and containing sodium pyruvate (2 mM) and 10% (v/v) fresh rabbit serum (heat inactivated at 56 °C for 30 min). Once established the bloodstream forms were subcultured every 1–3 days, never allowing the cell density to exceed 3×10^6 cells ml^{-1}.

2.4 Immunization of animals

New Zealand White rabbits (3.5 kg) were immunized with 6×10^4 purified bloodstream forms of *T. brucei* (MITat 1.1) by intravenous injection. Blood (0.5 ml) was withdrawn daily from the marginal ear vein of the rabbit from day 3 post-immunization and the agglutination titre of the serum was monitored as described in Section 2.7.

2.5 Purification of both IgM and IgG anti-VSG antibodies

IgM anti-MiTat 1.1 VSG antibodies were purified by a modification of the method of Jehanli and Hough [23], to be described in detail elsewhere. Briefly, a four step procedure was used that comprised of : (1) precipitation with polyethylene glycol 6000 (8% w/v) overnight at 4 °C with constant gentle stirring as described by Cripps et al. [24] to be followed by centrifugation and dissolution of the pellet in high ionic strength Tris–HCl buffer (100 mM, pH 8.0 ; NaCl, 150 mM) and filtration through a 0.22 μm pore size filter; (2) passage in turn through columns of Ultrogel AcA34 to isolate the high molecular weight fraction of protein in the exclusion volume, protein A Sepharose to remove the last traces of IgG and a Zn^{2+} affinity column to remove other proteins (primarily α_2-macroglobulin) ; (3) dialyzed into low ionic strength Tris–HCl buffer (10 mM, pH 8.0) and then chromatographed on DEAE cellulose, eluting IgM with a linear gradient of KCl (50–250 mM) in the same Tris buffer; and (4) applied to a VSG (MITat 1.1) affinity column and eluted with glycine HCl buffer (0.1 M, pH 3.0).

IgG anti-MITat 1.1 VSG antibodies were purified by a three step procedure : (1) rabbit antisera was chromatographed on Ultrogel AcA34, retaining the inclusion peak; (2) this peak, which contained the IgG antibody, was then applied to a protein A Sepharose column and the bound IgG antibody eluted at low pH; and (3) the purified IgG antibody was further purified on a VSG affinity column.

2.6 Enzyme-linked immunosorbent assay (ELISA)

ELISA was performed essentially as described previously [25]. The concentration of protein in rabbit plasma was measured by absorbance at 280 nm and assuming that 1 mg ml^{-1} of total protein would give an absorbance of 1.0. For the measurements of total IgM and total IgG concentrations in rabbit plasma ELISA wells were coated overnight at 4 °C in a first stage with 5 μg total serum protein in a final volume of 100 μl in carbonate coating buffer (pH 9.6). The second stage used either anti-IgM Fc-specific or anti-IgG Fc-specific peroxidase-linked antibodies (Sigma) at a 1 : 1000 dilution in phosphate buffered saline (pH 7.0) for 2.5 h. For the measurement of IgM and IgG anti-VSG antibodies ELISA wells were coated overnight at 4 °C in a first stage with 1 μg purified VSG (MITat 1.1) in 100 μl carbonate coating buffer (pH 9.6). In this case the second stage contained 10 μg total serum protein in 100 μl in phosphate buffered saline (pH 7.0) for 2.5 h and the third stage contained either anti-IgM Fc-specific or anti-IgG Fc-specific peroxidase-linked antibodies (Sigma) at a 1 : 1000 dilution in phosphate buffered saline (pH 7.0) for 2.5 h.

2.7 Treatment of cells with agglutinating concentrations of antibody

Cells were incubated at a concentration of $1-2 \times 10^7$ cells ml^{-1} (unless otherwise stated) in the presence or absence of the compound under investigation in a stirred chamber at 30 °C. A 10 μl sample was withdrawn from the incubation medium and examined microscopically; the viability of the cells was checked and the free cells present were counted. Whole plasma, purified IgM antibody or purified IgG antibody was added to the incubation medium at the concentrations indicated in the legends to the figures and tables at a time designated (t_0) and samples (10 μl) were removed from the incubation medium at subsequent specified times (t_x) and the numbers of free, unaggregated cells were counted during microscopic examination. The percentage of cells aggregated was calculated according to the equation :

$$\left(\frac{N_0 - N_x}{N_0} \right) \times 100$$

where N_0 is the number of free unaggregated cells at time zero before adding antibody and N_x is the number of free unaggregated cells at time x after adding antibody.

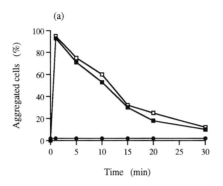

(a)

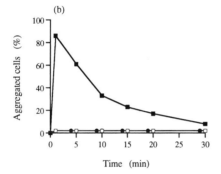

(b)

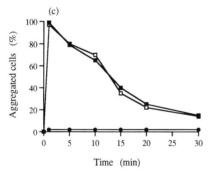

(c)

FIGURE 2

The effect of various treatments of purified IgM and purified IgG anti-VSG (MITat 1.1) antibody on the cycle of aggregation–disaggregation of bloodstream forms of T. brucei. Bloodstream forms of T. brucei (MITat 1.1) were incubated (107 ml–1) in isosmotic Tes buffer (pH 7.5, 37 °C) containing glucose (10 mM). In the experiment shown in panel (a) purified IgM antibody solutions (4 ml ml–1 final incubation, all stock antibody solutions adjusted to 2.12 mg protein ml–1) that had been treated in several ways were added to the cells; untreated IgM antibody (■), IgM antibody heat-treated at 56 °C for 30 min (□) or IgM antibody treated with 2-mercaptoethanol (●). In the experiment shown in panel (b) purified IgM anti-VSG (MITat 1.1) antibody was added to the cells (100 ml stock solution ml–1 final incubation, stock solution adjusted to 25 mg protein ml–1) of variant type (MITat 1.1) (■), MITat 1.4 (□) or MITat 1.5 (●). In the experiment shown in panel (c) purified IgG antibodies (20 ml stock solution ml–1 final incubation, stock antibody solution adjusted to 1 mg protein ml–1) that had been either untreated (■), or heat inactivated at 56 °C for 30 min (□) or the purified IgG fraction from pre-immune serum (20 ml stock solution ml–1 final incubation, stock solution adjusted to 1 mg protein ml–1) (●) was added to the incubation medium. In all cases at the times indicated samples were withdrawn and the percentage of aggregated cells calculated as described in Section 2. The data shown in panel (a) and panel (c) are representative experiments repeated on at least three separate occasions with similar results on each occasion and the data shown in panel (b) is a representative experiment which was repeated on two separate occasions with similar results on each occasion. For the purposes of clarity in the presentation of the data the symbols for MITat 1.5 in panel (b) were arbitrarily displaced by a 1 min interval from the symbols for MITat 1.4.

2.8 Measurement of the intracellular concentration of ATP in *T. brucei*

Trypanosomes ($1-2 \times 10^7$ ml^{-1}) were incubated in isosmotic Tes buffer at 30 °C with constant stirring for 10–15 min in the presence or absence of the indicated inhibitors. Incubations were terminated and the ATP released from the cells by the method of Wanders et al. [26]. Samples (0.8 ml) of the cell suspension were mixed rapidly with 240 μl stop medium (phenol–chloroform–isoamyl alcohol, 38 : 24 : 1 v/v/v) and 80 μl of an EGTA solution (50 mM, pH 7.5). Following centrifugation ($12\,000 \times g$ for 2 min) samples of the soluble intracellular contents were removed and assayed for ATP using the luciferin–luciferase assay. Samples (50 μl) of the reconstituted monitoring reagent (40 mg ml^{-1}, Sigma) were added to 425 μl of assay buffer (Tris–HCl, 100 mM; EDTA, 2 mM; pH 7.5). The reaction was initiated by adding 25 μl of the released soluble cell extract or the ATP standard and the light emission was detected using an LKB luminometer. The results were quantified by reference to a standard curve constructed using known concentrations of ATP.

2.9 SDS-PAGE and autoradiography

SDS-PAGE was conducted using a standard methodology [27] at a constant bis-acrylamide : acrylamide ratio with a resolving gel of polyacrylamide (10–15% w/v) and a stacking gel of polyacrylamide (5% w/v). Radiolabelled proteins were visualized by exposing the dried gel to Kodak X-OMAT X-ray film at $-20\,^{\circ}$C for approximately 4 days and then processing the film according to the manufacturers instructions.

2.10 Microscopy and photomicroscopy

Cell suspensions were viewed with phase contrast optics on an Olympus Optiphot microscope and photographed using 1600 ASA black and white film.

3 • Results

3.1 Bloodstream forms of *T. brucei* aggregated with IgM or IgG anti-VSG antibody actively disaggregate

Bloodstream forms of *T. brucei* (MITat 1.1) were incubated with increasing concentrations of acute immune serum, isolated from a rabbit which had been immunized 5–6 days previously with 6×10^4 viable bloodstream forms of *T. brucei* (MITat 1.1), and the percentage of aggregated cells determined as described in Section 2. A typical bell shape curve was obtained when the percentage of aggregated cells was plotted against the log of the dilution of the immune serum (Fig. 1a) with 100% agglutination at the equivalence point. No agglutination of cells was observed with preimmune serum (Fig. 1b) or in those regions of concentration of immune serum where there

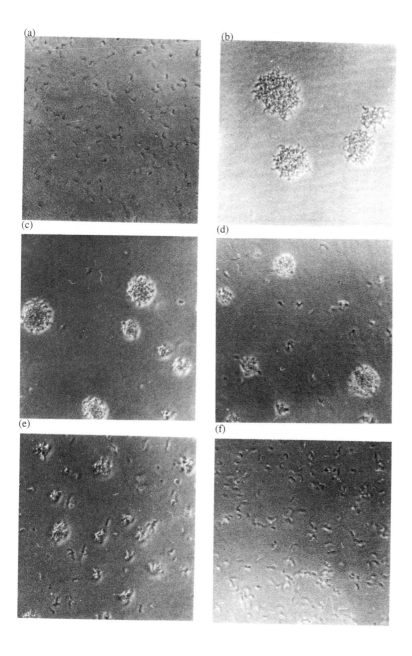

FIGURE 3

Morphology of bloodstream forms of *T. brucei* during the cycle of aggregation–disaggregation that occurs during incubation with purified IgM anti-VSG antibodies. Bloodstream forms of *T. brucei* (MITat 1.1) were incubated (10^7 ml^{-1}) in isosmotic Tes buffer (pH 7.5) containing glucose (10 mM) at 37 °C in a final volume of 1 ml. Purified IgM anti-VSG antibody (4 μl stock solution ml^{-1} final incubation, stock solution adjusted to 2.12 mg protein ml^{-1}) was added to the incubation medium and the cycle of aggregation–disaggregation allowed to occur. At the times indicated the suspension of cells was photographed as described in Section 2. Panel (a) shows the unaggregated cells just before addition of antibody. The remaining panels show cells 1 (b), 5 (c), 10 (d), 20 (e) and 30 min (f) after addition of antibody.

was a substantial excess of antigen, i.e. trypanosomes or a substantial excess of antibody (Fig. 1a). It was also observed that bloodstream form trypanosomes aggregated in the presence of antibody at the point of equivalence or just below the point of equivalence eventually disaggregated when incubated at 37 °C with a $t_{1/2}$ for disaggregation of 15 min (Fig. 1b).

FIGURE 4

The time course of changes in the concentration of IgM and IgG anti-VSG antibodies as well as total IgM and total IgG in acute immune rabbit plasma following infection with bloodstream forms of *Trypanosoma brucei* (MITat 1.1). A rabbit was infected with 6×10^4 cloned bloodstream forms of *T. brucei* (MITat 1.1) intravenously and samples of blood (0.5 ml) withdrawn daily, allowed to clot and the serum removed and stored frozen for up to 3 weeks at −20 °C. The concentration of total IgM (○) and total IgG (●) as well as the concentration of both IgM anti-VSG antibodies (□) and IgG anti-VSG antibodies (■) in each sample was determined by ELISA as described in Section 2.

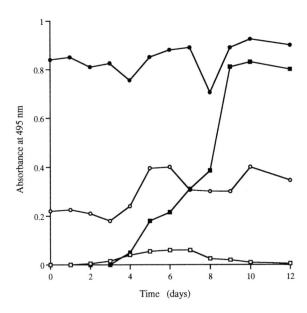

Immune plasma was fractionated, as described in Section 2, to isolate the component responsible for the observed aggregation. Our initial finding was that IgM antibody was the only component of the immune plasma responsible for the aggregation–disaggregation (Fig. 2a) previously observed with immune serum but further experiments to be described later revealed that IgG anti-VSG in sufficient concentration also gave rise to the phenomenon of aggregation–disaggregation. Treatment of the IgM antibody fraction with 2-mercaptoethanol before conducting experiments completely destroyed all agglutinating activity, confirming the involvement of IgM antibody in aggregation (Fig. 2a). In contrast to the proposed complement dependent mechanism of disaggregation described by Takayanagi et al. [14, 15] the same time course of aggregation–disaggregation was also observed when cells were incubated with IgM antibody that had been heat treated at 56 °C for 30 min to inactivate any contaminating complement that might have been present (Fig. 2a). Furthermore, when the IgM antibody fraction was further purified by affinity chromatography on a VSG affinity column only those IgM antibodies specific for the surface coat caused any aggregation of the cells (Fig. 2b). No aggregation of trypanosomes expressing a different variant surface coat, e.g. MITat 1.4 or MITat 1.5, was observed upon incubation with the IgM anti-MITat 1.1 VSG antibody. These results emphasize that the observed aggregation–disaggregation, at least with plasma isolated on day 6 post-immunization, was dependent solely on the interaction of IgM anti-VSG antibody with the currently expressed

VSG and not dependent upon any other serum component or any other trypanosomal surface protein.

The various stages of the aggregation–disaggregation phenomenon are depicted in the series of photographs obtained in one of these experiments (Fig. 3). Before addition of antibody, all of the trypanosomes were present as unaggregated, free swimming individual motile cells (Fig. 3a). However, large writhing spherical clumps of cells were formed within 1 min of addition of IgM antibody (Fig. 3b). These clumps gradually decreased in size and an increasing number of free cells were observed (Fig. 3c–e). Eventually, after 30 min, most of the cells had disaggregated and the very few remaining clumps consisted of only five to ten cells (Fig. 3f). Careful microscopic examination of the few small clumps still present at this stage revealed that the cells were only attached to each other by cross-links at the posterior end of the cell. Cells were never observed attached along the anterior part of the flagellum. After 45–60 min no aggregated cells whatsoever could be detected and all of the disaggregated cells were actively motile.

In the presence of antisera or anti-VSG antibody, bloodstream form trypanosomes showed a dramatic change in the frequency and amplitude of individual undulating waves that pass over the body of the cell, presumably driven by flagellar beating and forming the basis of their motility. The frequency of these waves increase and the amplitude of individual waves decrease as though attachment of antibody stiffened the pellicular structure of the cell; under these conditions the motile appearance somewhat resembles that seen in procyclic forms. Following disaggregation the undulating waves passing over the cell return to their former state and display a lower frequency and a heightened amplitude characteristic of healthy bloodstream forms in the absence of antibody.

The IgG antibody fraction of the acute immune serum isolated on day 5/6 post immunization appeared to have little or no agglutinating activity (data not shown) despite the fact that IgG anti-VSG antibodies could be detected without difficulty by ELISA. This finding raised the possibility that either the IgG antibody fraction was not as effective as the IgM antibody fraction due to the difference in valency and/or that the titer of IgG anti-VSG antibody was not sufficient to agglutinate cells due to the short immunization regime adopted simply because IgM anti-VSG and IgG anti-VSG production obey different kinetics of production in the host following the initial infection. Consequently, these questions were addressed by first examining the time course of the production of both IgM and IgG anti-VSG antibodies in a rabbit acutely infected with 6×10^4 cloned bloodstream form trypanosomes expressing MITat 1.1 VSG and then in a subsequent series of experiments by lengthening the time following immunization to 10 days before purifying IgG anti-VSG antibodies.

A small rise in total IgM and IgG may have occurred steadily over the period of the first 12 days following infection but the day to day variation was large enough that such a conclusion could not be made with any certainty (Fig. 4). In contrast to these findings, the levels of both specific IgM anti-VSG and specific IgG anti-VSG did change in a regular fashion over this period. IgM anti-VSG was first detected unequivocally on day 3 post infection and rose to a broad plateau between days 4–7 after which the low to moderate levels of this class of anti-VSG antibodies declined (Fig. 4). At the same time IgG anti-VSG antibodies were first detected on day 4 post infection and rose steadily to high levels by day 8 where they remained throughout the period of observation which was terminated on day 12. In some animals the specific anti-VSG responses of both classes of antibody were delayed by a day. Since it appears that VSG switching, as manifested by the average duration of the peaks of parasitemia, occurs every 8–9 days during infection of rabbits with a cloned population of most strains of *T. brucei*, it is clear that during the greater part of this period the major variant trypanosomes will be living successfully in the presence of anti-VSG antibodies directed against the major variant. This observation is important because it follows that these pathogens probably possess a mechanism for survival in the presence of anti-VSG antibodies that is additional to both antigenic variation itself as well as any immune suppression of the host that occurs.

When bloodstream forms of *T. brucei* were incubated with purified (Section 2) IgG anti-VSG antibody, aggregation of the cells was also observed. These aggregated cells disaggregated with a similar time course to that of cells aggregated by purified IgM antibody (Fig. 2a, b). Similarly, heat-treatment of the IgG antibody at 56 °C for 30 min had no affect on subsequent aggregation–disaggregation (Fig. 2b), which directly contrasted with the results of Takayanagi et al. [14, 15].

Approximately three times the concentration of VSG specific IgG antibody to IgM antibody was required to cause aggregation of the cells, which parallels the difference in valency of the two antibodies. It was calculated that approximately 25% of the total IgM antibody and 15% of the total IgG antibody fraction was VSG specific. These values were based on the percentage of antibody that bound to the VSG affinity columns and the percentage of radiolabelled antibody that bound to live trypanosomes. It was also calculated that approximately 2.5×10^5 molecules of IgM antibody and 6×10^5 molecules of IgG antibody were bound per trypanosome under incubation conditions used to achieve 100% agglutination. These results should probably be viewed within the framework of both the lower valency and higher molar concentration of VSG specific IgG antibodies in comparison to the VSG specific IgM antibodies found during the first parasitemic wave of an actual infection.

It was found that the $t_{1/2}$ for disaggregation lengthened with increasing concentrations of agglutinating antibody. In addition the $t_{1/2}$ for disaggregation lengthened at a fixed antibody concentration as the energy levels of the cells decreased with increasing time post-purification of the cells. For these reasons in the majority of the experiments performed in this study both IgM and IgG anti-VSG antibody were used at concentrations of antibody that were only just approaching the equivalence point, i.e. slight antigen excess, so that the disaggregation of cells could proceed at a rate compatible with survival in simple salt buffers.

3.2   Bloodstream forms of *T. brucei* aggregated by IgM or IgG anti-VSG antibody were viable following disaggregation

There have been reports in the literature that describe the cytotoxic effects of anti-VSG antibody on *T. vivax* [28] and *T. brucei* [6, 29, 30]. However, in this study the disaggregated cells appeared morphologically identical to cells that had not been incubated with IgM or IgG antibody and the motility of the disaggregated cells was not impaired when assessed by microscopic examination, provided that an incubating medium was selected that maintained metabolic integrity and viability (Section 2).

Additions to medium	O_2 consumption (μmol mg^{-1} cell protein per min)		Pyruvate production (μmol mg^{-1} cell protein per min)
	During disaggregation	After disaggregation	During disaggregation
No additions	0.120 ± 0.001	0.135 ± 0.003	0.273 ± 0.0
+IgM anti-VSG	0.123 ± 0.003	0.136 ± 0.004	0.278 ± 0.0

Bloodstream forms of *T. brucei* (MITat 1.1) were incubated (3×10^7 ml^{-1}) in isosmotic Tes buffer (pH 7.5) with added bovine serum albumin (1 mg ml^{-1}) at 30 °C in a final stirred volume of 3 ml in either the absence or presence of IgM anti-VSG Ig (4 μl ml^{-1} final incubation; stock antibody solution, 2.12 mg ml^{-1}). O_2 consumption and pyruvate production were measured during (in-flight) disaggregation. In addition O_2 consumption was also measured after disaggregation was complete. Results represent the mean $\pm$ SD of three separate experiments.

TABLE 1

The effect of IgM anti-VSG antibodies on glucose supported aerobic respiration of bloodstream forms of T. brucei

TABLE 2

The effect of agglutinating concentrations of IgM and IgG anti-VSG antibodies on intracellular ATP levels and infectivity

Additions to medium	Intracellular ATP concentration (% of control without additions)	Parasitemia after 3 days (trypanosomes ml^{-1} blood)
No additions	100 ± 3.5	$7.3 \pm 0.5 \times 10^8$
+IgM anti-VSG	98.2 ± 4.5	$8.2 \pm 1.5 \times 10^8$
+IgG anti-VSG	95.5 ± 3.8	$7.5 \pm 0.8 \times 10^8$

Bloodstream forms of *T. brucei* (MITat 1.1) were incubated (10^7 ml^{-1}) in isosmotic Tes buffer (pH 7.5, 30 °C) in the absence or presence of agglutinating concentrations of IgM or IgG anti-VSG antibodies. After a 1 h incubation two sets of samples of cells were withdrawn. The first set of samples were used immediately to measure the concentration of intracellular ATP. The intracellular concentration of ATP in cells that had been incubated for 1 h in the absence of antibody was found to be 0.76 mM. The results of the ATP measurements are expressed as the percentage of intracellular ATP measured in the presence of either IgM anti-VSG antibodies or IgG anti-VSG antibodies compared to that measured in the absence of added immunoglobulin and represent the mean ± range of the mean of two separate determinations from a single experiment. The cells in the second set of samples were washed twice by centrifugation/resuspension ($12\,000 \times g$, 20 s) in isosmotic Tes buffer. Male Wistar rats (300 g) were then infected with 2.5×10^6 of either untreated trypanosomes, IgM anti-VSG antibody treated trypanosomes or IgG anti-VSG antibody treated trypanosomes. After 3 days the rats were exsanguinated and the number of trypanosomes per ml of blood determined. The results of the measurements of parasitemia are expressed as the mean ± range of the mean of a single experiment performed in duplicate.

In addition to this simple observational test other metabolic parameters were selected to establish whether IgM or IgG anti-VSG antibodies themselves had a deleterious affects on the trypanosomes. Glucose supported respiration was measured by monitoring O_2 consumption both in-flight, i.e. injecting IgM antibody into the incubation medium, and after disaggregation and by measuring the production of pyruvate, the end product of glycolysis under aerobic conditions (Table 1). Intracellular ATP concentrations (Table 1) were also measured. The results of these experiments show that agglutinating concentrations of both IgM and IgG anti-VSG antibodies had no immediate short term affect on either the respiration of bloodstream forms of trypanosomes or their levels of ATP.

Extended viability tests were also performed in addition to those of a microscopic and metabolic nature. Rats were infected with cells that had been incubated with agglutinating concentrations of IgM and IgG anti-VSG antibody and then allowed to disaggregate fully before inoculation. Normal parasitaemias were found in these rats 3 days post-infection (Table 3).

TABLE 3

Additions to medium	Cells disaggregated at 30 min (% of total)
Glucose	80.3 ± 10.8
Glucose + oligomycin	0.8 ± 0.02
Glycerol	82.7 ± 7.5
Glycerol+oligomycin	79.7 ± 14.4

The effect of oligomycin on the disaggregation of bloodstream forms of *T. brucei* incubated with IgM anti-VSG antibodies

Bloodstream forms of *T. brucei* (MITat 1.1) were incubated (10^7 ml^{-1}) in isosmotic Tes buffer (pH 7.5, 30 °C) for 5 min with added glucose (10 mM) or glycerol (10 mM) in a final volume of 1 ml in either the absence or presence of oligomycin (0.6 μg ml^{-1}). Following the addition of IgM anti-VSG antibodies (4 μl ml^{-1} final incubation; stock antibody solution, 2.12 mg ml^{-1}) to the incubation medium the incubation was continued for 30 min after which the number of free, unaggregated cells was determined. Results represent the mean ± SD of three experiments.

In addition there were no differences in the growth curves of bloodstream forms of trypanosomes grown in culture that had been aggregated by IgM antibody compared to those that had never been exposed to antibody (Fig. 5).

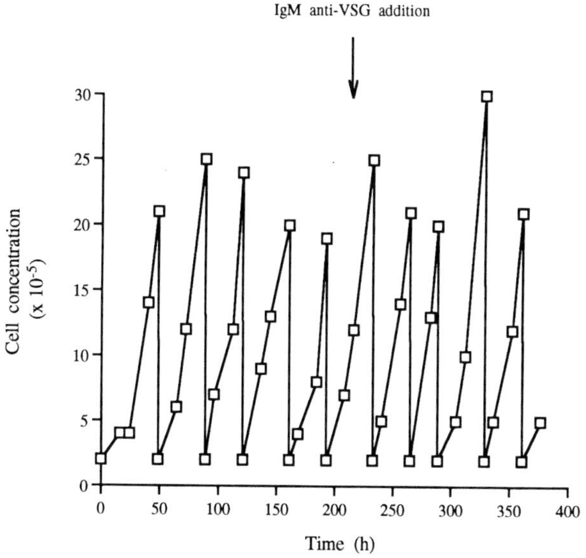

FIGURE 5

The effect of agglutinating concentrations of IgM anti-VSG antibody on the growth of *T. brucei* at 37 °C in vitro in axenic culture. Bloodstream forms of *T. brucei* (MITat 1.1) were grown in culture as described in Section 2. The cells were subcultured every 40–48 h. After approximately 210 h sterile filtered purified IgM anti-VSG antibody (4 μl stock solution ml^{-1} final culture, stock solution adjusted to 2.12 mg protein ml^{-1}) was added to the cells (see arrow on figure) to give 100% aggregation as assessed microscopically. The cells were observed to disaggregate without any apparent deleterious effect on the viability of the cells. Following disaggregation the cells were maintained in culture for an additional 6–7 days, subculturing as before. The result shown is a representative experiment performed in triplicate on a single batch of cells. Similar results were obtained during each of the three trials.

3.3 Bloodstream forms of *T. brucei* aggregated by IgM antibody require a source of metabolic energy to disaggregate

The energy requirement of the disaggregation mechanism was investigated by incubation of bloodstream form trypanosomes with inhibitors that are known to affect the energy status of these cells. Bloodstream form trypanosomes are thought to be totally dependent on glycolysis for ATP production since they lack an active H^+-pumping respiratory redox chain. Interestingly, oligomycin has been reported to inhibit ATP production by an unknown mechanism in bloodstream form trypanosomes respiring glucose but not in cells respiring glycerol [31–33]. No disaggregation of the cells occurred when trypanosomes respiring glucose were preincubated with oligomycin prior to the addition of IgM antibody (Table 3). However, oligomycin had no inhibitory effects on disaggregation when the cells were respiring glycerol. In addition, salicylhydroxamic acid also inhibited the disaggregation of cells cross-linked by IgM antibody (Fig. 6a).

The only reported effect of salicylhydroxamic acid in trypanosomes is to inhibit the terminal oxidase in bloodstream forms,

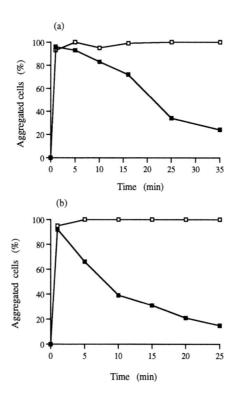

thereby lowering the cellular ATP levels to half of their normal value [34]. Similarly, incubation of cells in glucose free medium without the inclusion of an alternative respiratory substrate inhibited disaggregation (Fig. 6b). Finally, as expected for an energy-dependent process, the rate of disaggregation was markedly temperature-dependent (Fig. 1c).

It was observed that under all of the de-energized incubation conditions tested, where the ATP levels of the cells were lowered, very large, non-spherical clumps of cells were formed and that the cells forming the clumps did not disaggregate and eventually died upon prolonged incubation.

3.4 Measurement of the release of radiolabelled VSG during the disaggregation of bloodstream forms of *T. brucei*

One potential mechanism that would account for the observed disaggregation is that the VSG-antibody complexes were shed from the cells into the surrounding medium, thereby permitting disaggregation. Support for such an hypothesis can be found in the literature where the formation of filopodia has been proposed as a mechanism to avoid immune destruction [35]. In addition, filopodia have been observed when *T. congolense* is incubated with agglutinating concentrations of antibody [36].

The possibility that agglutinating concentrations of IgM anti-VSG antibody caused release of the VSG during disaggregation was tested by incubating surface radiolabelled cells with IgM antibody and then at subsequent times assaying the pellet and supernatant fractions for radiolabel following centrifugation of the disaggregating cells through a 35% (w/v) sucrose cushion. This procedure was adopted in order to eliminate the co-precipitation of the released but extensively cross-linked VSG–IgM antibody complexes together with their parent cells during the centrifugation step. This assay was based on the finding that the buoyant density of the released VSG–IgM complex, though larger than the free VSG, also was significantly smaller than the buoyant density of whole cells with their attached VSG. These differences in buoyant density were exploited and the efficacy of the method established by subjecting some of the aggregated cells to lysis in distilled deionized water, which has been shown previously to result in the release of the VSG from cells mediated via the GPI-specific phospholipase C [37, 38], followed by centrifugation of both the lysed and the unlysed aggregated cells separately through sucrose cushions (35% w/v). The results show that in those aggregated cells that had been lysed with water the majority (~88%) of the radiolabelled VSG was recovered in the supernatant above the cushion while in those aggregated cells that had not been lysed ~95% of the radioactivity was recovered below the sucrose cushion (Table 4) and, therefore, must have remained associated with the cells without being released into the surrounding medium. In addition SDS-PAGE and subsequent auto-radiography of cells that had been surface labelled with [^{125}I] also revealed that no significant loss or degradation of the surface coat occurred during aggregation/disaggregation (Fig. 8).

TABLE 4

The relative amount of radiolabelled Ag–Ab complexes, formed under aggregating conditions and composed of the VSG and IgM anti-VSG antibodies, that are retained on the surface or released from the surface of bloodstream forms of *T. brucei*

Samples	Radioactivity recovered (% of total)	
	Pellet	**Supernatant**
Lysed cells alone	12.8 ± 0.8	87.2 ± 0.8
Lysed cells + IgM anti-VSG Ig	11.0 ± 2.3	89.0 ± 2.3
Intact cells alone	96.5 ± 0.3	3.5 ± 0.3
Intact cell s+ IgM anti-VSG Ig	94.5 ± 0.5	5.5 ± 0.5

Surface labelled trypanosomes (10^7 cells 100 ml^{-1}) were incubated at 37 °C in isosmotic Tes buffer pH 7.5 in either the presence or absence of IgM anti-VSG antibodies (4 μl 0.1 ml^{-1}; stock antibody solution, 2.1 mg ml^{-1}). The extent of aggregation was checked microscopically and then either 900 μl of isosmotic Tes buffer or 900 μl of distilled water was added to the cells. Following a 10 min incubation at 37 °C the cells were centrifuged at 12 000 × g for 2 min through a sucrose cushion (0.2 ml; 35% w/v). The resulting pellet and supernatant fractions were processed and their radioactivity measured as described in Section 2. The results are expressed as the mean ± range of the mean of two separate determinations.

At no stage during the disaggregation phase itself was the radiolabelled VSG resistant to release by trypsin (O'Beirne and Voorheis, unpublished data) suggesting that the VSG remained on the surface of the cells at all stages during the process of disaggregation. Such a result could in fact be anticipated since endocytosis of the VSG of one cell while still cross-linked by antibody to the VSG of a second cell would require one trypanosome to ingest another, which has never been observed.

However, these results do not distinguish between the possibility that the VSG did in fact remain at the surface at all times during disaggregation and the, perhaps less likely, possibility that half of the VSG in any one immune complex at the surface of a trypanosome might be released from the first cell and then, while still a member of the complex, be internalized by the second cell to which it was still attached via antibody. Such a scenario might then employ an exchange reaction of all or part of the remaining portion of the current GPI anchor for a new one and subsequent export to the exterior surface. If such a process occurred continuously during aggregation so that all of the VSG in any immune complex was eventually internalized but that the amount of VSG inside cells at any single point in time was small, then the experimental design employed in this study would be unable to detect significant internalized VSG compared to the external background. Consequently, this particular issue is not yet resolved.

3.5 Inhibitors of endosomal/lysosomal homoeostasis inhibited the disaggregation of bloodstream forms of *T. brucei* aggregated by IgM antibody

Although the fate of the VSG partner in a surface immune complex during aggregation–disaggregation has not been completely determined, it was possible to test the possibility that an event within the endocytotic/exocytotic cycle was required as a part of the mechanism of disaggregation of cells agglutinated by IgM or IgG antibody.

Four different classes of inhibitors which have been reported to affect the endosomal/lysosomal organelles involved in intracellular trafficking were selected to test this possibility. Diethylstilbestrol and *N*-ethylmaleimide (NEM), inhibitors of the V-ATPases; the anion channel blocker, 4,4'-diisothiocyanostilbene-2,2'-disulphonate (DIDS); the weak bases, chloroquine and methylamine which are thought to exert their effects by raising the internal pH of these organelles; the sodium ionophore, monensin, which allows the electroneutral exchange of Na^+ for H^+ and amiloride, the classic inhibitor of the Na^+/H^+ exchanger, all inhibited disaggregation of cells crosslinked by IgM antibody (Table 5).

These results indicate that proper endosomal/lysosomal functioning is required during disaggregation but do not distinguish, for example, between export of a factor that might be required for disaggregation such as a protease or the GPI-PLC and some currently unidentified endosomal process that may be required.

T A B L E 5

The effect of endosomal inhibitors, protease inhibitors, cyclic nucleotides and protein kinase inhibitors on the disaggregation of bloodstream forms of *T. brucei* and on the intracellular levels of ATP following incubation with IgM anti-VSG antibodies

Additions to medium	Concentration (mM)	Cells disaggregated at 30 min (% of total)	ATP levels (% of control)
Endosomal inhibitors			
None		89.0 ± 2.3 (3)	100 ± 1.3
Diethylstilbestrol	0.01	5.0 ± 3.5 (3)	90 ± 6.5
NEM	0.01	3.7 ± 3.3 (3)	
DIDS	0.01	1.3 ± 2.5 (3)	89 ± 4.8
Chloroquine	0.1	0.8 ± 0.6 (3)	95 ± 3.5
Methylamine	5.0	6.6 ± 4.9 (3)	
Monensin	0.01	2.3 ± 3.0 (3)	
Amiloride	1.0	7.5 ± 5.6 (3)	97 ± 5.6
Protease inhibitors			
None		88.7 ± 1.3 (3)	100 ± 1.3
PMSF	0.1	90.1 ± 7.9 (3)	
TLCK	0.1	1.2 ± 0.8 (4)	101 ± 7.5
TPCK	0.1	84.6 ± 8.3 (3)	
E-64	0.01	87.6 ± 7.7 (3)	
Antipain	0.01	92.2 ± 6.8 (3)	
Leupeptin	0.042	86.5 ± 9.0 (3)	
Cystatin	0.01	90.5 ± 6.5 (3)	
Nucleotides and cyclic nucleotides			
None	1	83.6 ± 5.7 (8)	100 ± 1.3
Adenosine	1	85.9 ± 3.7 (3)	
Adenosine 5'-triphosphate	1	86.5 ± 4.6 (3)	
Adenosine 3'-monophosphate	1	84.9 ± 5.6 (3)	
3',5'-cAMP	1	1.0 ± 0.7 (3)	
CPT 3',5'-cAMP	1	0.0 ± 0.0 (3)	96 ± 4.6
Dibutryl 3',5'-cAMP	1	0.7 ± 0.4 (3)	
2',3'-cAMP	1	2.7 ± 2.3 (3)	
Guanosine 5'-monophosphate	1	89.0 ± 6.8 (3)	
Guanosine 5'-triphosphate	1	90.2 ± 3.6 (3)	
3',5'-cGMP	1	3.2 ± 1.9 (3)	
3',5'-cCMP	1	83.0 ± 5.8 (10)	
3',5'-cUMP	1	81.8 ± 9.9 (5)	
Uridine 5'-triphosphate	1	85.9 ± 5.7 (3)	
Theophylline	5	100 ± 0 (3)	87 ± 7.8
Protein kinase inhibitors			
None		91.0 ± 6.1 (7)	100 ± 1.3
Trifluoperazine	1	3.7 ± 2.3 (3)	91 ± 6.6
Clomiphene	0.001	4.0 ± 2.1 (6)	
TMB-8	0.01	1.8 ± 0.7 (4)	99 ± 3.4

Bloodstream forms of *T. brucei* ($1–2 \times 10^7$ ml^{-1}) were initially incubated in isosmotic Tes buffer (pH 7.5) at 30 °C in the absence or presence of either an endosomal inhibitor, a protease inhibitor or a protein kinase inhibitor as indicated in the table. Bloodstream forms of *T. brucei* ($1–2 \times 10^7$ ml^{-1}) were also incubated initially at 37 °C for 0.5–1 h in either the absence or presence of each of the indicated nucleotides and cyclic nucleotides, except for CPT-cAMP which was initially incubated with the cells for only 10 min. Following all of these initial incubations of cells, IgM antibody (for nucleotides, cyclic nucleotide and theophylline 5 μl ml^{-1} final incubation, stock antibody solution 1.30 mg ml^{-1}; for all other cases 4 μl ml^{-1} final incubation, stock antibody solution 2.12 mg ml^{-1}) was added and in each case the incubation was continued for a further 30 min after which the number of free cells was determined microscopically on samples of each suspension of cells and the percentage of disaggregated cells was calculated as described in Section 2. Each disaggregation result represents the mean ± SD of the number of determinations indicated in brackets. In addition separate samples (0.8 ml) of some of the cell suspensions were removed and the intracellular levels of ATP measured as described in Section 2. The intracellular concentration of ATP in cells that had not been exposed to any inhibitor was calculated to be 1.3 mM. The ATP results are expressed as the percentage of intracellular ATP measured in the presence of the inhibitors compared to that measured in the absence of any added inhibitor and represent the mean ± range of the mean of two determinations from a single experiment.

3.6 The role of intracellular secondary messengers during the disaggregation of bloodstream forms of *T. brucei* cross-linked by IgM antibody

The results obtained in the previous section indicate that the assay for disaggregation may provide a simple test to evaluate the inhibitory properties of compounds thought to affect endocytosis/exocytosis which in turn could also provide further evidence for the underlying cause of the observed disaggregation.

The various factors that control and regulate the mechanisms of endocytosis and exocytosis are not completely understood. However, candidates worthy of consideration should include phosphorylation by protein kinases and/or a role of Ca^{2+}. In support of this assumption was the finding that incubation of bloodstream forms of *T. brucei* with cAMP, which presumably slowly permeates these cells, before addition of IgM anti-VSG inhibited the subsequent disaggregation of cells when exposed to this antibody (Fig. 7 and Table 5).

A sigmoidal dose response curve was obtained when the concentration of cAMP in the extracellular medium was varied (Fig. 7b). It was found that the external concentration of cAMP that caused half-maximal inhibition of disaggregation was 0.63 ± 0.23 mM. These results suggest that an increase in intracellular concentrations of cAMP has an inhibitory role in either endocytosis or exocytosis. This hypothesis was strengthened by the observation that theophylline, an inhibitor of the phosphodiesterase which catalyses the breakdown of cAMP to 5'-AMP, also inhibited disaggregation (Fig. 7c and Table 5). In addition, analogues of cAMP and other cyclic nucleotides were also tested to investigate their ability to inhibit disaggregation (Table 5). Cyclic GMP, membrane permeable analogues of cAMP and the non-physiological cyclic nucleotide, 2',3'-cAMP inhibited disaggregation but none of the other nucleotides tested were found to be inhibitory. These results suggest that only cyclic purine nucleotides inhibit the disaggregation of cells.

The role of phosphorylation in the mechanism of disaggregation was further investigated by using known inhibitors of protein kinases. Trifluoperazine, clomiphene and 3,4,5-trimethoxybenzoic acid 8-(diethylamio)octyl ester (TMB-8) all inhibited disaggregation at concentrations which have been reported to inhibit protein kinase C and other related kinases in other cell systems (Table 5).

The requirement for calcium in the disaggregation process was investigated by incubating cells with either EGTA or the calcium

FIGURE 7

The effect of elevated intracellular cyclic AMP levels on the cycle of aggregation–disaggregation that occurs when bloodstream forms of *T. brucei* are incubated with purified IgM anti-VSG antibodies. Bloodstream forms of *T. brucei* (MITat 1.1) were incubated (10^7 ml^{-1}) for approximately 45 min in isosmotic Tes buffer (pH 7.5, 37 °C) containing glucose (10 mM); panel (a), in either the absence (■) or the presence (□) of cAMP (1 mM); panel (b), in the presence of varying concentrations of cAMP; panel (c), in the absence (■) or presence (□) of theophylline (5 mM). All of the experiments were initiated by the addition of IgM antibody (4 µl stock solution ml^{-1} final incubation, stock solution adjusted to 2.12 mg protein ml^{-1}) to the incubation medium and at the times indicated the percentage of aggregated cells was calculated as described in Section 2. Panel (a) is a representative experiment repeated four times on three separate occasions which gave similar results on each occasion. Panel (b) is a representative experiment repeated three times and panel (c) is a representative experiment repeated six times on four separate occasions with similar results on each occasion.

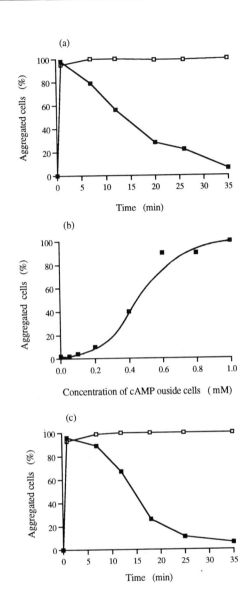

antagonist, calmidazolium, prior to addition of IgM antibody. In both cases the results indicated that an influx of calcium from the external medium was not required for disaggregation (data not shown). The result with calmidazolium further indicates that the effect of TMB-8, which has been reported to act as a calcium antagonist in addition to its role as a protein kinase inhibitor, was not mediated through a calcium requiring event (Section 4).

3.7 Measurement of intracellular ATP levels in the presence of inhibitors of disaggregation

Due to the energy sensitivity of the disaggregation mechanism the possibility existed that many or even all of the compounds tested were exerting their inhibitory effects solely by inhibiting energy metabolism in the cells. To investigate such a possibility intracellular ATP levels were measured in the absence and presence of selected inhibitors of disaggregation. It was found that the concentration of the various inhibitors used in the study had little or no effect on intracellular ATP levels during the short incubation periods of time used in the experiments (Table 5). Consequently, the inhibitors of the endocytotic/exocytotic cycle, inhibitors of protein kinases and the cyclic purine nucleotides cannot be acting on the mechanism of disaggregation secondarily through inhibition of the energy metabolism of the cell.

3.8 The effect of protease inhibitors on the disaggregation of bloodstream forms of *T. brucei* incubated with IgM antibody

The effect of a variety of protease inhibitors on disaggregation were tested because normal endosomal function, which in certain divisions of the endosome involves proteolysis, was found to be required during disaggregation and because the mechanism of disaggregation might easily be conceived to involve limited proteolysis of the cross-linking antibody molecule either by a membrane bound or a secreted protease. Support for such an hypothesis can be found in the literature where a variety of different organisms proteolyze bound antibodies to escape immune destruction [39–41].

Trypanosomes, were therefore incubated with various protease inhibitors, specific for the main classes of proteases, before addition of IgM antibody to test this hypothesis. The results in Table 5 show that of the inhibitors tested only tosyl lysine chloromethylketone (TLCK) could inhibit disaggregation at reasonable concentrations of the inhibitor. This result suggests that either a serine or a thiol protease is involved in the mechanism of disaggregation since TLCK can inhibit both classes of protease or, alternatively, that TLCK may be acting as a weak base in a similar manner to that known for chloroquine and methylamine. At very high concentrations of phenylmethanesulphonyl fluoride (PMSF), inhibition of disaggregation was also observed (data not shown) but the significance of this result is unclear. On the one hand this inhibitor will not act as a weak base and neither will its hydrolysis product which will have a p K far below any reasonable estimate of the endosomal/lysosomal pH but on the other hand at high concentration a nonspecific secondary effect can not be eliminated.

3.9 Analysis of the bound radiolabelled IgG anti-VSG antibody by SDS-PAGE and autoradiography during the process of disaggregation

The fate of the cross-linking IgG anti-VSG antibody bound to the surface of trypanosomes was investigated directly in order to determine if either disulphide cleavage or proteolysis of the antibody was responsible for the observed disaggregation. Bloodstream forms of *T. brucei* were incubated with agglutinating concentrations of unla-

FIGURE 8

The effect of agglutinating concentrations of IgM antibody on the processing–degradation of the VSG. Bloodstream forms of *T. brucei* (MITat 1.1) were surface radiolabelled with ^{125}I by the Iodogen method. The cells were washed three times with ice cold isosmotic Tes buffer (pH 7.4) and then resuspended in isosmotic Tes buffer containing glucose (10 mM) at 30 °C and then divided into two equal portions at a concentration of $1-2 \times 10^7$ cells ml^{-1}. Following a 10 min incubation, an agglutinating amount of IgM antibody (4 μl stock solution ml^{-1}, stock solution adjusted to 2.12 mg protein ml^{-1}) was added with mixing to one of these incubations. Samples (0.75 ml) of each incubation were withdrawn at the times indicated and the cells in the samples washed twice with ice cold buffer and then prepared for SDS-PAGE (10% w/v polyacrylamide) as described in Section 2. Panels (a) and (b) show autoradiographs of radiolabelled cells subsequently incubated in the absence of IgM antibody or in the presence of IgM antibody, respectively. The position to which molecular weight standards migrated are indicated by arrows in the figure and correspond to phosphorylase b (97.4 kDa), bovine serum albumin (68 kDa), ovalbumin (45 kDa), carbonic anhydrase (29 kDa), cytochrome *c* (12.4 kDa) and glucagon (3.5 kDa).

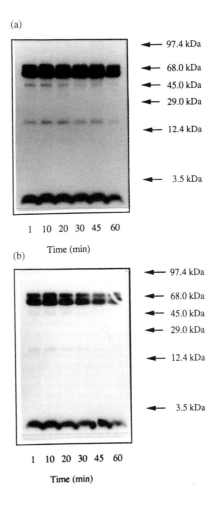

belled IgG anti-VSG that had been previously mixed with tracer amounts of radiolabelled IgG anti-VSG. These experiments were performed at 22 °C rather than at 37 °C, to decrease the $t_{1/2}$ for disaggregation and permit easier visualization of any cleavage of the cross-linking IgG antibody by SDS-PAGE and autoradiography. The extent of disaggregation was followed microscopically. Samples of cells were removed from the incubation medium at various stages during disaggregation, washed and then subjected to SDS-PAGE under both reducing and non-reducing conditions in order to test simultaneously the possibility that the IgG dimer was being converted to monomers by the cells in either a disulphide reduction reaction or a disulphide exchange reaction. The results of the electrophoresis of the bound antibody in the absence of any reducing or disulphide exchange reagent reveals that at all time periods only the IgG dimer was present on the surface of cells (Fig. 8b).

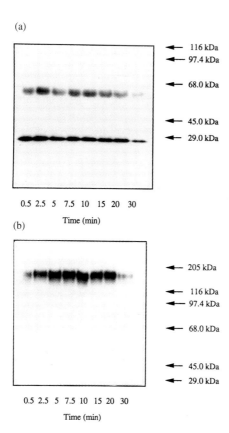

(a)

116 kDa
97.4 kDa

68.0 kDa

45.0 kDa
29.0 kDa

0.5 2.5 5 7.5 10 15 20 30

Time (min)

(b)

205 kDa

116 kDa
97.4 kDa

68.0 kDa

45.0 kDa
29.0 kDa

0.5 2.5 5 7.5 10 15 20 30

Time (min)

FIGURE 9

Assessment of the extent of proteolysis and amount of disulphide cleavage of radiolabelled IgG anti-VSG antibody while attached to the outer surface of bloodstream forms of *T. brucei* and present initially at agglutinating concentrations. Bloodstream forms of *T. brucei* were incubated in isosmotic Tes buffer (pH 7.5, 22.5 °C) at a concentration of 2×10^7 cells ml^{-1}. Agglutinating amounts of unlabelled purified IgG anti-VSG antibody containing a small volume of ^{125}I-labelled purified IgG anti-VSG antibody was added with mixing. The extent of aggregation was monitored microscopically. Samples (0.75 ml) were withdrawn at the times indicated and washed twice by centrifugation/resuspension (12 000 × g, 20 s). Separate samples were processed for SDS-PAGE (7.5% w/v polyacrylamide) as described in Section 2 under reducing and non-reducing conditions. The autoradiographs show typical results from two separate experiments of cells that had been incubated with purified IgG anti-VSG antibodies followed by subsequent analysis by SDS-PAGE under reducing (panel a) and non-reducing (panel b) conditions. The position to which molecular weight standards migrated are indicated by arrows in the figure and correspond to myosin (205 kDa), β-galactosidase (116 kDa), phosphorylase b (97.4 kDa), bovine serum albumin (68 kDa), ovalbumin (45 kDa) and carbonic anhydrase (29 kDa).

At no time is there the appearance of either IgG monomers or individual heavy or light chains. In addition no radiolabelled peptides other than the heavy and light chains of the IgG antibody were visible under reducing conditions at any time (Fig. 9a).

However, it was also clear that there was a gradual reduction in the amount of both heavy and light chain present, which was particularly noticeable in this experiment at 30 min, suggesting that cleavage resulted in the rapid release of the cleaved chains rather than their retention at the surface of cells. This result is particularly important because the $t_{1/2}$ for disaggregation is temperature dependent and shifts from 15 min at 37 °C to between 35 and 40 min at 22.5 °C (Fig. 1c). Consequently, the time course of loss of both IgG chains from cells occurred concurrently with the disaggregation in this experiment.

4 • Discussion

In this study it was observed that bloodstream forms of *T. brucei* incubated with agglutinating concentrations of acute immune serum disaggregated during a short incubation ($t_{1/2}$=15 min at 37 °C) in an energy dependent manner and without any deleterious effects on the cells. It was found that both IgM and IgG anti-VSG antibodies were the sole components of the acute immune serum responsible for this observation and that, following purification, either could act alone to produce the full effect.

The phenomenon of disaggregation has, to the best of our knowledge, only been reported by two independent workers in the literature. In an account of the interaction of *T. lewisi* with antisera in their excellent book on various aspects of trypanosomes, Laveran and Mesnil [12] summarized their early work [10, 11] and stated that aggregated trypanosomes remained motile and eventually disaggregated in a temperature dependent manner after a period of time that was inversely related to the amount of anti-sera present. This phenomenon of disaggregation was independently confirmed in the presence of low concentrations of antisera by Francis [13]. Furthermore, Laveran and Mesnil reported that following disaggregation the trypanosomes also remained motile [10–12]. These authors emphasized that disaggregation only occurred if the cells appeared healthy before the experiment commenced and that during disaggregation they were maintained under conditions that kept unaggregated cells healthy and motile. Finally, they observed that heat treatment of the antisera at 56 °C for up to 45 min had no effect on the aggregation–disaggregation phenomenon but that heat treatment at 65 °C for 30 min abolished the aggregation. Consequently, with the hindsight of modern immunological knowledge we can conclude from their observations that disaggregation is independent of the action of complement but that aggregation is dependent upon the conformational integrity of antibodies. Laveran and Mesnil [12] stated that *T. lewisi*, aggregated by antisera, remained infective to animals. However, they did not investigate either their plating efficiency or the mechanism responsible for initiating disaggregation. It is noteworthy that they did also observe that *T. brucei* displayed similar behavior to that seen with *T. lewisi.*

No other report or even confirmation of the phenomenon of disaggregation in almost a century since these early reports has appeared in the literature to our knowledge despite the many subsequent descriptions of agglutination of different species of trypanosomes by antisera (e.g. [3–9, 42–44]). In two of these studies and possibly a third study agglutination was probably mediated by IgM anti-VSG antibodies. However, in the majority of the other studies it is highly probable that IgG anti-VSG antibodies were responsible for the observed aggregation of cells due to the immunization regime employed which would have elicited a strong IgG response.

It is not known with certainty why the phenomenon of disaggregation following the initial aggregation phase was not observed or at least not reported in the last 90 years, particularly since the mechanism of such a disaggregation in recent years should have been recognized as interesting as well as novel. It is very unlikely that differences in affinity or specificity of the antibodies directed against epitopes on the VSG in our preparations compared to others reported in the literature were responsible for the differing observations, particularly because polyclonal antibodies contain such a wide variety of different antibodies. Consequently, it is almost inconceivable that all preparations would not have antibodies directed against at least two different epitopes exposed on the surface of bloodstream form trypanosomes expressing a single VSG, thus ensuring the formation of extensive cross-linked surface lattices and cap formation which could be conceived to be required as part of the disaggregation mechanism. In fact many of the studies reported in the literature used antisera from animals that were immunized with live trypanosomes and this strategy was adopted initially in the present study in order to ensure that the results would be applicable to an understanding of events occurring during a natural infection where the immunogen is the live trypanosome. In the final analysis, however, we have demonstrated that the complete cycle of energy-dependent aggregation–disaggregation only requires the presence of either IgG or IgM anti-VSG antibody and the precaution of immunization with live trypanosomes was not necessary.

A plausible explanation for the failure either to observe or to report disaggregation of bloodstream form trypanosomes following their aggregation by antibody may be found in one or a combination of the following three possibilities. Firstly, in many cases the fate of the aggregated cells may not have been followed for a long enough period of time or the study may have been conducted close to 0 °C where only the aggregation phase can be observed. For example in all of the studies reported in the literature only assays stopped after short periods of time were employed to measure the extent of aggregation and no comments were included to indicate that observations were subsequently made after longer periods of time. Furthermore, it is the practice of many immunologists assaying the agglutinating antibody content of an antiserum to keep their experimental incubations either on ice or in the refrigerator. Secondly, differences in the concentration of the agglutinating antibody used in the current study and those reported in the literature may have contributed to the differences in the results. Maximum agglutination of trypanosomes can be observed exactly at the equivalence point or closely adjacent on one or the other sides of the equivalence point, i.e. in the region between a slight excess of either antibody or antigen. Because the $t_{1/2}$ for disaggregation is inversely proportional to the concentration of antibody used, even a reasonable excess of the agglutinating antibody would significantly prolong the $t_{1/2}$ for disaggregation beyond the time periods commonly used for such studies. Furthermore, unless the cells were incubated under optimal conditions the increased period of time required for disaggregation to occur under such incubation conditions would have mitigated against any possible disaggregation due to the decaying energy status of such cells in simple salts solution and the strict energy dependence of the mechanism responsible for disaggregation. In such a situation the metabolic death of the cells would lead to a significant amount of VSG release, thereby allowing immune complexes access to the lipid bilayer and a consequent antibody plus complement dependent lysis.

More recently, Takayanagi et al. [14, 15] have reported that trypanosomes agglutinated by IgG anti-VSG can disaggregate without cell lysis upon the addition of a source of complement, i.e. additional fresh serum that had not been heat-inactivated. However, these results may not be related to the primary mechanism responsible for the disaggregation of trypanosomes crosslinked by IgM or IgG antibody reported here or by Laveran and Mesnil [10, 11] for the following reasons. First, aggregation and subsequent disaggregation was found to occur in the present study when affinity purified IgM or IgG antibody was added to the cells in the absence of any other serum component. Secondly, disaggregation proceeded normally when IgM or IgG antibody that had been heat-inactivated at 56 °C for 30 min, which destroys complement, was added to cells. Thirdly, disaggregation occurred in the presence of EGTA and EDTA, chelators of calcium and other metal ions, which are required at various stages in the complement cascade. Finally, no lysis of trypanosomes was observed in the current study even when freshly isolated pre-immune rabbit or guinea pig serum was added to cells incubated with agglutinating concentrations of purified anti-VSG antibody.

The results of Takayanagi et al. [15] can be interpreted in other ways. For example, the possibility exists that disaggregation under their specific experimental conditions was mediated via an alternative mechanism than that proposed by these workers. In *T. congolense* crosslinking of the VSG by Con A or by IgG anti-VSG antibody in conjunction with protein A resulted in the shedding of the VSG and the ligand into the surrounding medium [36]. Within this context the complement mediated disaggregation of cells crosslinked by IgG anti-VSG antibody [15] may have been caused by crosslinking of the IgG–VSG complex by C1q, the first component of complement under conditions where the further reactions of the complement cascade were inhibited.

The consequence of these observations and lines of reasoning is the conclusion that one of the major physiological roles of the VSG is to prevent full complement fixation via any pathway, i.e. insertion of the final C9 complex into the plasma membrane, by physically blocking access of immune complexes to the surface of the lipid bilayer. Furthermore, it appears that complement-mediated lysis does not occur in healthy bloodstream form trypanosomes regardless of the concentration of antibody or complement and only occurs in cells that are either previously or simultaneously damaged by a separate stress that results in VSG release.

The main conceptual problem in explaining the mechanism of complement independent disaggregation is that such a mechanism would necessitate that the effective crosslinks between any single antibody molecule and two VSG molecules resident upon two different cells be broken by some mechanism outside of the cell. Reduction of the interchain disulphide linkages of the crosslinking IgM antibody could theoretically allow the aggregated cells to disaggregate. The bonus effect of multivalency would be abolished under such conditions. Consequently, the equilibrium of binding of the IgMs for the VSG would then be shifted towards free antibody and antigen. The fact that IgM antibody reduced with mercaptoethanol does not agglutinate cells lends experimental support to the theoretical basis of this hypothesis. However, this mechanism does not account for the fact that cells aggregated by IgG antibody also disaggregate. Furthermore, the experiments designed to examine the state of the interchain disulphides of IgM anti-VSG antibody have shown that reduction of these disulphide bridges does not occur either before or during the period of dissaggregation (Fig. 9).

A second possibility is that the IgM or IgG antibody is subjected to limited proteolysis by an antibody specific protease. Support for the theoretical basis of such a proposal can be found in other types of organisms. Secretion of proteases in response to bound IgA and IgG antibody has been reported in certain bacteria and protozoons [39–41, 45–47]. The lack of evidence of an IgM specific protease may simply reflect the fact that most of the studies on secreted proteases have centred on certain pathogenic bacteria which reside on mucosal surfaces where there is a high concentration of IgA antibodies and a scarcity of IgM antibodies. Although secretion of proteases has been reported in African trypanosomes this release was probably due to the incubation conditions employed [48]. Similarly, proteases of trypanosomal origin detected in the plasma of infected animals are most likely due to release by dying or dead trypanosomes since cell death would be a natural occurrence during infection of the host [49]. Other experimental evidence from our laboratory but not presented in this report, using substrates for both serine and thiol proteases, indicate that treatment of bloodstream form trypanosomes with antibodies under incubation conditions where metabolic integrity is unequivocally maintained, does not lead to an increase in the low levels of those proteases that can be detected extracellularly. Although the protease inhibitor TLCK, which can inhibit both the thiol and serine classes of proteases that are present in trypanosomes [50–52], was found to inhibit disaggregation, other inhibitors of these classes of proteases had little or no effect on disaggregation. These results suggest that either : (1) very specific protease(s) was involved; (2) that these other inhibitors did not have access to the protease(s) in question; (3) that TLCK is acting in a similar manner to that found for penetrating weak bases where they apparently inhibit the processing of internalized anti-VSG antibodies. In view of the fact that various inhibitors which affect different aspects of the homoeostasis of endosomes/lysosomes all inhibited disaggregation, it seems most likely that the few protease inhibitors that inhibit disaggregation do so because of their behavior as weak penetrating bases rather than because of their direct anti-protease action. A final more speculative possibility is that TLCK as used in the current study and PMSF at higher concentrations than used in the current study are acting via one of the acyl transferase reactions that are known to be sensitive to serine protease inhibitors and, possibly, not on the main GPI biosynthetic pathway [53–57]. If this proved to be the case, it might mean that one of these reactions was involved in the antibody-stimulated recycling of VSG.

There is a considerable amount of other evidence for a role of the cycle of endocytosis/exocytosis in the mechanism of disaggregation based upon the effects of inhibitors of this cycle acting through a number of different routes. For example diethylstilbestrol and NEM have been reported to inhibit the V-type ATPases of the endosomal/lysosomal compartment [58–61]. At high concentrations both of these compounds can inhibit other classes of ATPase or even different metabolic processes. Nevertheless, they are considered to be specific for the V-ATPases of endosomes and lysosomes when used at the low concentrations employed in the present study. In support of this hypothesis were the preliminary findings that ouabain, an inhibitor of the E_1E_2 type ATPase (p-type ATPase) had no affect on disaggregation nor did oligomycin, an inhibitor of the F_1F_0 type ATPase, when glycerol was used as an energy yielding substrate. However, diethylstilbestrol inhibited disaggregation when either glucose or glycerol was used (result not shown). It has been reported that bafilomycin A1 is a specific inhibitor of V-ATPases and that it inhibits acidification of lysosomes and degradation of internalized ligands in lysosomes [62]. Use of this inhibitor in future work may eliminate any residual ambiguities with respect to the mode of inhibition of these ATPase inhibitors.

Disaggregation was also inhibited by the anion channel blocker DIDS which has been reported to affect the internal pH of lysosomes and endosomes [58, 63, 64]. In addition, monensin (10 μM) inhibited disaggregation. Monensin has been reported to cause instant swelling of the Golgi and lysosomes in trypanosomes [65] when used at this concentration and other workers have shown that monensin can dissipate the pH gradient of acidic organelles [66, 67]. Furthermore, this ionophore immediately and completely abolished the pH gradient in those endosomes through which internalized FITC-labelled IgM and IgG anti-VSG antibody traversed when used at higher concentrations (data not shown).

Amiloride, the classical inhibitor of the Na^+/H^+ exchanger, also inhibited disaggregation, although high concentrations were required (~0.5 mM), despite the fact that there is no evidence at present of a Na^+/H^+ exchanger in the plasma membrane of bloodstream forms of *T. brucei* (Nolan DP, PhD Thesis, Trinity College, Dublin, 1989). Therefore, amiloride may be exerting its inhibitory effects at an endosomal or lysosomal level and the high concentrations required may be due to the slow uptake of this inhibitor into trypanosomes. Another possibilty is that amiloride is inhibiting some other process. There are reports of inhibition of protein kinases by amiloride [68–70] and, as found in the current study, inhibition of protein kinases can also inhibit disaggregation. It may be possible to differentiate between the two modes of inhibition by using the new generation of amiloride analogues, which have initially been reported to be much more specific in their inhibitory properties [71, 72], if they become commercially available and their inhibitory specificity confirmed in other laboratories.

Chloroquine, the related base primaquine, and methylamine have all been reported to inhibit the intracellular processing of various internalized ligands [73–75]. Methylamine and other related amines have also been reported to inhibit the clustering of α_2-macroglobulin and EGF following binding to their receptors on the surface of fibroblasts [76]. These weak bases are freely permeable across biological membranes in their unprotonated form. However, in the acidic environment of endosomes/lysosomes these bases become protonated and trapped, raising the internal pH of these organelles in the process [77–79]. Both bases inhibited disaggregation at concentrations which have been reported to cause both vacuolation and a rise of the pH inside endosomal/lysosomal compartments in other types of cells [66, 78].

A combination of all of these facts provides strong evidence for the requirement of normal endosomal/lysosomal functioning during the mechanism of disaggregation and point to a mechanism that involves the endocytotic/exocytotic cycle in some way that is not yet defined. However, it is clear that even if surface immune complexes are eventually endocytosed, this step cannot occur until any antibody connections that exist between trypanosomes are eliminated. Consequently, it appears most likely that the involvement of the endocytotic/exocytotic cycle in this specific event involves the export of some component to the outer leaflet of the plasma membrane that is required for disaggregation.

It might be expected that the disaggregation event would be controlled by known signalling mechanisms such as phosphorylation. The finding that elevated cyclic nucleotide levels inhibited disaggregation provided indirect evidence that such a phosphorylation event was indeed involved although a phosphorylation of substrate protein(s) was not identified per se during the disaggregation process. The sigmoidal dose response curve for the inhibitory effects of cAMP on the mechanism of disaggregation is indicative of a highly cooperative process which would be expected if cAMP-dependent protein kinases were the major receptor proteins mediating the inhibitory effects of cAMP on disaggregation.

Although long preincubation times and apparently unphysiological concentrations of this cyclic nucleotide were required to inhibit disaggregation this finding was almost certainly a reflection of the relatively slow uptake of these cyclic nucleotides into the trypanosomes and/or the breakdown of the internalized cyclic nucleotides by a phosphodiesterase within the cells. The finding that the more permeable analogue, 8-(4-chlorophenylthio) adenosine-3',5'-cyclic monophosphate (CPT-cAMP), could inhibit disaggregation without the requirement of a long preincubation also suggested that uptake of the cyclic nucleotides was indeed rate limiting. Another cAMP analogue, dibutryl cAMP, which is also supposedly membrane permeable, did require a long preincubation to exert its inhibitory affects on disaggregation. The reason for this result is not known but it may reflect a difference in the permeability properties of the trypanosomal membrane in comparison to that of other types of cells where the membrane permeability of this particular cAMP analogue has been studied. The actual intracellular concentration of cAMP that would be found if equilibrium conditions obtained and no internal breakdown occurred was calculated to be in the region of 20–40 μM. This value was calculated using the Nernst equation for a singly negatively charged species and a value of -82 mV for the plasma membrane potential [33] along with an external concentration of cAMP of 0.63 ± 0.23 mM, the concentration of cAMP outside cells which was found to cause half-maximal inhibition of disaggregation. This value of 20–40 μM is at least a factor of two times greater than the intracellular concentration of cAMP measured in freshly isolated trypanosomes (Voorheis, unpublished) and well in excess of the physiological concentrations of cAMP required to half maximally activate either type I (0.01–0.03 μM cAMP) or type II (0.09–0.15 μM cAMP) cAMP dependent kinase (reviewed in [80]). Therefore, any reasonable prediction of the steady state intracellular concentrations of cAMP during an incubation with half mM external concentration of cAMP are well within the range of that required to activate either type I or II cAMP dependent kinases, after allowing for a considerable rate of breakdown of cAMP.

The survey of cyclic nucleotides revealed that only cyclic purine nucleotides were inhibitory for disaggregation; cyclic pyrimidine nucleotides had no effect. The exact positions of the cyclic phosphodiester linkage appeared to be unimportant since the non-physiological cyclic nucleotide, 2',3'-cAMP, also inhibited disaggregation with equal potency to that observed with 3',5'-cAMP. Such a lack of specificity is not unusual and there have been several reports that indicate that different cyclic nucleotides will bind to either cAMP or cGMP dependent kinases and induce similar enzyme activation [81–84].

Further support for the regulatory role of cAMP in the disaggregation mechanism stems from the observation that theophylline, an inhibitor of cAMP phosphodiesterase, also inhibited disaggregation of cells incubated with IgM antibody. The concentration of theophylline required to achieve inhibition of disaggregation is in agreement with recent results which show that similar concentrations raise the intracellular concentrations of cAMP in trypanosomes (Voorheis and Allen, unpublished work).

The exact mode of inhibition of the cyclic nucleotides was not determined with certainty. However, the results indicate that cAMP may mediate its inhibitory effects on disaggregation by activating protein kinase A. Protein kinase A may then directly or indirectly, through some sort of cascade reaction, modulate the phosphorylation of some key regulatory component required for disaggregation. The anion channels of the endosomes and lysosomes represent one potential site for control by phosphorylation during disaggregation. Recent evidence suggests that these channels are under the control of a cAMP dependent kinase in mammalian cells [64, 85]. There is also evidence for the control of the Na^+/H^+ exchanger by protein kinases [86–89]. Furthermore, cAMP and cGMP have both been implicated in the regulation of the Na^+/H^+ exchanger in cultured kidney cells [90]. Interestingly, the concentration of the cyclic nucleotides required to inhibit the Na^+/H^+ exchanger in these cells was almost identical to the concentration required to inhibit disaggregation. This latter explanation would be in agreement with the earlier findings which suggested a role for the Na^+/H^+ exchanger in the regulation of endosomal/lysosomal pH. Control of the anion channels or the Na^+/H^+ exchanger by phosphorylation may provide a mechanism for the more subtle regulation of the internal pH of early and late endosomes and lysosomes.

Alternative explanations may include one or more of the following less well defined modes of inhibition mediated by elevated cyclic nucleotide levels. It has been reported that the release of histamine from mast cells and basophils in response to binding of antigen to IgE antibody receptors on the surface of these cells can be inhibited by increased intracellular cAMP levels [91]. Similarly, cGMP has been reported to inhibit secretion in rat pancreatic acini [92]. Both cGMP and cAMP have been reported to inhibit the receptor linked degradation of inositol phospholipids in the plasma membrane, thereby blocking the activation of protein kinase C and the release of Ca^{2+} from intracellular stores [93].

The observations that various protein kinase inhibitors also inhibited disaggregation provides additional evidence for a phosphorylation event. However, caution should be exercised in the interpretation of these results because of the known non-specific effects of the protein kinase inhibitors used in this study. For example, trifluoperazine, in addition to its inhibitory effects on protein kinase C, also inhibits calmodulin mediated events as well as having membrane perturbing properties in its own right [94, 95]. Interestingly, preliminary results reported in the literature [96] indicated that trifluoperazine inhibited the V-ATPase of lysosomes but the mode of inhibition remains to be elucidated. Similarly, TMB-8 was first proposed to be an intracellular calcium antagonist [94, 97, 98] before its inhibitory effects on protein kinase C and other protein kinases were discovered [99, 100].

Preincubation of cells in calcium free medium in the presence of EGTA had no effect on the mechanism of disaggregation indicating that an influx of calcium from the extracellular medium is not required for disaggregation to occur. Furthermore, disaggregation was also not inhibited by the intracellular calcium antagonist, calmidazolium, suggesting that an efflux of calcium from intracellular stores was also not required for disaggregation. Calmidazolium is up to a thousand times more specific in its inhibition of calmodulin mediated events than TMB-8, which lends further support for a role of TMB-8 in the inhibition of a protein kinase as previously discussed.

We conclude that the disaggregation mechanism in trypanosomes is a regulated process, inhibited by cAMP and its analogues and apparently requiring the presence of a functional protein kinase C or similar kinase but independent of the action of Ca^{2+}.

No definitive conclusion can be made with respect to the fate of the VSG within surface immune complexes based on the results presented in this study. Although the results indicate that no gross release of the VSG occurred during disaggregation the possibility does exist that a small percentage of the total surface coat may indeed have been released or internalized since the error associated with the results approximately corresponds to the theoretical value of any released/internalized cross-linked VSG (1–10% of the total surface coat, i.e $\sim 10^5$–10^6 copies of the VSG). Clustering of the VSG on the surface of trypanosomes may act as a trigger for the controlled trafficking of the VSG specific phospholipase C or a protease which would then release a small part of the VSG and the bound IgM or IgG antibody into the surrounding medium and so permit disaggregation. Alternatively, following cleavage of some portion of the VSG-antibody complex, internalization may occur. The fact that many inhibitors of endosomal/lysosomal homoeostasis were also inhibitory for disaggregation suggested that the VSG was internalized by a similar mechanism to that of non-agglutinating VSG-antibody complexes. Presumably, the VSG would then be delivered either to a degradative compartment within the cell or recycled back to the plasma membrane. The lack of any visible proteolysis of the VSG, as detected by autoradiography of the labelled VSG that remains on the surface of the cell during the disaggregation phase, certainly suggests that gross degradation does not occur. However, it is also possible that only a small fraction of VSG molecules in any single immune complex need be proteolysed for disaggregation to proceed. Such a possibility arises because of the dramatic effect even a single clip of a few peptides would have on the stability constant of an immune complex, which, although only directly dependent upon the concentration of the intact participating peptides, is exponentially dependent upon the concentration of the effective cross-links. Clearly, additional work, designed to detect relatively rare and probably very specific proteolytic events occurring at the cell surface in either the VSG or the immunoglobulin, is required in order to finally understand the physiologically important mechanism of disaggregation of anti-VSG aggregated trypanosomes, which form a part of this organism's defence against the immune mechanisms of its mammalian host.

Acknowledgements

This work was supported by the European Union's programme, Science and Technology for Development and by the Health Research Board of Ireland.

R E F E R E N C E S

[1] Laveran A., Mesnil F. De la longue conservation a la glacière des trypanosomes du rat et de l'agglomération de ces parasites. C R Seances Soc Biol; 52; 1900; 816-819.

[2] Massaglia M.A. Des causes des crises trypanolytiques et des rechutes qui les suivent. C R Acad Sci; 145; 1907; 687-689.

[3] Offermann. Über die serologischen Untersuchungsmethoden als hilfsmittel zum nachweis der trypanosomenkrankheiten, im besonderen der beschälseuche. Arb K GesundhAmt 1915; 50 : 1–30.

[4] Dahmen H., David W. Zur serodiagnostik der beschälseuche. IV. Mitteilung. Agglomeration und agglutination. Berl Tieraerztl Wochenschr; 37; 1921; 305-306.

[5] Soltys M.A. Immunity in trypanosomiasis II. Agglutination reaction with African trypanosomes. Parasitology; 47; 1957; 390-395.

[6] Cunningham M.P., Vickerman K. Antigenic analysis in the *Trypanosoma brucei* group, using the agglutination reaction. Trans R Soc Trop Med Hyg; 56; 1962; 48-59.

[7] Gray A.R. The influence of antibody on serological variation in *Trypanosoma brucei*. Ann Trop Med Parasitol; 56; 1962; 4-13.

[8] Gray A.R. Antigenic variation in a strain of *Trypanosoma brucei* transmitted by *Glossina morsitans* and *G. palpalis*. J Gen Microbiol; 41; 1965; 195-214.

[9] Miller J.K. Variation of the soluble antigens of *Trypanosoma brucei*. Immunology; 9; 1965; 521-528.

[10] Laveran A., Mesnil F. Sur l'agglutination des trypanosomes du rat par divers sérums. C R Seances Soc Biol; 52; 1900; 939-942.

[11] Laveran A., Mesnil F. Recherches morphologiques et expérimentales sur le trypanosome des rats (*T. lewisi* Kent). Ann Inst Pasteur; 15; 1901; 673-713.

[12] Laveran A, Mesnil F. Trypanosomes and Trypanosomiases. Nabarro D, translator and enlarger. London : Baillière, Tindall and Cox, 1907.

[13] Francis E. An experimental investigation of *Trypanosoma lewisi*. Bull Hyg Lab; 11; 1903; 1-29.

[14] Takayanagi T., Kawaguchi H., Yabu Y., Itoh M., Appawu M.A. Contribution of the complement system to antibody-mediated binding of *Trypanosoma gambiense* to macrophages. J Parasitol; 73; 1987; 333-341.

[15] Takayanagi T., Kawaguchi H., Yabu Y., Itoh M., Yano K. Dissociation of IgG antibody-mediated clumps of *Trypanosoma brucei gambiense* by complement. Parasitol Res; 77; 1991; 645-650.

[16] Holder A.A., Cross G.A.M. Glycopeptides from variant surface glycoproteins of *Trypanosoma brucei*. C-terminal location of antigenically cross-reacting carbohydrate moieties. Mol Biochem Parasitol; 2; 1981; 135-150.

[17] Lanham S.M. Separation of trypanosomes from the blood of infected rats and mice by anion-exchangers. Nature; 218; 1968; 1273-1274.

[18] Owen M.J., Voorheis H.P. Active-site-directed inhibition of the plasma-membrane carrier transporting short-chain, neutral amino acids into *Trypanosoma brucei*. Eur J Biochem; 62; 1976; 619-624.

[19] Lonsdale-Eccles J.D., Grab D.J. Purification of African trypanosomes can cause biochemical changes in the parasites. J Protozool; 34; 1987; 405-408.

[20] Baltz T., Baltz D., Giroud C., Crockett J. Cultivation in a semi-defined medium of animal infective forms of *Trypanosoma brucei, T. equiperdum, T. evansi, T. rhodesiense* and *T. gambiense*. EMBO J; 4; 1985; 1273-1277.

[21] Duszenko M., Ferguson M.A.J., Lamont G.S., Rifkin M.R., Cross G.A.M. Cysteine eliminates the feeder cell requirement for cultivation of *Trypanosoma brucei* bloodstream forms in vitro. J Exp Med; 162; 1985; 1256-1263.

[22] Hirumi H., Hirumi K. Continuous cultivation of *Trypanosoma brucei* bloodstream forms in a medium containing a low concentration of serum protein without feeder cell layers. J Parasitol; 75; 1989; 985-989.

[23] Jehanli A., Hough D. A rapid procedure for the isolation of human IgM myeloma proteins. J Immunol Methods; 44; 1981; 199-204.

[24] Cripps A.W., Neoh S.H., Smart I.J. Isolation of human IgA and IgM from normal serum using polyethylene glycol precipitation and affinity chromatography. J Immunol Methods; 57; 1983; 197-204.

[25] Dolan M.T., Reid C.G., Voorheis H.P. Calcium ions initiate the selective depolymerization of the pellicular microtubules in bloodstream forms of *Trypanosoma brucei*. J Cell Sci; 80; 1986; 123-140.

[26] Wanders R.J.A., Van den Berg G.B., Tager J.M. A re-evaluation of conditions required for an accurate estimation of

[27] the extramitochondrial ATP/ADP ratio in isolated rat-liver mitochondria. Biochim Biophys Acta; 767; 1984; 113-119.

[27] Laemmli U.K. Cleavage of structural proteins during the assembly of the head of bacteriophage T4. Nature; 227; 1970; 680-685.

[28] Desowitz R.S. Effect of antibody on the respiratory rate of *Trypanosoma vivax*. Nature; 177; 1956; 132-133.

[29] Thurston J.P. The effect of immune sera on the respiration of *Trypanosoma brucei* in vitro. Parasitology; 48; 1958; 463-467.

[30] Barry J.D. Capping of variable antigen on *Trypanosoma brucei*, and its immunological and biological significance. J Cell Sci; 37; 1979; 287-302.

[31] Miller P.G.G. Alternate metabolic pathways in protozoan metabolism (Workshop 1, EMPO 3). Parasitology; 82; 1980; 23-24.

[32] Miller P.G.G., Klein R.A. Effects of oligomycin on glucose utilization and calcium transport in African trypanosomes. J Gen Microbiol; 116; 1980; 391-396.

[33] Nolan D.P., Voorheis H.P. The mitochondrion in bloodstream forms of *Trypanosoma brucei* is energized by the electrogenic pumping of protons catalysed by the F_1F_0-ATPase. Eur J Biochem; 209; 1992; 207-216.

[34] Opperdoes F.R., Borst P., Fonck K. The potential use of inhibitors of glycerol-3-phosphate oxidase for chemotherapy of African trypanosomiasis. FEBS Lett; 62; 1976; 169-172.

[35] Wright K.A., Lumsden W.H.R., Hales H. The formation of filopodium-like processes by *Trypanosoma (Trypanozoon) brucei*. J Cell Sci; 6; 1970; 285-297.

[36] Frevert U., Reinwald E. Formation of filopodia in *Trypanosoma congolense* by cross-linking the variant surface antigen. J Ultrastruc Mol Struc Res; 99; 1988; 124-136.

[37] Cross G.A.M. Identification, purification and properties of clone-specific glycoprotein antigens constituting the surface coat of *Trypanosoma brucei*. Parasitology; 71; 1975; 393-417.

[38] Bowles D.J., Voorheis H.P. Release of the surface coat from the plasma membrane of intact bloodstream forms of *Trypanosoma brucei* requires Ca^{2+}. FEBS Lett; 139; 1982; 17-21.

[39] Plaut A.G., Gilbert J.V., Artenstein M.S., Capra J.D. *Neisseria gonorrhoeae* and *Neisseria meningitidis*: extracellular enzyme cleaves human immunoglobulin A. Science; 190; 1975; 1103-1105.

[40] Molla A., Kagimoto T., Maeda H. Cleavage of immunoglobulin G (IgG) and IgA around the hinge region by proteases

from *Serratia macrescens*. Infect Immunol; 56; 1988; 916-920.

[41] Cicarelli R.M.B., Lopes J.D. Characterization of a protein from *Trypanosoma cruzi* trypomastigotes that cleaves non-immune IgG bound through its Fab fragment. J Immunol; 142; 1989; 1685-1690.

[42] Seed J.R., Cornille R.L., Risby E.L., Gam A.A. The presence of agglutinating antibody in the IgM immunoglobulin fraction of rabbit antiserum during experimental African trypanosomiasis. Parasitology; 59; 1969; 283-292.

[43] Takayanagi T., Enriquez G.L. Effects of the IgG and IgM immunoglobulins in *Trypanosoma gambiense* infections in mice. J Parasitol; 59; 1973; 644-647.

[44] Takayanagi T., Nakatake Y., Kato H. *Trypanosoma gambiense*: inaccessibility as a factor in agglutination and binding to host macrophages. Exp Parasitol; 43; 1977; 196-202.

[45] Plaut A.G. The IgA1 proteases of pathogenic bacteria. Ann Rev Microbiol; 37; 1983; 603-622.

[46] Kilian M., Mestecky J., Russell M.W. Defence mechanisms involving Fc-dependent functions of immunoglobulin A and their subversion by bacterial immunoglobulin A proteases. Microbiol Rev; 52; 1988; 296-303.

[47] Proctor M., Manning P.J. Production of immunoglobulin A protease by *Streptococcus pneumonie* from animals. Infect Immunol; 58; 1990; 2733-2737.

[48] Boutignon F., Huet-Duvillier G., Demeyer D., Richet C., Degand P. Study of the proteolytic activities released by incubation of trypanosomes (*Trypanosoma brucei brucei*) in pH 5.5 and pH 7.0 phosphate/glucose buffers. Biochim Biophys Acta; 1035; 1990; 369-377.

[49] Knowles G., Black S.J., Whitelaw D.D. Peptidase in the plasma of mice infected with *Trypanosoma brucei brucei*. Parasitology; 95; 1987; 291-300.

[50] Lonsdale-Eccles J.D., Mpimbaza G.W.N. Thiol-dependent proteases of African trypanosomes. Eur J Biochem; 155; 1986; 469-473.

[51] Lonsdale-Eccles J.D., Grab D.J. Lysosomal and non-lysosomal peptidyl hydrolases of the bloodstream forms of *Trypanosoma brucei brucei*. Eur J Biochem; 169; 1987; 467-475.

[52] Robertson C.D., North M.J., Lockwood B.C., Coombs G.H. Analysis of the proteinases of *Trypanosoma brucei*. J Gen Microbiol; 136; 1990; 921-925.

[53] Masterson W.J., Ferguson M.A.J. Phenylmethanesulphonyl fluoride inhibits GPI anchor biosynthesis in the African trypanosome. EMBO J; 10; 1991; 2041-2045.

[54] Güther M.L.S., Masterson W.J., Ferguson M.A.J. The effects of Phenylmethylsulfonyl fluoride on inositol-acylation and fatty acid remodeling in African trypanosomes. J Biol Chem; 269; 1994; 18694-18701.

[55] Güther M.L.S., Ferguson M.A.J. The role of inositol acylation and inositol deacylation in GPI biosynthesis in *Trypanosoma brucei*. EMBO J; 14; 1995; 3080-3093.

[56] Buxbaum L.U., Raper J., Opperdoes F.R., Englund P.T. Myristate exchange A second glycosyl phosphtidylinositol myristoylation reaction in African trypanosomes. J Biol Chem; 269; 1994; 30212-30220.

[57] Buxbaum L.U., Milne K.G., Werbovetz K.A., Englund P.T. Myristate exchange on the *Trypanosoma brucei* variant surface glycoprotein. Proc Natl Acad Sci USA; 93; 1996; 1178-1183.

[58] Schneider D.L. ATP-dependent acidification of intact and disrupted lysosomes. Evidence for an ATP-driven proton pump. J Biol Chem; 256; 1981; 3858-3864.

[59] Cidon S., Nelson N. A novel ATPase in the chromaffin granule membrane. J Biol Chem; 258; 1983; 2892-2898.

[60] Bowman B.J., Bowman E.J. H^+-ATPases from mitochondria, plasma membranes, and vacuoles of fungal cells. J Membrane Biol; 94; 1986; 83-97.

[61] Nelson N., Taiz L. The evolution of H^+-ATPases. Trends Biochem Sci; 14; 1989; 113-116.

[62] Yoshimori T., Yamamoto A., Moiyama Y., Futai M., Tashiro Y. Bafilomycin A_1, a specific inhibitor of vacuolar-type H^+-ATPase, inhibits acidification and protein degradation in lysosomes of cultured cells. J Biol Chem; 266; 1991; 17707-17712.

[63] Chan R.Y.Y., Loh T.T. Perturbation of intracellular pH by DIDS on endocytosis of transferrin and iron uptake in rabbit reticulocytes. Biochem Biophys Res Commun; 150; 1988; 1256-1262.

[64] Bae H.-R., Verkman A.S. Protein kinase A regulates chloride conductance in endocytotic vesicles from proximal tubule. Nature; 348; 1990; 637-639.

[65] Duszenko M., Ivanov I.E., Ferguson M.A.J., Plesken H., Cross G.A.M. Intracellular transport of a variant surface glycoprotein in *Trypanosoma brucei*. J Cell Biol; 106; 1988; 77-86.

[66] Ohkuma S., Poole B. Fluorescence probe measurement of the intralysosomal pH in living cells and the perturbation of pH by various agents. Proc Natl Acad Sci USA; 75; 1978; 3327-3331.

[67] Ohkuma S., Moriyama Y., Takano T. Identification and characterization of a proton pump on lysosomes by fluorescein

isothiocyanate-dextran fluorescence. Proc Natl Acad Sci USA; 79; 1982; 2758-2762.

[68] Pouysségur J., Chambard J.C., Franchi A., Paris S., Van Obberghen-Schilling E. Growth factor activation of an amiloride-sensitive Na$^+$/H$^+$ exchange system in quiescent fibroblasts : coupling to ribosomal protein S6 phosphorylation. Proc Natl Acad Sci USA; 79; 1982; 3935-3939.

[69] Besterman J.M., May W.S., LeVine H., Cragoe E.J., Cuatrecasas P. Amiloride inhibits phorbol ester-stimulated Na$^+$/H$^+$ exchange and protein kinase C. J Biol Chem; 260; 1985; 1155-1159.

[70] Higashihara M. Inhibition of myosin light chain kinase by amiloride. Biochem Biophys Res Commun; 162; 1989; 1253-1259.

[71] Yoshida K.-i., Cragoe E.J. Amiloride analogues stimulate protein phosphorylation and serotonin release in human platelets. Biochem Int; 16; 1988; 913-920.

[72] Yoshida K.-i., Matoba R., Cragoe E.J., Nachmias V.T. Paradoxical effects of amiloride analogs on protein phosphorylation and serotonin release induced by agonists in human platelets. Biochem Biophys Res Commun; 154; 1988; 101-107.

[73] King A.C., Hernaez-Davis L., Cuatrecasas P. Lsomotrophic amines cause intracellular accumulation of receptors for epidermal growth factor. Proc Natl Acad Sci USA; 77; 1980; 3283-3287.

[74] Reid P.A., Watts C. Cycling of cell-surface MHC glycoproteins through primaquine-sensitive intracellular compartments. Nature; 346; 1990; 655-657.

[75] Reif J.S., Schwartz A.L., Fallon R.J. Low concentrations of primaquine inhibit degradation but not receptor-mediated endocytosis of asialoorosomucoid by HepG2 cells. Exp Cell Res; 192; 1991; 581-586.

[76] Maxfield FR, Willingham MC, Davies PJA, Pastan I. Amines inhibit the clustering of α_2-macroglobulin and EGF on the fibroblast cell surface. Nature 1979; 277 : 661–63.

[77] De Duve C., De Barsy T., Poole B., Trouet A., Tulkens P., Van Hoof F. Lysomotrophic agents. Biochem Pharmacol; 23; 1974; 2495-2531.

[78] Ohkuma S., Poole B. Cytoplasmic vacuolation of mouse peritoneal macrophages and the uptake into lysosomes of weakly basic substances. J Cell Biol; 90; 1981; 656-664.

[79] Dean R.T., Jessup W., Roberts C.R. Effects of exogenous amines on mammalian cells, with particular reference to membrane flow. Biochem J; 217; 1984; 27-40.

[80] Lohmann S.M., Walter U. Regulation of the cellular and subcellular concentrations and distribution of cyclic nucleo-tide-dependent protein kinases. Adv Cyclic Nucleotide Protein Phosphor Res; 18; 1984; 63-117.

[81] Nishiyama K., Katakami H., Yamamura H., Takai Y., Shimomura R., Nishizuka Y. Functional specificity of guanosine 3' : 5'-monophosphate-dependent and adenosine 3' : 5'-monophosphate-dependent protein kinases from silkworm. J Biol Chem; 250; 1975; 1297-1300.

[82] Gill G.N., Holdy K.E., Walton G.M., Kanstein C.B. Purification and characterization of 3' : 5'-cyclic GMP-dependent protein kinase. Proc Natl Acad Sci USA; 73; 1976; 3918-3922.

[83] Khoo J.C., Gill G.N. Comparison of cyclic nucleotide specificity of guanosine 3',5'-monophosphate-dependent protein kinase and adenosine 3',5'-monophosphate-dependent protein kinase. Biochim Biophys Acta; 584; 1979; 21-32.

[84] Gill G.N., McCune R.W. Guanosine 3',5'monophosphate-dependent protein kinase. Curr Top Cell Regul; 15; 1979; 1-45.

[85] Mulberg A.E., Tulk B.M., Forgac M. Modulation of coated vesicle chloride channel activity and acidification by reversible protein kinase A-dependent phosphorylation. J Biol Chem; 266; 1991; 20590-20593.

[86] Grinstein S., Cohen S., Goetz J.D., Rothstein A. Osmotic and phorbol ester-induced activation of Na$^+$/H$^+$ exchange : possible role of protein phosphorylation in lymphocyte volume regulation. J Cell Biol; 101; 1985; 269-276.

[87] Siffert W., Scheid P. A phorbol ester and 1-oleoyl-2-acetyl-glycerol induce Na$^+$/H$^+$ exchange in human platelets. Biochem Biophys Res Commun; 141; 1986; 13-19.

[88] Vigne P., Breittmayer J.-P., Frelin C., Lazdunski M. Dual control of the intracellular pH in aortic smooth muscle cells by a cAMP-sensitive HCO$_3^-$/Cl$^-$ antiporter and a protein kinase C-sensitive Na$^+$/H$^+$ antiporter. J Biol Chem; 263; 1988; 18023-18029.

[89] Sardet C., Counillon L., Franchi A., Pouysségur J. Growth factors induce phosphorylation of the Na$^+$/H$^+$ antiporter, a glycoprotein of 110 kDa. Science; 247; 1990; 723-726.

[90] Moran A., Montrose M.H., Murer H. Regulation of the Na$^+$ – H$^+$ exchange in cultured opossum kidney cells by parathyroid hormone, atrial natriuretic peptide and cyclic nucleotides. Biochim Biophys Acta; 969; 1988; 48-56.

[91] Marone G., Findlay S.R., Lichtenstein L.M. Adenosine receptor on human basophils : modulation of histamine release. J Immunol; 123; 1979; 1473-1477.

[92] Rogers J., Hughes R.G., Matthews E.K. Cyclic GMP inhibits protein kinase C-mediated secretion in rat pancreatic acini. J Biol Chem; 263; 1988; 3713-3719.

[93] Nishizuka Y. The role of protein kinase C in cell surface signal transduction and tumour promotion. Nature; 308; 1984; 693-698.

[94] Owen N.E., Villereal M.L. Evidence for a role of calmodulin in serum stimulation of Na$^+$ influx in human fibroblasts. Proc Natl Acad Sci USA; 79; 1982; 3537-3541.

[95] Douglas W.W., Nemeth E.F. On the calcium receptor activating exocytosis : inhibitory effects of calmodulin-interacting drugs on rat mast cells. J Physiol; 323; 1982; 229-244.

[96] Schneider D.L. The proton pump ATPase of lysosomes and related organelles of the vacuolar apparatus. Biochim Biophys Acta; 895; 1987; 1-10.

[97] Rittenhouse-Simmons S., Deykin D. The activation by Ca^{2+} of platelet phospholipase A$_2$. Effects of dibutryl cyclic adenosine monophosphate and 8-(*N, N*-diethylamino)-octyl-3,4,5-trimethoxybenzoate. Biochim Biophys Acta; 543; 1978; 409-422.

[98] Owen N.E., Villereal M.L. Efflux of ^{45}Ca^{2+} from human fibroblasts in response to serum or growth factors. J Cell Physiol; 117; 1983; 23-29.

[99] Simpson A.W.M., Hallam T.J., Rink T.J. TMB-8 inhibits secretion evoked by phorbol ester at basal cytoplasmic free calcium in quin-2 loaded platelets much more effectively than it inhibits thrombin-induced calcium mobilization. FEBS Lett; 176; 1984; 139-143.

[100] Kojima I., Kojima K., Rasmussen H. Intracellular calcium and adenosine 3',5'-cyclic monophosphate as mediators of potassium-induced aldosterone secretion. Biochem J; 228; 1985; 69-76.

14

Keywords : Trypanosome; Glucose transporter; Glycosylation

Trypanosome glucose transporters

Michael P. Barret [b],
Emmanuel Tetaud [c],
Andreas Seyfang [d],
Frédéric Bringaud [a],
Théo Baltz [a]

[a] *Laboratoire de Parasitologie Molécu-laire, UPRESA CNRS 5016, Université de Bordeaux II, 146 Rue Léo Saignat, 33076 Bordeaux Cedex, France*

[b] *Division of Infection and Immunity, Institute of Biomedical and Life Sciences, Joseph Black Building, University of Glasgow, Glasgow G12 8QQ, UK*

[c] *Department of Biochemistry, Medical Sciences Institute, University of Dundee, Dundee DD1 4HN, UK*

[d] *Oregon Health Sciences University, Mail code L-220, Portland, OR 97201, USA*

1 • Introduction

The genus *Trypanosoma* comprises a group of parasitic protozoa which cause widespread disease in man and animals. African trypansomes are transmitted by tsetse flies, or other biting insects, or by coitus in the case of the equine parasite *T. equiperdum*. The South American trypanosome, infectious to humans, *T. cruzi* is transmitted fecally by reduviid bugs. The different trypanosome species have different life cycles. African trypanosomes live free in the blood, central nervous system and other tissue fluids of their mammalian hosts. *T. cruzi*, by contrast adopts an intracellular environment within their mammalian hosts. Invasion and passage through different anatomical locations within insect vectors also distinguishes the parasites.

All trypanosome species use glucose as a crucial source of energy, and all have specific plasma membrane transporters to facilitate the uptake of this molecule. Four different trypanosome glucose transporter genes have been cloned, and their function verified by expression in either *Xenopus* oocytes or Chinese hamster ovary (CHO) cells. It appears that the transporters have adapted to best suit the needs of the parasites in the different environments with which they are confronted. For example, availability of free glucose in serum differs greatly from that in a mammalian cell's cytoplasm or within the midgut of insect vectors.

The trypanosome glucose transporters belong to the glucose transporter superfamily, exemplified by the mammalian erythrocyte transporter, GLUT1 [1]. Nevertheless they have particular structural and functional features which distinguish them from their mammalian counterparts. These include : a conserved array of cysteine residues in the first exofacial loop; a relative insensitivity to various pharmacological reagents such as cytochalasin B; and a substrate recognition profile which includes the ability to transport D-fructose. It is possible that the trypanosome glucose transporters may represent either chemotherapeutic targets themselves, or gateways which allow the targeting of other toxic molecules to these parasites.

2 • Cloning of the trypanosome glucose transporter genes

A gene cloned from a *T. brucei* EATRO 164 cDNA library [2] was found to have high homology to a glucose transporter gene previously isolated from the related kinetoplastid parasite *Leishmania enriettii* [3]. The gene was found to be a member of a clustered gene family in the *T. brucei brucei* genome. In fact, two separate isoforms, called THT1 and THT2 (THT = trypanosome hexose transporter) were isolated [4], differing predominantly in the carboxy terminal domain, and a cysteine rich first exofacial loop. Identical genes have been found in *T. brucei rhodesiense, T. b. gambiense, T. equiperdum* and *T. evansi* [5].

The *T. brucei* THT1 gene was used to probe a library of *T. cruzi* genomic DNA, and a related gene was identified [6], although only a single isoform (TcrHT1), also in multiple copies, could be identified in *T. cruzi.*

Having identified genes encoding glucose transporters from *T. brucei* and *T. cruzi,* and given the availability of related sequences from *Leishmania* parasites, regions of high conservation were identified. Oligonucleotides based on these motifs were designed and used to amplify related sequences from *Trypanosoma vivax* using the polymerase chain reaction [7]. Sequencing of three tandemly arranged TvHT1 copies present in the Y481 strain of *T. vivax* showed that there is only a single TvHT isoform (Bringaud et al., unpublished data).

The different trypanosome glucose transporter amino acid sequences are all highly homologous to one another (52–80% identity). The genes which flank the glucose transporter gene clusters from all three species of trypanosome are conserved and found in the same positions relative to the glucose transporter genes revealing a high conservation of genome organisation within the genus *Trypanosoma* (Bringaud et al., unpublished data).

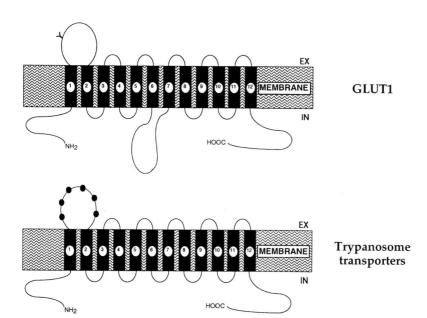

GLUT1

Trypanosome
transporters

FIGURE 1

Schematic representation of the mammalian GLUT1 glucose transporter and the trypanosome transporters. The 12 transmembrane hydrophobic helices are numbered. A «Y» represents the glycoslylation site of the first exofacial loop of the mammalian transporter. Shaded circles in the trypanosomal first exofacial loop represent the cysteine residues. A particularly long intracellular loop between helices 6 and 7 of GLUT1 is not present in the trypanosome transporters.

All of the trypanosome glucose transporter genes conform to the widely held view of membrane topology of the glucose transporter superfamily in that hydrophobicity plots predict 12 transmembrane helices (Fig. 1). The sequences are aligned in Fig. 2.

2.1 *T. brucei* contains two glucose transporter isoforms : *T. vivax* and *T. cruzi* contain only one

The glucose transporters from all of the trypanosome species studied exist as multiple tandem copies. In *T. brucei* two different isoforms exist while *T. cruzi* and *T. vivax* contain just one. The copy number varies greatly between individual isolates in the case of *T. brucei* [8].

Northern blot analysis (Fig. 3) revealed that in *T. brucei* THT1 is the most abundantly expressed isoform in bloodstream form parasites, while THT2 is the most abundant in procyclics.

THT2 levels are similar throughout the life-cycle while THT1 transcripts are some 40-fold more abundant than THT2 transcripts in bloodstream forms and absent or present at very low levels in procyclic forms [4]. The 3' untranslated region of the THT1 gene is responsible for its differential expression, rendering transcripts stable in bloodstream but not procyclic cells [9]. The expression of two

FIGURE 2

Amino-acid sequence alignment of the trypanosome glucose transporters. Identical amino acids are underscored with an asterisk. The cysteines of the first exofacial loop are marked with an arrow above the first sequence. Transmembrane, hydrophobic domains are indicated. Potential *N*-linked glycosylation sites are underlined.

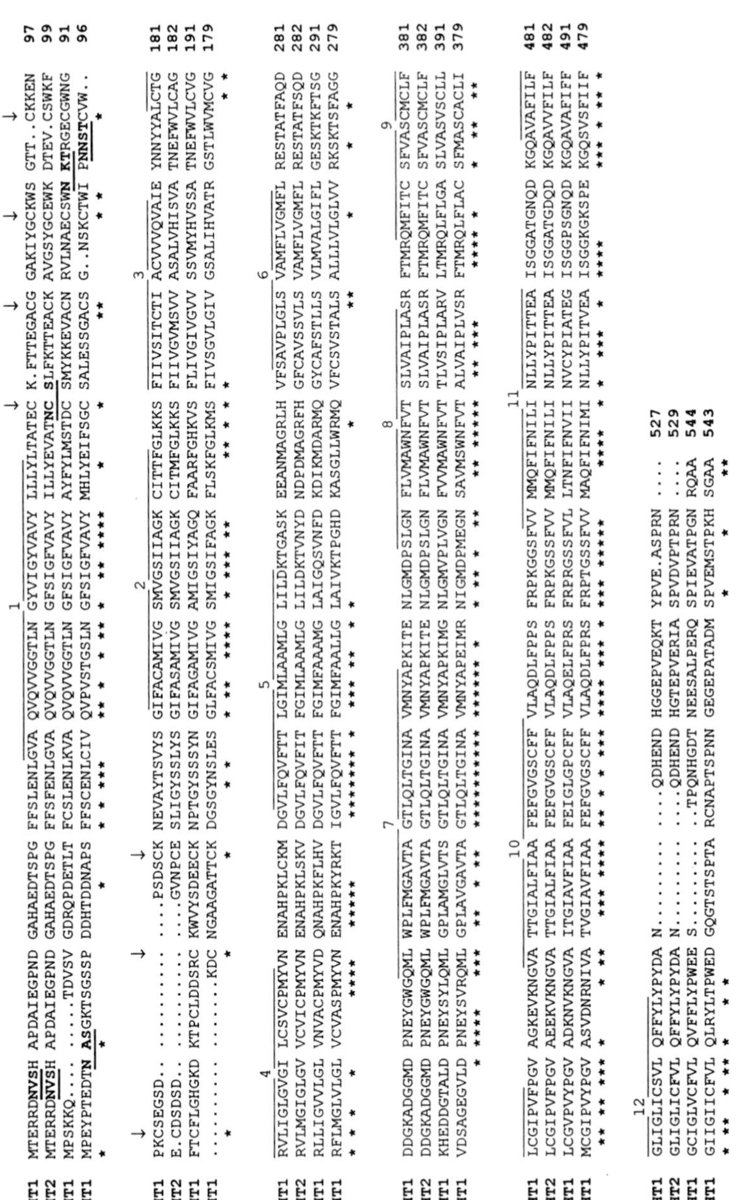

```
                                                    →                                            →                          →
THT1    MTERRDNVSH APDAIEGPND GAHAEDTSPG FFSLENLGVA QVQVVGGTLN GVYIGVAVY  LLLYLTATEC K.FTTEGACG GAKIYGCKWS GTT..CKKEN   97
THT2    MTERRDNVSH APDAIEGPND GAHAEDTSPG FFSFENLGVA QVQVVGGTLN GFSIGFVAVY ILLYEVATNC SLFKTTEACK AVGSYGCEWK DTEV.CSWKF   99
TcrHT1  MPSKKQ.... .....TDVSV GDRQPDETLT FCSLENLKVA QVQVVGGTLN GFSIGFVAVY AYFYLMSTDC SMYKKEVACN RVLNAECSWN KTRGECGWNG   91
TvHT1   MPEYPTEDTN ASGKTSGSSP DDHTDDNAPS FFSCENLCIV QVPVSTGSLN GFSIGFVAVY MHLYEIFSGC SALESSGACS G..NSKCTWI PNNSTCVW..   96
         *                  *                  *          *   ****  *      *         *                                 *
                                                                                            1
                              →                                                                                3
THT1    PKCSEGSD.. .......... ..PSDSCK   NEVAYTSVYS GIFACAMIVG SMVGSIIAGK CITTFGLKKS FIIVSITCTI ACVVVQVAIE YNNYYALCTG  181
THT2    E.CDSDSD.. .......... ..GVNPCE   SLIGYSSLYS GIFASAMIVG SMVGSIIAGK CITMFGLKKS FIIVGVMSVV ASALVHISVA TNEFWVLCAG  182
TcrHT1  FTCFLGHGKD KTPCLDDSRC KWVYSDEECK NPTGYSSSYN GIFAGAMIVG AMIGSIYAGQ FAARFGHKVS FLIVGIVGVV SSVMYHVSSA TNEFWVLCVG  191
TvHT1   .......... .......KDC NGAAGATTCK DGSGYNSLES GLFACSMIVG SMIGSIFAGK FLSKFGLKMS FIVSGVLGIV GSALIHVATR GSTLWVMCVG  179
                                                    *     ***    ** *   **  *          *    *                             *
                                                                 2
                          →                                                     5                         6
THT1    RVLIGLGVGI LCSVICPMYN ENAHPKLCKM DGVLFQVFTT LGIMLAAMLG LILDKTGASK EEANMAGRLH VFSAVPLGLS VAMFLVGMFL RESTATFAQD  281
THT2    RVLMGIGLGV VCVICEMYVN ENAHPKLSRV DGVLFQVFIT FGIMLAAMLG LILDKTVNYD NDPDMAGRFH GFCAVSSVLS VAMFLVGMFL RESTATFSQD  282
TcrHT1  RLLIGVVLGL VNVACPMYVD QNAHPKFLHV DGVLFQVFTT FGIMFAAAMG LAIGQSVNFD KDIKMDARMQ GYCAFSTLLS VLMVALGIFL GESKTKFTSG  291
TvHT1   RFLMGLVLGL VCVASPMYVN ENAHPKYRKT IGVLFQVFTT FGIMFAALLG LAIVKTPGHD KASGLLWRMQ VFCSVSTALS ALLLVLGLVV RKSKTSFAGG  279
         *       *          * ***       * *****  *   ***        *                                           *
                                                      7                                                 8               9
THT1    DDGKADGGMD PNEYGWGQML WPLFMGAVTA GTLQLTGINA VMNYAPKITE NLGMDPSLGN FLVMAWNFVT SLVAIPLASR FTMRQMFITC SFVASCMCLF  381
THT2    DDGKADGGMD PNEYGWGQML WPLFMGAVTA GTLQLTGINA VMNYAPKITE NLGMDPSLGN FLVMAWNFVT SLVAIPLASR FTMRQMFITC SFVASCMCLF  382
TcrHT1  KHEDDGTALD PNEYSYLQML GPLAMGLVTS GTLQLTGINA VMNYAPKIMG NLGMVPLVGN FVMAWNFVT  TLVSIPLARV LTMRQLFLGA SLVASVSCLL  391
TvHT1   VDSAGEGVLD PNEYSVRQML PLAVGAVTA  GTLQLTGINA VMNYAPEIMR NIGMDPMEGN SAVMSWNFVT ALVAIPLVSR FTMRQLFLAC SFMASCACLI  379
              *     ***       *          *******   *  ***       **          **   ****           *           **
                                                                 10                              11
THT1    LCGIPVFPGV AGKEVKNGVA TTGIALFIAA FEFGVGSCFF VLAQDLPPPS FRPKGGSFVV MMQFIFNILI NLLYPITTEA ISGGATGNQD KGQAVAFILF  481
THT2    LCGIPVFPGV AEEKVKNGVA TTGIALFIAA FEFGVGSCFF VLAQDLPPPS FRPKGSSFVV MMQFIFNILI NLLYPITTEA ISGGATGDQD KGQAVVFILF  482
TcrHT1  LCGVPVYPGV ADRNVKNGVA ITGIAVFIAA FEIGLGPCFF VLAQBLFPRS FRPRGSSFVL LTNFFNVII  NVCYPIATEG ISGGPSGNQD KGQAVAFIFF  491
TvHT1   MCGIPVYPGV ASVDNRNIVA TVGIAVFIAA FEFGVGSCFF VLAQDLPPRS FRPTGSSFVV MAQFIFNIMI NLLYPITVEA ISGGKGKSPE KGQSVSFIIF  479
          ** * * **             *  * ***  *     ***   ***         **  *                  **        *        *
                  12
THT1    GLIGLICSVL QFFYLYPYDA N......... ....QDHEND HGGEPVEQKT YPVE.ASPRN .....   527
THT2    GLIGLICFVL QFFYLYPYDA N......... ....QDHEND HGTEPVERIA SPVDVPTPRN .....   529
TcrHT1  GCIGLVCFVL QVFFLYPWEE S......... ..TPQNHGDT NEESALPERQ SPIEVATPGN RQAA    544
TvHT1   GIIGIICFVL QLRYLTPWED GQGTSTSPTA RCNAPTSPNN GEGEPATADM SPVEMSTPKH SGAA    543
         * ***  *   *                                                             *
```

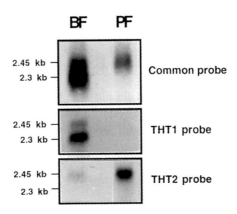

BF   PF

2.45 kb —
2.3 kb —   Common probe

2.45 kb —
2.3 kb —   THT1 probe

2.45 kb —
2.3 kb —   THT2 probe

FIGURE 3

Expression of the THT genes in the *T. brucei* EATRO-164 bloodstream forms (BF) and *T. brucei* Stib-247 procyclic forms (PF). The Northern blot was successively hybridized with different ^{32}P-labeled probes common to THT1 and THT2 genes (common probe), specific to THT1 genes (THT1 probe) and specific to THT2 genes (THT2 probe).

glucose transporter isoforms in *T. brucei* is reflected by the presence of different measurable kinetic properties of transport in bloodstream form and procyclic organisms. Bloodstream form cells possess a low affinity, high capacity glucose uptake system [10–13], while procyclics possess a higher affinity lower capacity system [14–17] (Table 1).

TABLE 1

Kinetic parameters and substrate specificities of the trypanosome glucose transporters

Organisms	Genes	K_m D-glucose or 2-DOG (mM)	V_{max} (nmol min^{-1} per mg protein)	Transport of D-fructose or inhibition	Type of transport
T. brucei bloodstream forms		0.49–0.9[a,b,c,d]	~250[a,b,c,d]	+[b]	Facilitated[a]
T. brucei procyclic forms		0.045–0.080[e,f,g]	4–10[e,f,g]	+[e,f]	Facilitated/Active[e,f]
T. brucei	THT1 (*Xenopus*)	ND	ND	+[h]	Facilitated[h]
	THT2 (CHO)	0.151 (2-DOG)[f]	4.3[f]	+[f]	Facilitated[f]
T. cruzi trypomastigote forms		0.294 (2-DOG)	1.4	ND	Facilitated
T. cruzi epimastigote forms[i,j]		0.312 (2-DOG)	3.65	+	Facilitated
T. cruzi	TcrHT1 (CHO)	0.315 (2-DOG)	7.7	+	Facilitated
T. vivax bloodstream forms[k]		0.585	88.5	+	Facilitated
T. vivax	TvHT1 (CHO)	0.545 (2-DOG)	4.3	+	Facilitated

Values are from : [a] [10]; [b] [11]; [c] [13]; [d] [31]; [e] [14]; [f] [16]; [g] [17]; [h] [4]; [i] [6]; [j] [26]; [k] [7].

Sequence information alone was insufficient to assign functions to the putative transporters, hence all of the trypanosome glucose transporter genes have been expressed in heterologus systems, including CHO cells and *Xenopus* oocytes to test function. Expression of the THT2 isoform in CHO cells [16] (in which the endogenous transporter was inhibited by cytochalasin B) revealed it to be kinetically and pharmacologically similar to the transporter identified in procyclic cells. THT1 cRNA, expressed in *Xenopus* oocytes [4] had a substrate recognition profile and pharmacology similar to the transporter measured in bloodstream form trypomastigotes.

The parasites therefore have two transporter genes that are expressed in a fashion which allows maximal exploitation of the host's extracellular environment. Bloodstream forms express predominantly THT1, a high capacity low affinity transporter to exploit the high concentration (~5 mM) of glucose in mammalian serum. Procyclic forms express the higher affinity transporter, THT2, in the insect midgut where glucose is relatively scarce, and amino acids such as proline become the major energy source [18].

T. cruzi, by contrast, has a single glucose transporter gene isoform [6], which is expressed at similar levels in epimastigotes, which dwell in the insect midgut, and trypomastigotes which live transiently in the bloodstream of the mammal before invading cells (particularly neurons and myocytes) where they transform to cytoplasmic amastigotes. Glucose transport has not been measured in amastigotes.

The metabolism of glucose by *T. cruzi* differs significantly from that of *T. brucei* bloodstream forms [19, 20] which lack a functional Krebs' cycle or a full mitochondrial respiratory chain and generate, under aerobic conditions just two moles of ATP per mole of glucose consumed via the glycolytic flux which ends at pyruvate. All life-stages of *T. cruzi* have a less profligate use of glucose, using functional mitochondrial systems to generate more ATP per mole of glucose. (Procyclic form *T. brucei* have a similar metabolism to *T. cruzi*.)

T. cruzi bloodstream form trypomastigotes are transiently bathed in the high glucose concentrations of mammalian serum, however, intracellular forms are exposed to relatively low free glucose (most cellular glucose is locked up by the host in a phosphorylated or polymeric form). Presumably for this reason they need only a single, relatively high affinity transporter (Table 1), and since bloodstream form trypomastigotes do not divide, and as their duration in the bloodstream is only transient, they have not evolved a low affinity, high capacity transporter to exploit this environment.

The metabolism of *T. vivax* is unlike that of bloodstream form *T. brucei* in that a partial Krebs' cycle is present [21, 22] and glucose utilisation is more efficient in terms of ATP production. Nevertheless, it is exposed to high glucose concentrations in the mammalian bloodstream and expresses a correspondingly low affinity transporter [7] (Table 1). Intriguingly, the parasite has only a single isoform glucose transporter gene, which might reflect the fact that its passage through the tsetse fly, unlike *T. brucei,* does not take it beyond the proboscis and is relatively fast (several days as opposed to several weeks).

2.2 Facilitative versus secondary active transport

The uptake of nutrients into cells may occur by a variety of mechanisms [23]. Large polar molecules, such as glucose, and indeed most biochemical substrates are too large and polar to simply diffuse across the lipid bilayer, and thus require specific transport proteins to catalyse uptake. Cells may accumulate nutrients without energy expenditure, allowing the thermodynamic energy in a diffusion gradient to propel substrates into cells. Alternatively, if a diffusion gradient cannot be relied upon (i.e. if substrate is scarce or a cell needs to concentrate it beyond the extracellular level) energy is expended. Such active transport can be direct (the transporter uses either ATP or pyrophosphate to accumulate substrate), or indirect. Indirect active transport involves the co-transport of two substrates (either in the same, symport, or opposite, antiport, direction). The co-transport of glucose with sodium ions in the mammalian intestine, and lactose with protons in *Escherichia coli* serve as classic examples of secondary active transport [23]. The energy to drive these systems comes from the diffusion gradients of co-transported ions which are maintained by secondary energy dependent pumping systems.

The different types of transport may be distinguished experimentally. Active transporters accumulate substrates against a concentration gradient and comparison of intracellular and extracellular concentrations of substrate can show when a substrate has been actively concentrated. If a second substrate (usually an ion) is required, transport in the presence and absence of that ion will be markedly different. Finally pharmacological reagents which either dissipate the ion gradients required to drive secondary active transport, or agents which inhibit energy production within the cell can also inhibit secondary active transport.

It is generally agreed that bloodstream forms of *T. brucei* depend on a facilitative diffusion molecule to accumulate glucose [10–13]. Given these organisms have evolved in a glucose rich environment, and that glucose is metabolised virtually instantaneously, ensuring a perpetual concentration gradient, energy expenditure on glucose accumulation would be unnecessary. One study did suggest a dependence on sodium ions at low external glucose concentration [24].

The case of the procyclic trypanosome is more controversial. Procyclics are exposed to low levels of glucose in the tsetse midgut, however, after a tsetse feed they are exposed, transiently, to high levels of the sugar in mammalian serum. The first study on these organisms revealed a relatively high affinity transporter, which according to pharmacological investigation was dependent on the co-transport of protons [14]. Both the respiratory inhibitor KCN and the protonophore FCCP reduced transport. Two further studies, both employing high concentrations of substrate failed to show either an accumulation of glucose beyond the external levels [15], or inhibition by KCN or FCCP [17]. In fact, an inhibitory effect by both KCN and FCCP depends on the concentration of substrate [16]. It appears that these reagents inhibit transport at low external glucose concentration, but exert progressively less impact as the substrate concentration rises to 1 mM. This phenomenon is characteristic of «slippage» [25] whereby the dependence on the counter-ion is diminished as substrate concentration rises. In the case of the procyclic trypanosome, such a mechanism makes physiological sense given that normally the parasites are exposed to low external glucose and might expend energy upon its acquisition. During the transient explosion in glucose concentration following a tsetse meal, however, dependence on energy to acquire the abundant substrate would be futile. One difficulty with the «slippage» hypothesis is that transport via THT2, the procyclic transporter, expressed in CHO cells, had no dependency on protons or energy regardless of substrate concentration [16]. The situation in procyclic cells might be more complicated, involving other phenomena including putative auxiliary factors or membrane potential which would be effected by the same pharmacological reagents used to assess proton dependence.

All available evidence suggests that *T. cruzi* [6, 26] and *T. vivax* [7] have straight forward facilitative transporters, although controversy also surrounds the mechanism employed by leishmanial transporters [27, 28].

2.3 The first extracellular loop of trypanosome glucose transporters contains a conserved arrangement of cysteine residues

All of the trypanosome glucose transporters possess numerous, spatially conserved cysteine residues in their first exofacial loop.

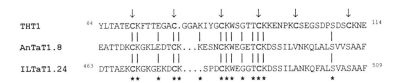

FIGURE 4

Alignment of the cysteine rich loop of THT1 with domains from two *T. brucei* variant surface glycoproteins. The amino acid sequence of the first exofacial loop, when used to search the protein data bases identified homology with small conserved regions of *T. brucei* variant surface glycoproteins. Alignment with the regions of the AnTaT1.8 and ILTaT1.24 sequences is shown here. The cysteine residues are over-scored with an arrow. An asterisk below the aligned sequences highlights identical residues.

Extensive analysis of the sequences of THT1 and THT2 reveal the loop to have been inserted independently [5], probably to replace a different type of first exofacial loop in an ancestral gene. Intriguingly, when the amino-acid sequence of the loop was used to scan protein sequence data-bases it identified a similar conserved arrangement of cysteine residues in variant surface glycoproteins from African trypanosomes (Fig. 4).

In fact, many trypanosomatid surface proteins reveal this arrangement of cysteines [29]. The motif has been conserved suggesting it performs a critical role in the architecture of kinetoplastid surface membranes.

3 • Glycosylation of trypanosomal glucose transporters

The mammalian GLUT1 transporter, and various other eukaryotic hexose transporters are glycosylated, usually in the first exofacial loop [30] which corresponds to the cysteine rich loop of the trypanosome transporters described above. Western blot analysis of THT1 after proteinase K digest of intact parasites, using site-specific antibodies against the amino terminus, carboxy terminus or two predicted extracellular loops connecting helices 5/6 and 7/8, has revealed that THT1 is oriented in the plasma membrane according to the predicted model based on GLUT1 (Seyfang et al., unpublished data).

Amino acid analysis of the various trypanosomal glucose transporters revealed significant differences in the occurrence of potential *N*-linked glycosylation sites (Fig. 2). Asn-69 in *T. brucei* THT2, Asn-81 in *T. cruzi* TcrHT1 and Asn-90, Asn-91 in *T. vivax* TvHT1 are the only potential exofacial *N*-glycosylation sites in these transporters, all located within the first extracellular loop.

The *T. brucei* bloodstream form transporter, THT1, lacks potential *N*-linked glycosylation sites on any of the predicted extracellular loops (only the loops which end up outside the cell are topologically available for glycoslylation within the endoplasmic reticulum). THT1 does contain one *N*-glycosylation consensus sequence (Asn-7), although this is located on the amino terminal tail and is predicted to face the cytoplasm. THT2 (Asn-7) and TvHT1 (Asn-10) also have additional *N*-glycosylation consensus sequences at similar positions.

De-glycosylation experiments with THT1-enriched plasma-membrane fractions [31] (using *N*-glycosidase, *O*-glycosidase and sialidase treatment) in combination with Western blot analysis showed no band shift (reduced molecular weight) for the THT1 protein [32]. In contrast, the GLUT1 protein purified from human erythrocytes and de-glycosylated had a reduction in apparent molecular weight of about 3 kDa after *N*-glycosidase F treatment. THT1-enriched plasma-membrane fractions were also analysed for glycoproteins by lectin blot analysis. A glycoprotein of 45 kDa (gp45) which co-migrated on reducing SDS-PAGE gels with THT1 [32] was detected. However, in non-denaturing gels, THT1 showed a lower electrophoretic mobility (shifting from 45 to 51 kDa) and under these conditions no glycoproteins co-migrated with THT1. These cumulative data demonstrated that THT1 is not glycosylated, in agreement with the predictions drawn from amino acid sequence data and membrane topology predictions.

It is believed that glycoslylation is critical in correctly orienting mammalian transporters in the plasma membrane [33]. Clearly in the case of bloodstream form *T. brucei* the transporter can be oriented without glycosylation. Possibly the dense packaging of the highly glycosylated variant surface glycoproteins of bloodstream form *T. brucei* might influence the need for glycosylation on transporter proteins in the plasma membrane. Interestingly, expression of THT2, TvHT1 and TcrHT1 was successful in CHO cells, while THT1 could not be functionally expressed (Tetaud et al., unpublished data). Possibly it is the lack of glycosylation to THT1 which hinders expression in mammalian cells.

4 • Therapeutic targets and therapeutic targeting

Any aspect of a parasite's biochemical make-up may be vulnerable to therapeutic attack, particularly where significant differences between host and parasite can be identified. In the case of trypanosome glucose transporters significant differences can be identified in terms of both the pharmacology and substrate recognition profiles when compared to the mammalian GLUT1 transporter. For example, all of the trypanosome transporters also carry D-fructose [7, 16, 26, 34] while GLUT1 does not. GLUT1 is very much more susceptible to cytochalasin B and phloretin than the trypanosome transporters. An extensive study of other reagents would undoubtedly identify

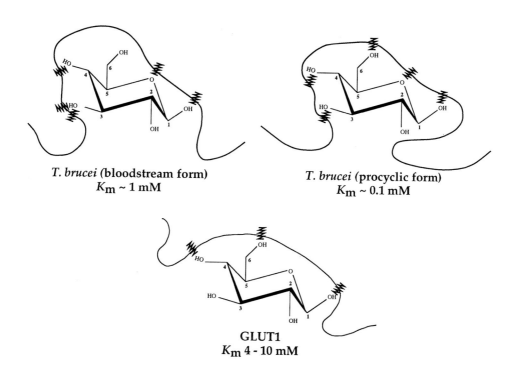

T. brucei **(bloodstream form)**
$K_m \sim 1$ mM

T. brucei **(procyclic form)**
$K_m \sim 0.1$ mM

GLUT1
K_m 4 - 10 mM

some which react more potently with the trypanosome transporters. None of the drugs used in the chemotherapy of human African trypanosomiasis inhibit the glucose transporter of bloodstream form trypomastigotes when used at concentrations usually toxic to the cells, suggesting that none of these drugs exert their activity at the level of this transporter (Barrett et al., unpublished observations).

Detailed analysis of substrate analogues, substituting the various hydroxyl groups has identified the key features involved in the structure-activity relationship of the various trypanosome glucose transporters (Fig. 5). Bloodstream form *T. brucei* depends exclusively on glucose metabolism to generate energy, hence inhibition of glucose uptake would certainly be expected to exert a lethal effect. So far, however, specific inhibitors of the *T. brucei* glucose transporter have not been identified. Armed with the substrate recognition information, and given the high capacity of the *T. brucei* bloodstream from glucose transporter to fulfill the prodigious appetite these cells have for this substrate, it might be possible to subvert the transporter, to carry toxic analogues of glucose into the cell.

A similar situation exists in the case of the melaminophenyl based arsenical and diamidine classes of drug which enter trypanosomes via an unusual amino-purine transporter, termed P2 [35]. The drugs share a chemical motif with the normal amino-purine

FIGURE 5

Substrate recognition of the *T. brucei* bloodstream form, and procyclic form glucose transporters, compared with mammalian GLUT1. Hydrogen bonds predicted to occur between the transporters and D-glucose are represented by jagged lines. The different carbon positions are numbered 1–6 (data from [11, 16, 39]).

substrates which is recognised by the transporter. Loss of the transporter renders the parasites resistant to these drugs.

Since the *T. brucei* bloodstream form transporter does not make hydrogen bonds with the hydroxyls at positions 2 and 6 of the glucose ring [11], these sites were considered available for the attachment of other chemical constituents, which would not interfere with recognition by the transporter. In fact, in the case of the C-6 position, a strict limit on the size of substituent groups has been noted (Barrett et al., unpublished data), whereas, provided substituent groups were neither charged nor aromatic, relatively large replacements could be added at position C-2. At least one compound containing a substituent group at position C-2 has been developed, which is toxic to bloodstream form parasites grown in vitro (Barrett et al., unpublished data). Fructose analogues have also been developed [36], and toxic examples are known. Further work is underway to assess the chemotherapeutic value of these compounds, and to distinguish whether the products actually inhibit the transporter itself or hit intracellular targets once taken into the cell via the transporter. A potential drawback with the glucose transporter relates to its low affinity for substrate, and the high abundance of glucose within serum, which would out-compete analogues for the transporter if such analogues were prescribed in quantities within the range of currently used antimicrobial drugs.

5 • Discussion

Glucose transporter genes have been cloned from several parasitic protozoa of the genus *Trypanosoma*. The function of the genes has been verified by expression in both *Xenopus* oocytes and CHO cells.

T. brucei contains two separate glucose transporter gene isoforms, which account for the different kinetic properties of the transporters measured in the different life cycle forms of the parasite. *T. cruzi*, and *T. vivax* contain only a single isoform. Substrate affinity and possibly mechanistic differences distinguish the transporters, in a manner which may reflect the different extracellular environments to which the parasites are exposed.

All of the trypanosome glucose transporters also recognise D-fructose which distinguishes them from the main mammalian glucose transporter, GLUT1. However, there are at least four other mammalian plasma membrane hexose transporters expressed in different tissues, with a range of substrate specificities, including two isoforms (GLUT2-liver and GLUT5-intestine) [37, 38] which also recognise D-fructose, highlighting the difficulties in pin-pointing unique features of the trypanosome transporters which might hinder their utility as chemotherapeutic targets.

The trypanosome transporters all contain a cysteine-rich first exofacial loop with a structure conserved in other trypanosomatid membrane proteins, which may play a critical role in the membrane architecture of these parasites. The comparative situation of the loop in THT1 and THT2 suggests it was inserted independently into ancestral genes. The presence of a similar structure in other trypanosomatid membrane proteins, might suggest that the insertion of «cassettes» which donate particular functions to proteins, has been involved in the evolution of trypanosome membrane proteins.

Structure activity relationship studies between the transporters and their substrates has allowed the development of analogues which are still recognised by the transporter, and may herald a new pathway in the development of novel anti-trypanosomal reagents, which exploit the glucose transporter as a specific gateway to carry toxic reagents into the parasites.

Acknowledgements

MPB was funded by a Royal Society European Exchange fellowship. This work was funded by the CNRS, the Commission of the European Community, the Ministère de l'Enseignement Supérieur et de la Recherche and the GDR CNRS/DGA-DSP.

REFERENCES

[1] Gould G.W., Holman G.D. The glucose transporter family: structure, function and tissue-specific expression. Biochem J; 295; 1993; 329-341.

[2] Bringaud F., Baltz T. A potential hexose transporter gene expressed predominantly in the bloodstream form of *Trypanosoma brucei*. Mol Biochem Parasitol; 52; 1992; 111-122.

[3] Cairns B.R., Collard M.W., Landfear S.M. Developmentally regulated gene from *Leishmania* encodes a putative membrane transport protein. Proc Natl Acad Sci USA; 86; 1989; 7682-7686.

[4] Bringaud F., Baltz T. Differential regulation of two distinct families of glucose transporter genes in *Trypanosoma brucei*. Mol Cell Biol; 13; 1993; 1146-1154.

[5] Bringaud F., Baltz T. African trypanosome glucose transporter genes: organisation and evolution of a multigene family. Mol Biol Evol; 11; 1994; 220-230.

[6] Tetaud E., Bringaud F., Chabas S., Barrett M.P., Baltz T. Characterization of glucose transport and cloning of a hexose transporter gene in *Trypanosoma cruzi*. Proc Natl Acad Sci USA; 91; 1994; 8278-8282.

[7] Waitumbi J.N., Tetaud E., Baltz T. Glucose uptake in *Trypanosoma vivax* and molecular characterization of its transporter gene. Eur J Biochem; 237; 1996; 234-239.

[8] Barrett M.P., Bringaud F., Doua F., Melville S.E., Baltz T. Hypervariability in gene copy number for the glucose transporter genes in trypanosomes. J Euk Microbiol; 43; 1996; 244-249.

[9] Hotz H.-R., Lorenz P., Fischer R., Krieger S., Clayton C. Role of 3'-untranslated regions in the regulation of hexose transporter mRNAs in *Trypanosoma brucei*. Mol Biochem Parasitol; 75; 1995; 1-14.

[10] Gruenberg J., Sharma P.R., Deshusses J. D-Glucose transport in *Trypanosoma brucei*. Eur J Biochem; 89; 1978; 461-469.

[11] Eisenthal R., Game S., Holman G.D. Specificity and kinetics of hexose transport in *Trypanosoma brucei*. Biochim Biophys Acta; 985; 1989; 81-89.

[12] Seyfang A., Duszenko M. Specificity of glucose transport in *Trypanosoma brucei* : effective inhibition by phloretin and cytochalasin B. Eur J Biochem; 202; 1991; 191-196.

[13] Ter Kuile B.H., Opperdoes F.R. Glucose uptake by *Trypanosoma brucei* : rate-limiting steps in glycolysis and regulation of the glycolytic flux. J Biol Chem; 266; 1991; 857-862.

[14] Parsons M., Nielsen B. Active transport of 2-deoxy-D-glucose in *Trypanosoma brucei* procyclic forms. Mol Biochem Parasitol; 42; 1990; 197-204.

[15] Ter Kuile B.H., Opperdoes F.R. Mutual adjustment of glucose uptake and metabolism in *Trypanosoma brucei* grown in a chemostat. J Bacteriol; 174; 1992; 1273-1279.

[16] Barrett M.P., Tetaud E., Seyfang A., Bringaud F., Baltz T. Functional expression and characterization of the *Trypanosoma brucei* procyclic glucose transporter, THT2. Biochem J; 321; 1995; 687-691.

[17] Wille U., Seyfang A., Duszenko M. Glucose uptake occurs by facilitated diffusion in procyclic forms of *Trypanosoma brucei*. Eur J Biochem; 236; 1996; 228-233.

[18] Cazzulo J.J. Aerobic fermentation of glucose by trypanosomatids. FASEB J; 6; 1992; 3153-3161.

[19] Fairlamb AH, Opperdoes FR. Carbohydrate metabolism in African trypanosomes, with special reference to the glycosome. In : Morgan MJ, editors. Carbohydrate Metabolism in Cultured Cells. New York : Plenum, 1986 : 183–219.

[20] Opperdoes F.R. Compartmentation of carbohydrate metabolism in trypanosomes. Ann Rev Microbiol; 41; 1987; 127-151.

[21] Gardiner P.R. Recent studies of the biology of *Trypanosoma vivax*. Adv Parasitol; 28; 1989; 229-317.

[22] Bowman IBR, Flynn IW. Oxidative metabolism of trypanosomes. In : Lumsden WHR, Evans DA, editors. Biology of the Kinetoplastida, vol. 1. New York : Academic, 1976 : 435–476.

[23] Stein WD. Channels, Carriers, and Pumps : An Introduction to Membrane Transport. San Diego : Academic, 1990.

[24] Munoz-Antonia T., Richards F.F., Ullu E. Differences in glucose transport between bloodstream and procyclic forms of *Trypanosoma brucei* rhodesiense. Mol Biochem Parasitol; 47; 1991; 73-82.

[25] Eddy A.A. Slip and leak models of gradient-coupled solute transport. Biochem Soc Trans; 8; 1980; 271-273.

[26] Tetaud E., Chabas S., Giroud C., Barrett M.P., Baltz T. Hexose uptake in *Trypanosoma cruzi* : structure-activity relationship between substrate and transporter. Biochem J; 317; 1996; 353-359.

[27] Zilberstein D., Dwyer D.M. Protonmotive force-driven active transport of D-glucose and L-proline in the protozoan parasite *Leishmania donovani*. Proc Natl Acad Sci USA; 82; 1985; 1716-1720.

[28] Ter Kuile B.H., Opperdoes F.R. Uptake and turnover of glucose in *Leishmania donovani*. Mol Biochem Parasitol; 60; 1993; 313-322.

[29] Carrington M., Boothroyd J. Implications of conserved structural motifs in disparate trypanosome surface-proteins. Mol Biochem Parasitol; 81; 1996; 119-126.

[30] Mueckler M. Facilitative glucose transporters. Eur J Biochem; 219; 1994; 713-725.

[31] Seyfang A., Duszenko M. Functional reconstitution of the *Trypanosoma brucei* plasma-membrane D-glucose transporter. Eur J Biochem; 214; 1993; 593-597.

[32] Seyfang A. Characterization and isolation of the glucose transporter from *Trypanosoma brucei*. PhD thesis. University of Tübingen, 1993.

[33] Hresko R.C., Kruse M., Strube M., Mueckler M. Topology of the GLUT1 glucose transporter deduced from glycosylation scanning mutagenesis. J Biol Chem; 269; 1994; 20482-20488.

[34] Fry A.J., Towner P., Holman G.D., Eisenthal R. Transport of D-fructose and its analogues by *Trypanosoma brucei*. Mol Biochem Parasitol; 60; 1993; 9-18.

[35] Carter N.S., Fairlamb A.H. Arsenical resistant trypanosome lack an unusual adenosine transporter. Nature; 361; 1993; 173-175.

[36] Page P., Blonski C., Perie J. An improved chemical and enzymatic synthesis of new fructose derivatives for import studies by the glucose transporter in parasites. Tetrahedron; 52; 1996; 1557-1572.

[37] Colville C.A., Seatter M.J., Jess T.J., Gould G.W., Thomas H.M. Kinetic analysis of the liver-type (GLUT2) and brain-type (GLUT3) glucose transporters in *Xenopus* oocytes : substrate specificities and effects of transport inhibitors. Biochem J; 290; 1993; 701-706.

[38] Burant C.F., Takeda J., Brot-Laroche E., Bell G.I., Davidson N.O. Fructose transporter in human spermatozoa and small intestine is GLUT5. J Biol Chem; 267; 1992; 14523-14526.

[39] Silverman M. Structure and function of hexose transporters. Annu Rev Biochem; 60; 1991; 757-794.

TABLE OF CONTENTS

CHAPTER 2
The molecular phylogeny of trypanosomes : evidence for an early divergence of the Salivaria 53

Jochen Haag, Colm O'hUigin, Peter Overatha

CHAPTER 6
VSG gene control and infectivity strategy of
metacyclic stage Trypanosoma brucei 129

David Barry, Sheila V. Graham Michael Fotheringham, Vincent S. Graham, Kerri Kobryn, Ben Wymer

CHAPTER 7
Controls of the expression of the Vsg in Trypanosoma brucei 147

Luc Vanhamme, Etienne Pays

CHAPTER 10

The glycosylation of the variant surface glycoproteins and procyclic acidic repetitive proteins of Trypanosoma brucei 197

Angela Mehlert, Nicole Zitzmann, Julia M. Richardson, Achim Treumann,
Michael A.J. Ferguson

CHAPTER 11

Glycosyl phosphatidylinositol myristoylation in African trypanosomes 207